Semiconductor Wafer Bonding: Science, Technology and Applications 17

Editors:

F. Fournel

R. Knechtel

C. Tan

T. Suga

H. Baumgart

M. Goorsky

K. D. Hobart

Sponsoring Division:

 Electronics and Photonics

Published by
The Electrochemical Society
65 South Main Street, Building D
Pennington, NJ 08534-2839, USA
tel 609 737 1902
fax 609 737 2743
www.electrochem.org

ecstransactions ™

Vol. 112, No. 3

Published by:

The Electrochemical Society
65 South Main Street
Pennington, New Jersey 08534-2839, USA

Telephone 609.737.1902
Fax 609.737.2743
e-mail: ecs@electrochem.org
Web: www.electrochem.org

ISSN 1938-6737 (online)

ISBN 978-1-62332-684-5 (PDF)

Printed in the United States of America.

Preface

The Seventeenth International Symposium on Semiconductor Wafer Bonding: Science, Technology, and Applications took place in Gothenburg, Sweden, as part of the 244th Meeting of the Electrochemical Society from October 10 to 12, 2023.

Over the past forty years, wafer bonding technologies have evolved from pioneering techniques to mature processes, enabling applications in diverse fields such as microelectronics, MEMS, micro-technologies, photonics, and packaging. The understanding of bonding mechanisms and process developments continues to grow. Among the different wafer bonding techniques, direct bonding has gained significant interest, especially for 3D applications with copper/copper hybrid bonding and III/V to silicon bonding for photonic applications. Initially focused on wafer-to-wafer bonding, this technique is now used for die-to-wafer bonding, further expanding the application field of direct bonding. This issue of ECS Transactions presents a wide variety of papers covering wafer bonding fundamental physics and chemistry, technologies, characterizations, and applications.

The issue of ECS Transactions comprises twenty-eight contributions, including eleven invited talks, which have been categorized into six technical sessions. We express our gratitude to the Electronics and Photonics Division of ECS and the three Industrial Sponsors: Electro-Vision Group (EVG), Tepla, and Screen, for their financial support, which has enabled us to maintain the Symposium tradition of funding students and presenting awards for the best presentations.

We extend our sincere appreciation to all the authors for sharing their latest research findings. Special thanks go to the Invited Speakers for their valuable contributions and for serving as Session Chairs during the Symposium.

F. Fournel,
H. Baumgart,
M. Goorsky,
K. Hobart,
R. Knechtel,
T. Suga,
C.S. Tan,
V. Larrey

ECS Transactions, Volume 112, Issue 3

Semiconductor Wafer Bonding: Science, Technology and Applications 17

Table of Contents

Facts about ECS

The Electrochemical Society (ECS) is an international, nonprofit, scientific, educational organization advancing the theory and practice of electrochemistry and solid state science and technology, and allied subjects. The Society was founded in Philadelphia in 1902 and incorporated in 1930. There are currently over 8,000 members from around the globe representing 13 technical division and 23 geographical sections and a growing student membership program with over 100 student chapters. The Society is also supported by more than 2,000 corporations, government agencies, and academic institutions through institutional membership, corporate programs, and subscriptions.

The technical activities of the Society are carried on by divisions. Sections of the Society host symposia, programs, and events focused on their respective geographic regions. Major international meetings of the Society are held in the spring and fall of each year. At these meetings, the divisions and partnered organizations hold general sessions and sponsor symposia on specialized subjects.

The Society has an active publications program that includes the following:

Journal of The Electrochemical Society — (JES) is the flagship journal of The Electrochemical Society and the oldest peer-reviewed journal in its field. Since its founding in 1902, JES has evolved into one of the most highly cited and prestigious journals in electrochemistry and materials science with a cited half-life of greater than 10 years.

ECS Journal of Solid State Science and Technology — (JSS) is a peer-reviewed journal covering fundamental and applied areas of solid state science and technology, including experimental and theoretical aspects of the chemistry, and physics of materials and devices.

ECS Transactions (ECST) — is the official conference proceedings publication of The Electrochemistry Society — a high-quality venue for authors and an excellent resource for researchers. ECST offers the full-text content of proceedings from ECS meetings and ECS sponsored conferences.

The Electrochemical Society Interface — *Interface* is an authoritative yet accessible publication for those in the field of solid state and electrochemical science and technology. Published quarterly, this full-color magazine contains technical articles about the latest developments in the field, and presents news and information about the Society.

ECS Books Series — ECS books and monographs provide authoritative, detailed accounts of specific topics in electrochemistry and solid state science and technology. These titles are sponsored by ECS and published in cooperation with noted publishers such as John A. Wiley & Sons.

For more information on these publications and other Society activities, visit the ECS website:

www.electrochem.org

ECS Transactions, 112 (3) 3-14 (2023)
10.1149/11203.0003ecst ©The Electrochemical Society

Bonding Strength of Cu-Cu Hybrid Bonding for 3D Integration Process

N. Fujii, S. Furuse, H. Yoshioka, N. Ogawa, T. Yamada, T. Hirano, S. Saito,
Y. Hagimoto, and H. Iwamoto

Research Division 2, Sony Semiconductor Solutions Corporation,
Atsugi, Kanagawa, 243-0014, Japan

Cu-Cu hybrid bonding is a significant technology for fabricating 3D
stacked semiconductor devices. In hybrid bonding, the calculation
of bonding strength is complex due to the various materials present
in the bonding interface. This interface not only includes Cu/Cu and
dielectric/dielectric interfaces, but also the Cu/dielectric interface
because of the misalignment of Cu pads. In this study, we developed
an integrated model regarding total bonding strength, considering
the different interfaces. Additionally, considering the thermal
expansion of Cu pads, we demonstrated the dependence of bonding
strength on misalignment using simulations. At the
dielectric/dielectric bonding interface, a phenomenon was observed,
in which the H_2O contained in the dielectric enhanced the bonding
strength. We proposed a model for the increase of the bonding
strength by filling the bonding interface gap with thermally
increased dielectrics. These results provide understanding regarding
a part of the mechanism involved in bonding strength in Cu-Cu
hybrid bonding.

Introduction

Adhesive-free direct bonding technology of silicon wafers has been researched and
developed to fabricate silicon-on-insulator (SOI) wafers (1). Following that, the technology
advanced the development of back side illuminated complementary metal oxide
semiconductor (CMOS) image sensors, enabling the fabrication of layer stacked image
sensors. Nowadays, with this technology, some leading-edge semiconductor devices are
being developed with 3D stacking, which require electrical connection between the stacked
layers.
Initially, the stacked wafers used to be connected electrically with through-silicon vias
(TSVs), constructed after bonding. However, the TSVs could not shrink adequately. This
was due to the difficulty of filling deep vias with conductors such as metals. Moreover, the
device dimensions could not be reduced, because some blanked areas were required for the
TSVs in the circuits. Consequently, the development of hybrid bonding technology was
desired. It would connect the devices electrically with just wafer bonding using the high
density of Cu pads (2) (3) (4). The hybrid bonding technology has been widely used for
the mass-production of stacked image sensors (5).
As mentioned above, Cu-Cu hybrid bonding is indispensable for the integration of 3D
heterogeneous stacked packages. A common 3D stacking procedure includes the thinning
of bonded wafers. Delamination can occur when the bonding strength of an interface is

insufficient. Therefore, the bonding strength is a key factor in 3D stacked integration and the mechanisms to improve the strength thoroughly have been investigated.

The bonding strength between Cu-Cu hybrid bonded wafers is complicated to describe because of the various materials present in the bonding interface.

The bonding interface includes not only Cu/Cu or dielectric/dielectric interfaces, but also the Cu/dielectrics interface. Due to the misalignment of the Cu pads, the strength of the Cu-Cu hybrid bonds needs to comprehensively account for these interfaces.

In this study, we proposed an equation for the total bonding strength of Cu-Cu hybrid bonding as a function of misalignment, and verified our assumption experimentally and theoretically. In this assumption, the bonding strength of the dielectric/dielectric interface is also an important factor, because its bonding area is larger than that of the Cu/Cu interface. Thus, we investigated the ways to improve the bonding strength between SiO_2 films existing in the interfaces of a Cu-Cu hybrid bonds. In this study, we investigated the bonding strength of a dielectric/dielectric interface in terms of H_2O amounts in the films.

Behavior of Bonding Strength on Cu-Cu hybrid bonding

When SiO_2 is used as a dielectric, the bonding strength of the Cu-Cu hybrid interface is represented by the following equation accounting for our assumption.

$$\gamma = A \cdot \gamma\,(Cu/SiO_2) + B \cdot \gamma\,(Cu/Cu) + C \cdot \gamma\,(SiO_2/SiO_2) \qquad [1]$$

where, γ: total bonding strength, $\gamma(Cu/SiO_2)$: bonding strength of the Cu/SiO$_2$ interface per unit, $\gamma(Cu/Cu)$: bonding strength of the Cu/SiO$_2$ interface per unit, $\gamma(SiO_2/SiO_2)$: bonding strength of the Cu/SiO$_2$ interface per unit, A: density of the Cu/SiO$_2$ contacted area, B: density of the Cu/Cu contacted area, and C: density of the SiO$_2$/SiO$_2$ contacted area.

This equation implies that the total bonding strength γ is represented by summarizing the bonding strengths of three different interfaces (Cu/SiO$_2$, Cu/Cu, and SiO$_2$/SiO$_2$).

Figure 1 shows the schematic of bonding interfaces before and after the annealing process. The interfaces before the annealing process are shown in the upper side of Figure 1. Although it is not included in Figure 1, there is copper oxide on the surface of the Cu

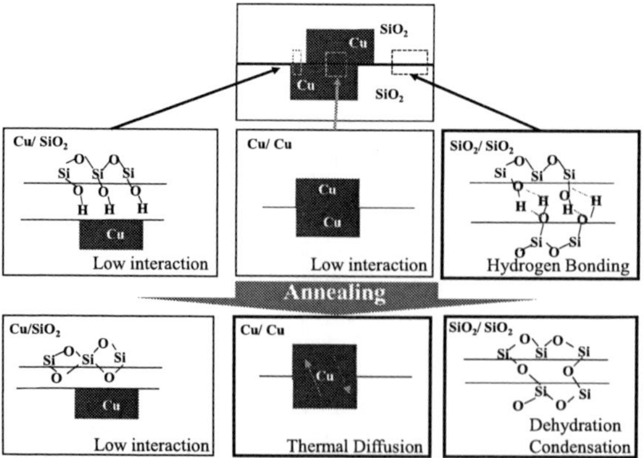

Figure 1 Schematic drawn of Cu-Cu hybrid bonding interface.

that interacts with the Si-OH on the SiO_2 surface. However, the Cu pad and SiO_2 on the bonding surface are not flat as shown in Figure 1. A recess exists on the Cu pad as a result of chemical mechanical polishing (CMP). Therefore, before annealing, the Cu/SiO_2 and Cu/Cu shown in Figure 1 have little or no contact. Thus, the equation of bonding strength before annealing is approximated only the third term in Equation [1]. The post-annealing interface has two high bonding strength areas, as shown in the lower part of Figure 1. One is the SiO_2/SiO_2 interface formed by the dehydration condensation of the hydrogen bonded silanol group. The other one is the Cu/Cu contacted area, in which Cu diffuses during thermal treatment. We have excluded the $\gamma(Cu/SiO_2)$ because its bonding strength is approximately 0.11 J/m^2, which is very low compared to the total strength of approximately 4.40 J/m^2. With this condition and assumption, Equation [1] can be written as follows.

$$\gamma = B \cdot \gamma\,(Cu/Cu) + C \cdot \gamma\,(SiO_2/SiO_2) \qquad [2]$$

When our hypothesis is applicable, the relationship between bonding strength and misalignment follow the abovementioned equation. Thus, we attempted to clarify the relationship between the bonding strength and misalignment both experimentally and theoretically.

<u>Experimental Procedures</u>

Figure 2 shows the sample structure prepared for this study. The patterned wafer used for this evaluation contains a 3-μm space and squared 3-μm Cu pad with a thickness of 350 nm. Two types of wafers with Cu pad structures were prepared, those with small- and large-recess Cu pads. These two types of Cu pad wafers were obtained by changing the condition of the CMP process. Surface-polished wafers were pre-bonded with a purposeful shift to evaluate the effect of misalignment. The alignment of bonded wafers was measured using an infrared (IR) microscope to obtain the degree of misalignment. Subsequently, the bonding strength was measured using a crack opening test (6). Subsequently, the bonded wafers were annealed at 400 °C and the bonding strength was measured again after annealing. The bonding strength was measured 5 min after a razor was inserted using IR under a room temperature of 23 °C and relative humidity of 55%. The measurement was carried out on a wafer 24 h after bonding and annealing. In this study, the SiO_2/SiO_2 bonding strengths used in formulas [1] and [2] were 0.40 J/m^2 for a single surface before annealing and 1.07 J/m^2 after annealing. The Cu/Cu bonding strength after annealing was determined as $\gamma(Cu/Cu) = 14.43$ J/m^2 based on the density of the hybrid surface from the bonding strength of 4.41 J/m^2 obtained in a sample with no misalignment.

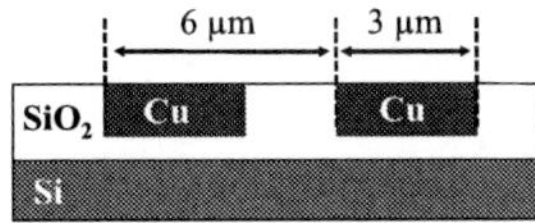

Figure 2 Cross-sectional image of sample structure

<u>Results and Discussions</u>

<u>Bonding Strength of Bonded Wafer before Thermal Treatment.</u> Figures 3 and 4 show the experimental and calculated results of bonding strength for small- and large-recess Cu

pads, respectively. The results were calculated using only the third term of Equation [1]. In both the figures, the vertical axis indicates the normalized bonding strength, including the maximum value of this measurement. The horizontal axis indicates the amount of proportional misalignment of the Cu/SiO_2 area in contact. An increase of the proportion of Cu/SiO_2 contact area indicates a decrease in bonding strength.

As shown in Figures 3 and 4, the bonding strength decreases linearly with an increase in the proportion of misalignment of Cu/SiO_2 contact area. The calculated results reproduce the experimental results well. Although the amount of recess of Cu pads are varied, the bonding strength in the pre-bonded wafers is not influenced. These results indicate that the recess of Cu pad does not affect the bonding strength. Additionally, the results suggest our proposed equation and assumptions are reasonable.

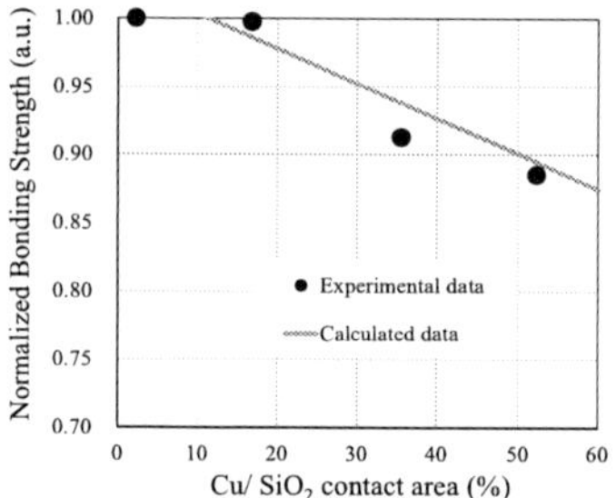

Figure 3. Experimental and calculated bonding strengths of the small-recess Cu Pad versus misalignment.

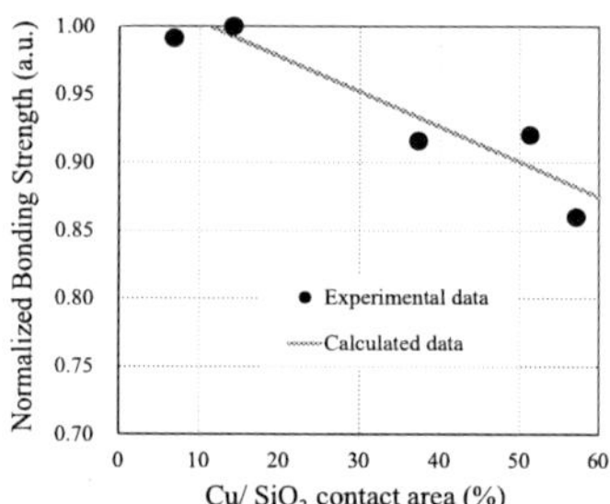

Figure 4. Experimental and calculated bonding strengths of the large-recess Cu Pad versus misalignment.

Bonding Strength of Bonded Wafer after Thermal Treatment. Figures 5 and 6 show the experimental and calculated results of the bonding strength after the annealing process for the small- and large-recess Cu pads, respectively. Bonding strengths of 4.70 J/m^2 and 4.41 J/m^2 were used in Figures 5 and 6 for normalization, respectively. The calculated results were determined using Equation [3]. As shown in Figure 5, the calculated results

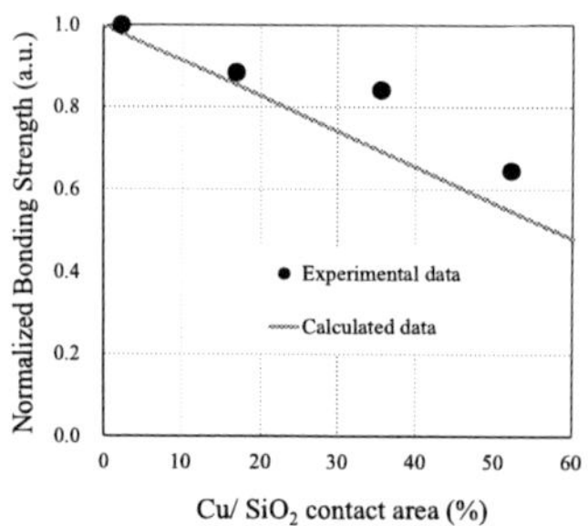

Figure 5. Experimental and calculated bonding strengths after the annealing process of the small-recess Cu pad versus misalignment.

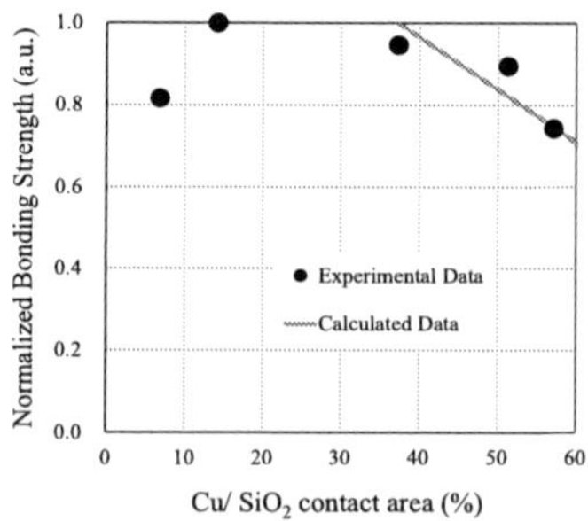

Figure 6. Experimental and calculated bonding strengths after the annealing process of large-recess Cu pad versus misalignment.

reproduce the experimental results well in the case of the small-recess Cu pad. However, the calculated bonding strength of the large-recess Cu pad does not correspond well with the experimental bonding strength. In other words, Equation [3] cannot represent the relationship between the bonding strength of the large-recess Cu pad and its misalignment. Considering that Equation [3] can represent the bonding strength of the small-recess Cu pad, there is another factor related to recess that affects the bonding strength.

<u>Influence of Thermal Expansion of Cu.</u> It is known that Cu expands at high temperature (3). The bonding strength is strongly affected by the thermal expansion of Cu in the case of the large recess. However, Equation [2] does not consider the effect of the thermal expansion of Cu. Considering its effect, the equation can be written by inserting a correction term, as Equation [3].

$$\gamma = B \cdot \gamma \, (Cu/Cu) + C \cdot \gamma \, (SiO_2/SiO_2) + \alpha \qquad [3]$$

To elucidate the effect of the thermal expansion of Cu and correction term α in Equation [3], we conducted a thermal stress simulation. Figure 7 shows the thermal expansion of Cu of a single non-bonded wafer during the annealing process. The amount of thermal expansion increases as the annealing temperature increases. Thermal expansion of Cu is the largest at the edge of the Cu pad at annealing temperatures more than 300 °C. Because a large recess substantially reduces the amount of thermal expansion of the Cu pad, at the edge, the bonding strength in case of the large-recess Cu pad is expected to be affected.

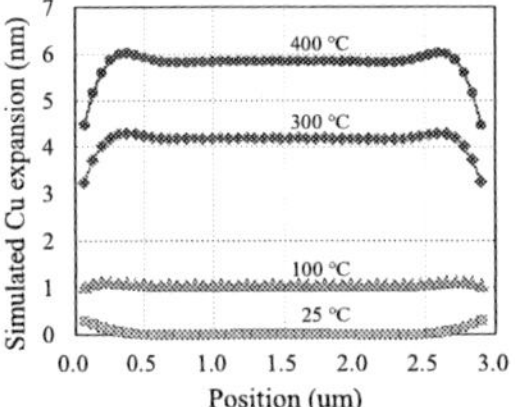

Misalignment	0%	25 %	35%	55%
Small recess				
Large recess				

Figure 7. Simulated thermal expansion of Cu during the annealing process.

Figure 8. Simulated contact pressure of small and large-recess Cu pads during annealing process. Dashed-lined squares are the edges of the top and bottom Cu pads, respectively

Figure 8 shows the simulated contact pressure of the Cu pad for small recess and large recess versus misalignment. The distribution of Cu contact pressure of the small-recess Cu pad is uniform and unchanged with misalignment, whereas that of the large-recess Cu pad changes with misalignment. In the case of the large recess pad, high- and low-contact pressurized areas exist at the edge and the middle, respectively. The high contact pressurized area arises from the maximum point of thermal expansion of Cu pad, as shown in Figure 7. These results indicate that the distribution of Cu contact pressure is strongly affected by that of the thermal expansion of Cu in the case of the large-recess Cu pad. This is as was expected above. Scanning acoustic microscope measurements were performed for all the samples, but no voids were observed in the samples after annealing, even when the low Cu contact pressure area was included.

Accounting for the thermal expansion of Cu, Equation [3] can be described as follows.

$$\gamma = B' \cdot \gamma' \ (Cu/Cu) + B'' \cdot \gamma'' \ (Cu/Cu) + C \cdot \gamma \ (SiO_2/SiO_2) \qquad [4]$$

Where, γ' (Cu/Cu): bonding strength of the high pressurized Cu/Cu interface per unit, γ'' (Cu/Cu): bonding strength of the low pressurized Cu/Cu interface per unit, B': density of the high pressurized Cu/Cu contacted area, and B'': density of the low pressurized Cu/Cu contacted area. The calculated bonding strengths of small recess and large recess are shown in Figures 9 and 10, respectively, which were determined by substituting a simulated high pressurized Cu/Cu contacted area into Equation [4]. At room temperature after thermal treatment, a stress difference inside the Cu pad appears. Cioccioa *et al.* (7) suggested that the high-pressure region has high tensile stress, and the low-pressure region has low tensile stress. These must also be considered when discussing the absolute strength value.

As shown in Figures 9 and 10, the calculated results reproduce the experimental results well. Bonding strengths of 4.70 J/m^2 and 4.41 J/m^2 were used in Figures 9 and 10 for normalization, respectively. It is concluded that the discrepancy between the bonding strength of the large-recess Cu pad calculated using by Equation [2] and that of the experiment is due to the second term in Equation [4]. This term is related to the effect of the thermal expansion of Cu and is not accounted for. In other words, the thermal expansion of Cu strongly affects the bonding strength as the recess of the Cu pad becomes larger.

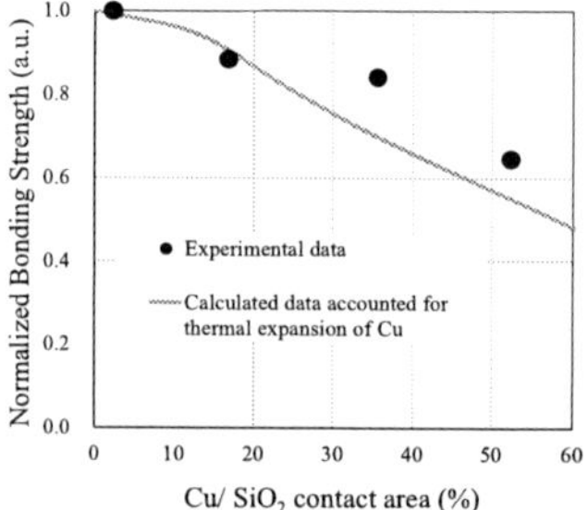

Figure 9. Experimental and calculated bonding strength after the annealing process of small-recess Cu pad versus misalignment. Calculated results account for thermal expansion of Cu.

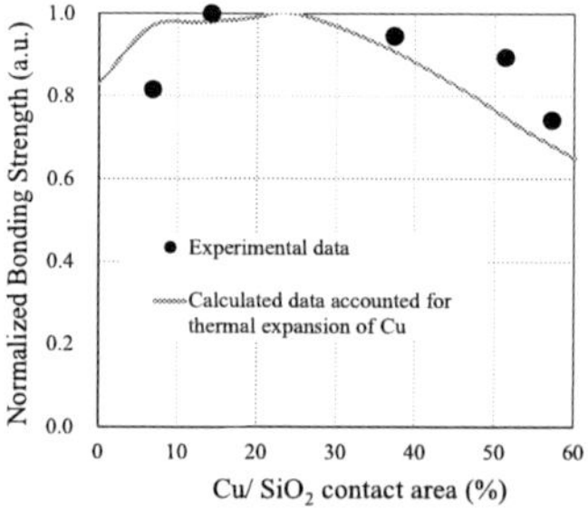

Figure 10. Experimental and calculated bonding strength after the annealing process of large-recess Cu pad versus misalignment. Calculated results account for thermal expansion of Cu.

<u>Summary of This Experiment</u>

Before the annealing process, the bonding strength decreased linearly as the misalignment increased and agreed well with our assumed equation. However, the bonding strengths of the small- and large-recess Cu pads behaved differently after the annealing process. To elucidate the behavior of bonding strength after annealing, we conducted a thermal stress simulation and obtained the results of a low contact pressure area that existed at the middle of the large-recess Cu pad. Simulated results revealed that the thermal expansion of Cu and the recess of Cu pad strongly affected the bonding strength, and our initial proposed equation could not describe enough the thermal expansion of Cu. By inserting the correlation term for the effect of thermal expansion by the recess into the proposed equation, the correlated equation could well reproduce the bonding strength of the large-recess Cu pad.

Improvement of Bonding Strength between SiO_2/SiO_2 Interface

Because the high bonding strength of SiO_2/SiO_2 interface provided a stable 3D stacking process, we also continued to study ways to improve the bonding strength of the interface between the SiO_2 films that exist in the interfaces of a Cu-Cu hybrid bond. The dielectric films are bonded using a dehydration condensation reaction on the plasma-activated surface by thermal annealing. This bonding process has been widely studied from the perspective of surface Si-OH amount by considering the activation method and condition, type of dielectric, and flatness of the surface (8)(9). Therefore, elucidating the mechanism of strength generation would offer a guideline to improve the bonding strength. Given that few investigations have considered factors other than the bonding interfaces, we focused on the influence of the H_2O contained in the dielectric film to be bonded and investigated the relationship between the H_2O amount in the film and the bonding strength. This study examined the relationship with the bonding strength by observing the amount of H_2O using thermal desorption spectrometry (TDS), rather than using FT-IR absorption, as reported in (10).

<u>Experimental Procedures.</u>

<u>Sample Preparation and Measurement Methods.</u> Figure 11 shows the flow of the experiment. A series of SiO_2 films (A, B, C, D, and E) was prepared with different deposition conditions of plasma-enhanced chemical vapor deposition (PE-CVD), CMP, and plasma activation treatment on each SiO_2 film. The H_2O content, surface silanol group content, and surface roughness were measured. Furthermore, each SiO_2 film was bonded to Film A. After annealing at 400 °C for 1 h, the bonding strengths was evaluated.

The amounts of H_2O in the SiO_2 films were measured by TDS using individual 10 mm × 10 mm dies cut from a single film. For evaluation of desorption, the temperature was increased to 400 °C at a rate of 30 °C/min. The Si-OH amounts was compared using an analytical method, in which the surface was modified using a derivative; it was measured

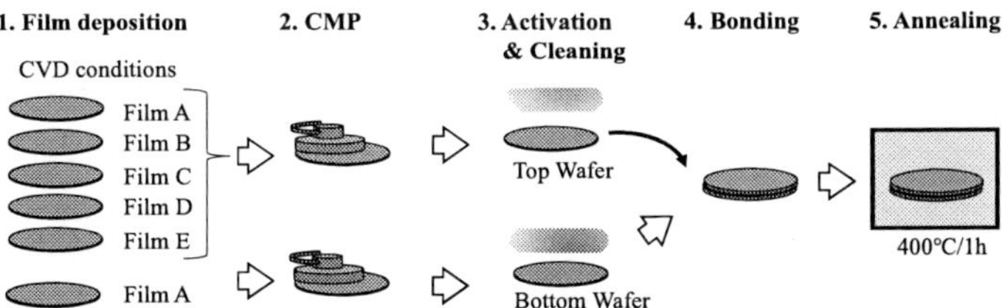

Figure 11. Sample preparing procedure of this experiment.

by X-ray photoelectron spectroscopy (XPS), and the Si-OH/Si ratio was calculated (11). The surface roughness was measured by atomic force microscopy (AFM). Then, the bonding strength of the bonded wafers after annealing was measured using the crack opening test (6), which was carried out at using the same procedure as the experiment on Cu-Cu hybrid bonding. Measurements were performed at four locations in each sample, and the average value was calculated. For bonded wafers, each combination is hereafter referred as A, B, C, D, and E, as shown in Table I.

Table I. Combinations of bonded SiO_2 films

Notation of samples	Bonding combinations	
	Wafer1	Wafer2
A	Film A	Film A
B	Film B	Film A
C	Film C	Film A
D	Film D	Film A
E	Film E	Film A

Results and Discussions

Relationship Between H_2O Amounts and Bonding Strength. Figure 12 shows the temperature dependence of mass-to-charge ratio (M/z) for molecular weight 18. It represents H_2O during the degassing of each film, as measured by TDS. Figure 13 shows the plots of each film with the maximum M/z for molecular weight 18 (Figure 12) on the horizontal axis and the bonding strength on the vertical axis. The bonding strength used for normalization in Figure 13 and the following figures had a maximum value of 1.95 J/m^2. The x-axis represents the maximum M/z for molecular weight 18 for the larger of the bonded combination wafers. The higher the H_2O amounts in the film, the higher the bonding strength.

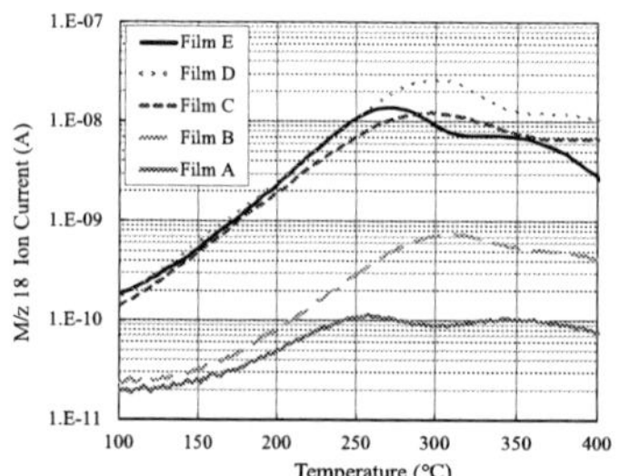

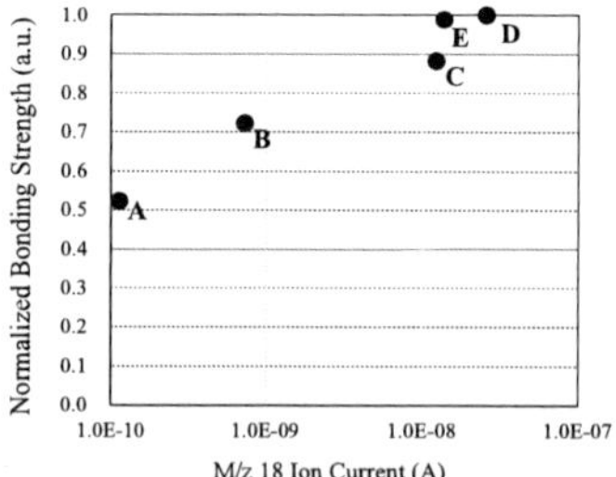

Figure 12. Comparison of H_2O amounts in the films.

Figure 13. Relationship between H_2O content in the film and the bonding strength.

Effect of Surface Silanol Groups and Roughness. Figure14 shows a plot of the Si-OH/Si content ratio on the horizontal axis and the bonding strength on the vertical axis; in which the Si-OH/Si ratio is the conditionally selected value of each bonded pair. No dependance is observed between the bonding strength and the amount of silanol groups on the surface.

The root mean square (RMS) value of surface roughness on each film is less than 0.3 nm. Figure 15 shows a plot of the surface roughness on the horizontal axis and bonding strength on the vertical axis. Herein, the RMS value is the value of "Wafer 1" in Table I. No relationship is observed between the bonding strength and the surface roughness, as is the case with the dependance on Si-OH content.

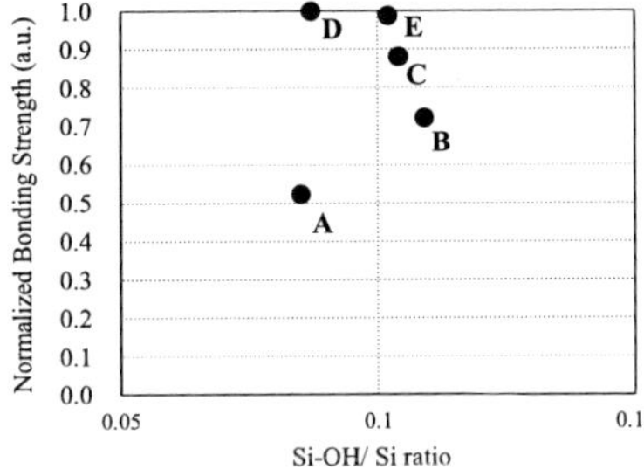

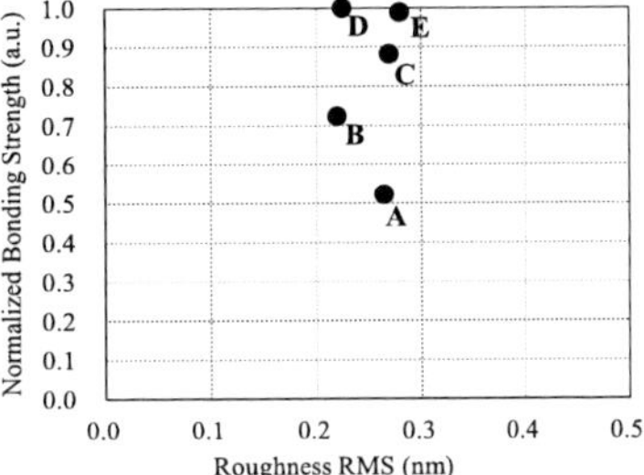

Figure 14. Relationship between bonding strength and Si-OH content.

Figure 15. Relationship between bonding strength and surface roughness.

<u>Changes in Bonding Interface due to Thermal Treatment.</u> If the H_2O content in the film affects the bonding strength, few phenomena may occur during the annealing process after bonding. Therefore, we evaluated whether the appearance of the bonding interface changed before and after annealing. To confirm the appearance of the bonding interface, scanning-transmission electron microscopy (STEM) imaging of the cross sections was conducted.

Figure 16 shows cross-sectional images of the bonded surfaces of sample E before and after annealing; the film expands owing to the thermal treatment. Further, Figure 17 shows cross-sectional images of the bonded surfaces of sample A before and after annealing; the film does not expand.

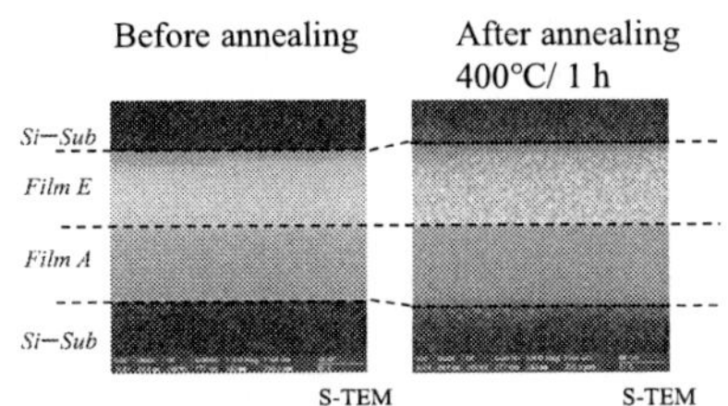

Figure 16. Cross-sectional images of bonded surface (Sample E).

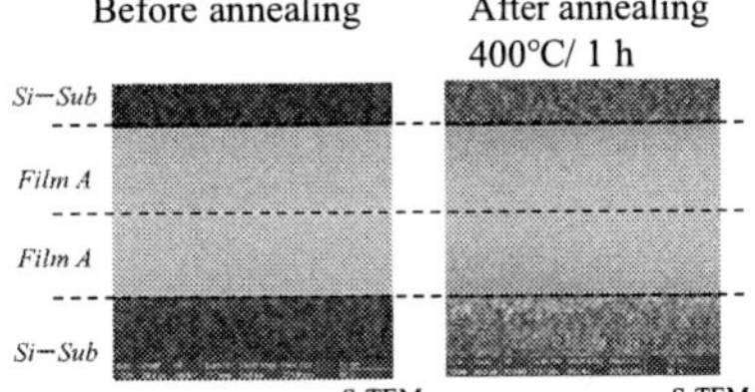

Figure 17. Cross-sectional images of bonded surface (Sample A).

Table II shows the film thickness of each sample before and after annealing (sum of Wafer 1 and Wafer 2 films as measured from the cross-sectional images) and the amount of expansion due to annealing. Figure 18 shows the relationship between the H_2O content

Table II. Film Thickness before and after Annealing

Sample	Before annealing (nm)	After annealing (nm)	Amount of increase (nm)
A	169.0	168.6	-0.4
B	161.5	165.7	4.2
C	170.9	175.5	4.7
D	163.8	172.7	8.9
E	162.4	175.3	12.9

in the film and the amount of expansion due to annealing. The maximum ion current for molecular weight 18 in Figure 12 is plotted on the horizontal axis and the amount of expansion in Table II is plotted on the vertical axis. The higher the H_2O content in the film, the greater the expansion due to thermal treatment. Figure 19 shows the relationship between the amount of expansion and the bonding strength; the increase in film expansion is associated with higher bonding strength.

Next, the STEM images of sample E, which had a large amount of expansion, were observed in the same way at different heat-treatment temperatures. Each thermal treatment was 1 h. The results are shown in Figure 20. The film thickness is the sum of the thickness of the bonded films as measured from the cross-sectional image. As the annealing temperature increases, the amounts of expansion increases, and the film becomes porous at temperatures of 300 °C and 400 °C.

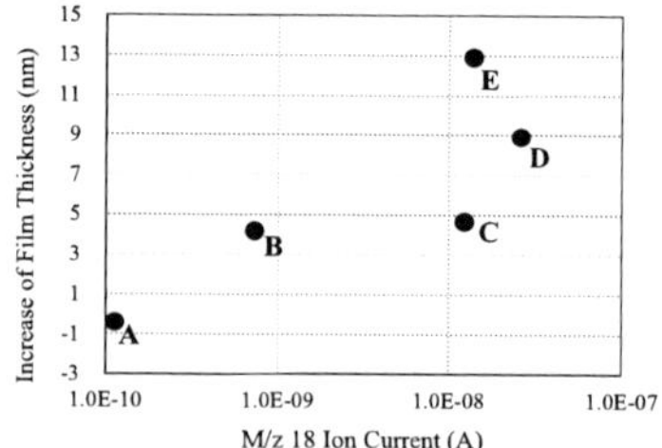

Figure 18. Relationship between increase of film thickness and H_2O amounts.

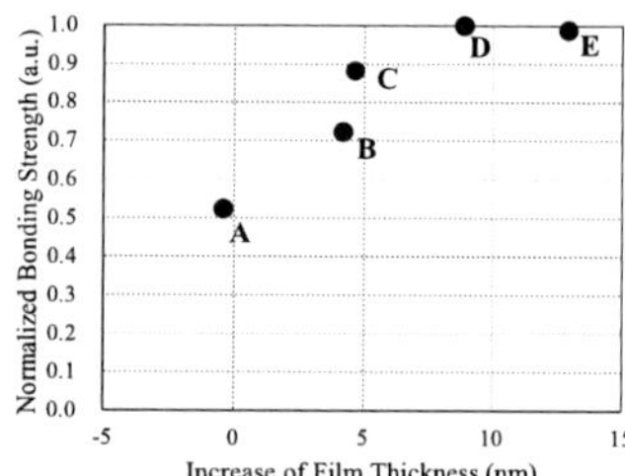

Figure 19. Relationship between bonding strength and increase of film thickness.

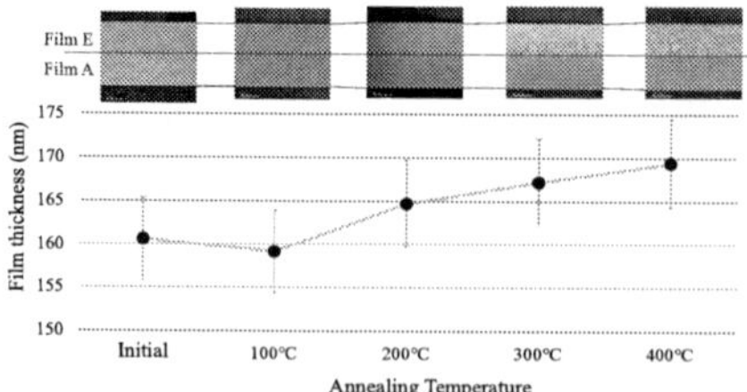

Figure 20.   Film thickness at different annealing temperatures (Sample E).

These results suggest that the difference in bonding strengths between the samples in this experiment does not depend on the amount of surface silanol groups or surface roughness, but on the difference in the H_2O content in the films.

<u>Proposed Mechanism for the Increase of Bonding Strength.</u> The following mechanisms are assumed for the abovementioned phenomena. If H_2O content in the film is high during the heat treatment in the bonded state, the degassed moisture is assumed to disperse into the film; the film expands because there is no escape route (Figure21). H_2O may also have caused oxidation on the Si substrate (12). As the surface roughness of each film before bonding is less than 0.3 nm, the effect of this gap filling is attributed to the small gaps that still exist after bonding, as shown in Figure 22. These gaps at the bonding interface were also assumed to be filled by the increase in the film, which expanded as a result of H_2O or the oxidation of the Si substrate, resulting in a high bonding strength. In addition, the hydrolysis of Si-O by H_2O in the film could occur, resulting in the recombination of Si-O in the bonding interface and improvement in the bonding strength (10)(12)(13).

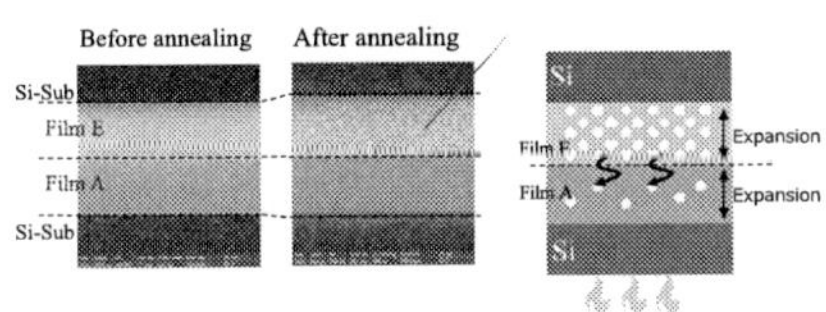

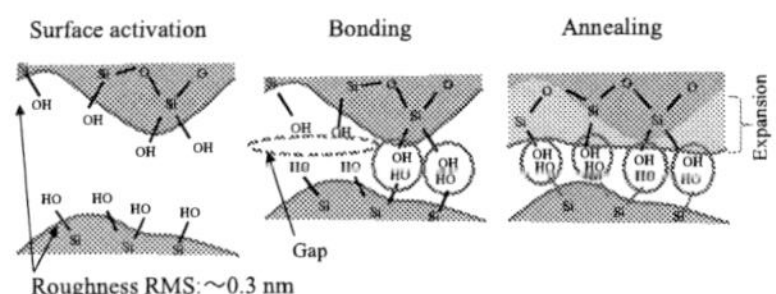

Figure 21. Proposed mechanism of film expansion.

Figure 22. Proposed mechanism, and the filling of the gap between the bonding surfaces.

<u>Summary of This Experiment</u>

In this study, the relationship between the H_2O content in a film and the bonding strength at its SiO_2/SiO_2 interface was investigated. The higher the H_2O content, the higher the bonding strength was obtained. A film with high H_2O content increased during annealing after bonding. Further, with increasing film, the bonding strength increased. During SiO_2 film increase, the gap at the bonding interface was considered filled and it improved the bonding strength. Based on the results of this study, we proposed a model in which film expansion contributed to the increase of the bonding strength. On the other hand, the increase in the film could be caused by the oxidation of the Si substrate, and the hydrolysis of Si-O by H_2O could have improved the bonding strength. These phenomena should be further investigated in detail.

Conclusions

This paper focused on the bonding strength of hybrid bonding in semiconductor 3D stacking technology. We confirmed the effect of misalignment of Cu-Cu hybrid bonding on the bonding strength after annealing, considering the recess of the Cu pad. According to these results, we presented an integrated model of the comprehensive bonding strength that included three interfaces involved in the Cu-Cu hybrid bonding. In dielectric bonded interface, we proposed that filling up the gap in the interface would be an effective approach for improving the bonding strength. These results, and the influence of H_2O amounts in the bonding dielectric films on SiO_2/SiO_2 bonding, offer deep understanding of the mechanism for the bonding strength of Cu-Cu hybrid bonds. This will contribute to the development of 3D stacking technology in the future.

Acknowledgments

This study is based on results obtained from "Research and Development Project of the Enhanced Infrastructures for Post-5G Information and Communication Systems" (JPNP20017), subsidized by the New Energy and Industrial Technology Development Organization (NEDO).

References

1. P. Ramm, J. J. -Q. Lu, and M. M. V. Taklo, *Handbook of Wafer Bonding*, Wiley-VCH Verlag & Co., p. 81, (2012).
2. H. Hashiguchi, M. Haneda, Y. Kagawa, M. Horiike, T. Hirano, S. Kobayashi, T. Hirano, and H. Iwamoto, Advanced Metallization Conference Plus, (2019).
3. V. C. Venezia, A. C-W. Hsiung, Kelvin Ai, Xiang Zhao, Z. Lin, D. Mao, A. Yazdani, E. A. G. Webster, and L. A. Grant, *IEEE International Electron Devices Meeting*, p. 10–4, (2018).
4. Y. Kagawa, H. Hashiguchi, T. Kamibayashi, M. Haneda, N. Fujii, S. Furuse, T. Hirano, and H. Iwamoto, *Proc. IEEE Int. Interconnect Technol. Conf. (IITC)*, p. 148, (2020).
5. J. Jourdon, S. Lhostis, S. Moreau, J. Chossat, M. Arnoux, C. Sart, Y. Henrion, P. Lamontagne, L. Arnaud, N. Bresson, V. Balan, C. Euvrard, Y. Exbrayat, D. Scevola, E. Deloffre, S. Mermoz, A. Martin, H. Bilgen, F. Andre, C. Charles, D. Bouchu, A. Farcy, S. Guillaumet, A. Jouve, H. Fremont, and S. Cheramy, *IEEE International Electron Devices Meeting (IEDM)*, p. 7-3-1, (2018).
6. W. P. Maszara, G. Goetz, A. Caviglia, and J. B. McKitterick, Journal of Applied Physics 64(10), p. 4943, (1988)
7. L. Di Cioccioa, P. Gueguena, R. Taibib, D. Landruc, G. Gaudinc, C. Chappazb, F. Rieutorda, F. de Crecya, I. Raduc, LL Chapelonb, and L. Clavelie, ECS Transactions, 33 (4) 3-16 (2010)
8. Q. Y. Tong and U. Gosele, *Semiconductor wafer bonding*, Wiley-VCH Verlag & Co., (1998)
9. N. Rauch, E. Andersen, I. G. Vicente-Gabás, J. Duchoslav, A. Minenkov, J. Gasiorowski, C. Flötgen, K. Hingerl, and H. Groiss, *Proc.WaferBond'22*, p. 47, (2022).
10. J. Desomberg, F. Fournel, H. Moriceau, A. Roule, E. Barthel, and F. Rieutord, Microsyst. Technol., **24** (1), p. 801, (2018)
11. T. Takei, M. Ataku, T. Konishi, M. Fuji, T. Watanabe, and M. Chikazawa, *Journal of the Society of Powder Technology*, **36**, p.179, (1999).
12. C. Ventosa, F. Rieutord, L. Libralesso, C. Morales, F. Fournel, and H. Moriceau. Journal of Applied Physics, **104** (12), 123524, (2008).
13. F. Fournel, C. Martin-Cocher, D. Radisson, V. Larrey, E. Beche, C. Morales, P. A. Delean, F. Rieutord, and H. Moriceau., ECS J. Solid State Sci. Technol., **4** (5), p.124, (2015)

ECS Transactions, 112 (3) 15-22 (2023)
10.1149/11203.0015ecst ©The Electrochemical Society

Edge Bonding Voids Management Using Humid Helium Bonding Atmosphere

F. Fournel[a], V. Larrey[a], C. Morales[a], and L. G. Michaud[b]

[a] Univ. Grenoble Alpes, CEA, LETI, F-38000 Grenoble, France
[b] EV Group, DI E. Thallner Straße 1, 4782 St. Florian/Inn, Austria

Hydrophilic direct wafer bonding involves two types of bonding voids: classical voids caused by contamination or surface topography, and edge voids resulting from the bonding wave dynamics. The adiabatic expansion of the bonding wave at the wafer edge can lead to condensation of humidity and the formation of small water droplets, resulting in bonding defects even without contamination. These defects persist even under dry gas conditions. Two methods are used to address this issue. The first is vacuum bonding (<0.1 mbar), and the second involves using gases with a negative Joule-Thomson coefficient, such as helium. Helium is preferred due to its low coefficient and cost-effectiveness. However, bonding under pure helium results in lower adhesion and adherence energy. In this study, humid helium, generated using a dedicated humidifier, is used to evaluate the adhesion energy and adherence of standard Si/SiO2 bonding.

Introduction

Both adhesion and adherence energy play a role in wafer direct bonding. While adherence energy pertains to the energy required to separate bonded wafers, adhesion energy refers to the energy available to facilitate the spontaneous bonding of the two surfaces. Adhesion energy allows the two surfaces to bond together spontaneously, provided that bringing them together does not consume excessive mechanical elastic energy. In reality, surfaces are never perfectly flat or smooth. At a very small scale, when roughness is measured by AFM with a 1 μm * 1 μm scan field, attractive forces (such as van der Waals forces, hydrogen bonds, and capillary bridges) are counterbalanced by the mechanical deformation of roughness asperities preventing surfaces from interpenetrating [1]. However, this phenomenon occurs when the two surfaces are already in contact. Beyond this point, they are bonded. But before this point, surfaces need to deform in order to approach each other. One could consider that this asperity deformation only determines the amount of adhesion used for macroscopic surface deformation. Therefore, roughness has an impact on the adhesion amplitude. An automotive analogy could be made by comparing roughness to the accelerator pedal. The lower the roughness is, the higher the adhesion will be. For a given type of surface (hydrophilic, hydrophobic, or with dangling bonds), roughness determines the amount of adhesion energy used to bring surfaces into contact. Roughness determines the distance between the surfaces and subsequently the amount of attractive force available immediately before the surfaces make contact. The smoother the surface, the higher the adhesion energy, but the surface itself does not change with the alteration of roughness. The van der Waals force, hydrogen bonds, water amount, or dangling bonds remains the same regardless of roughness. Roughness only influences the amount of van der Waals forces that can be generated, the formation of hydrogen bonds, and the density of capillary bridges. Roughness can truly be seen as the accelerator pedal for controlling the amount of bonding engine power: the adhesion energy. Macroscopic surface deformations (such as bow, warp, and nanotopology) can then be considered the brakes, continuing the automotive analogy. They consume a portion of the adhesion energy. After subtracting this mechanical energy, the remaining adhesion energy can be used to propagate the bonding. When direct bonding is performed under atmospheric pressure, the system needs also to push out the air trapped between the surfaces. The resistance from the air induces viscous friction. As the magnitude of viscous friction depends on the fluid speed, the speed of air expulsion adjusts automatically to the amplitude of the remaining adhesion energy. This speed is known as the bonding wave speed, which can be measured during room pressure direct bonding. The remaining adhesion energy is referred to as the adhesion energy as it is the one used to bring the surfaces together, drive the bonding wave speed [2], and can be measured using a modified double cantilever beam (DCB) setup [3]. However, in reality, it is only the residual adhesion energy, not the adhesion energy itself. Nevertheless, this residual adhesion energy will be referred to as the adhesion energy in this article, as it is the one that can be measured.

If the adhesion energy is greater than zero, the system will have enough energy to propagate the bonding, resulting in spontaneous bonding, which is the general definition of direct bonding. The propagation of bonding induces one or more bonding waves. Under vacuum, the bonding wave speed can be significant (>100 cm/s). However, during room pressure bonding, the speed is much smaller, around a few cm/s, and can be observed with the naked eye. This slower speed is due to the viscous friction, which leads to a gas overpressure at the bonding front. This overpressure deforms the silicon wafers, and this deformation can be seen from the wafer backside. In addition to infrared visualization, dynamic backside interferometry can be used to monitor the bonding wave speed [4]. This overpressure can reach a few bars [2]. When it reaches the end of the wafer, an adiabatic depressurization occurs. As demonstrated by Castex et al. [5], during this adiabatic expansion of the bonding wave at the wafer edge, humidity inside the bonding wave gas can liquefy, resulting in small water droplets nucleating. This is shown in Figure 1, which depicts the bonding of two 300 mm silicon wafers with 145 nm thermal oxide layers and after a post-bonding thermal annealing at 300°C.

Figure 1 : Acoustic characterization of edge bonding voids between two 300 mm silicon wafers. Each silicon wafer has a 145 nm thick thermal oxide layer. After the hydrophilic bonding performed in air with 40% of relative humidity, a post-bonding thermal annealing is performed at 300°C before the acoustic characterization.

These wafer edge droplets lead to bonding defects without the presence of particle contamination or surface topography. They are usually referred to as "edge bonding voids". Even if bonding is performed under a dry gas such as nitrogen or argon, these defects remain at the hydrophilic direct bonding interface because there is always a small amount of water on a hydrophilic surface. During the first stage of bonding wave propagation, gas compression increases its temperature and enables the gas to take water from the surfaces, as explained by V. Larrey et al. [3]. The humid gas results in edge bonding voids at the end of the propagation. There are only two methods to eliminate this phenomenon. The first one is to perform bonding under vacuum (<0.1 mbar). The second one is to use a gas with a negative Joule-Thomson coefficient. Gases with a negative coefficient, such as helium, hydrogen or neon, will be heated during the adiabatic expansion when the bonding wave exits the bonding interface. Among these gases, helium has the lowest Joule-Thomson coefficient at ambient conditions and is the safest and most cost-effective option. Bonding under a helium atmosphere will prevent water nucleation, as shown in Figure 2

Figure 2. Acoustic characterization of two 300 mm silicon wafers bonded under pure helium. No edge bonding voids can be detected. Each silicon wafer has a 145 nm thermal oxide layer. After the hydrophilic bonding performed in pure helium, a post-bonding thermal annealing is done at 300°C before the acoustic characterization.

Typically, pure helium, which is a dry gas, is used. This removes some water from the surface before bonding. As demonstrated by Radisson [8] and Fournel et al. [10], the adhesion and adherence will be reduced in this case. Adding water vapor to increase the relative humidity (RH) of helium could enable the recovery of standard bonding conditions with respect to the amount of trapped water.

Experiment

In our EVG850LT bonding tool, we have installed a humidifier on the helium gas line to introduce a varying RH gas mixture (ranging from 0 to 80%) into the bonding chamber. The process involves bonding 300 mm standard (001) silicon wafers that have been oxidized to form a 145 nm oxide layer. Prior to bonding, the wafers undergo classical RCA cleaning [6]. To control the bonding atmosphere inside the EVG850LT bonding chamber, we initially purge the chamber with pure helium until the RH value drops below 1%. Then, a mixture of helium and water vapor at different concentrations is introduced to achieve the desired RH values. The EVG850LT bonder is equipped with an infrared camera to monitor the bonding wave. During the recording, multiple images are captured, and the time scale of each image is recorded in the file number. We utilize a custom Matlab software to automatically detect the bonding wave and calculate its speed along radial lines starting from the initiation point. After bonding under different atmospheres at room temperature, the samples undergo annealing at 300°C for two hours in a nitrogen environment. An acoustic microscope with a 140 MHz transducer is used to characterize the bonding defectivity, particularly the presence of edge bonding voids. The wafers are then cut into small rectangular beams measuring 20 mm wide and 100 mm long using a standard dicing saw. The adherence (bonding energy) is measured using the double cantilever beam (DCB) technique under prescribed displacement. This technique is also known as the crack opening method or the Maszara technique. The measurement is performed under anhydrous nitrogen with a water concentration of less than 1 ppm to prevent any water-induced stress corrosion effects during the measurement [7].

Results

Figure 3 shows that when bonding is performed with 54% RH in helium, no edge bonding voids are detected using scanning acoustic microscopy. Even at 83% RH in helium, as shown in Figure 4, no edge bonding voids or specific bonding defects are observed.

Figure 3 : Acoustic characterization of two 300 mm silicon wafers bonded under helium at 54% RH. No edge bonding voids can be detected. Each silicon wafer has a 145 nm thermal oxide layer. After the hydrophilic bonding performed in 54% RH helium, a post-bonding thermal annealing is done at 300°C before the acoustic characterization.

Figure 4 : Acoustic characterization of two 300 mm silicon wafers bonded under helium at 83% RH. No edge bonding voids can be detected. Each silicon wafer has a 145 nm thermal oxide layer. After the hydrophilic bonding performed in 83% RH helium, a post-bonding thermal annealing is done at 300°C before the acoustic characterization.

During the bonding process, sequential images of the bonding wave propagation are recorded, as depicted in Figure 5a. A custom Matlab software is used to automatically detect the bonding wave within the region of interest or ROI (Figure 5b). The bonding wave speed is then calculated along radial lines starting from the bonding initiation point (Figure 5c). By fitting the bonding wave with a polynomial equation, the intersection of the wave with the radial lines can be obtained (Figure 5d). The derivative of the bonding point movement along each line provides the bonding wave speed value, which can be plotted as shown in Figure 6. Statistical calculations can be performed to determine average and median speeds, for example.

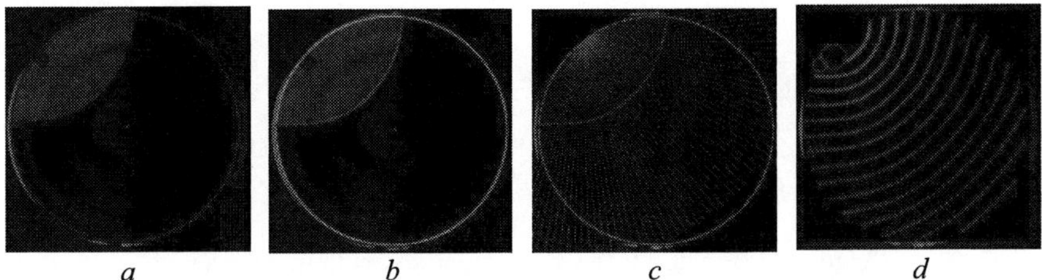

Figure 5 : Example of bonding wave speed detection using custom Matlab software. a) bonding wave image inside ROI. b) Automatic bonding wave detection. c) Speed lines. d) Detection of the bonding wave position along each speed lines.

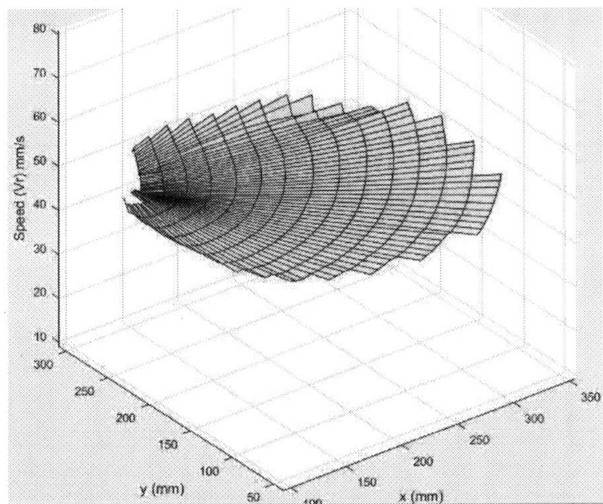

Figure 6 : Example of bonding wave speed evaluation using homemade Matlab software.

Figure 7 displays the average bonding wave speeds for different bonding atmospheres. As the speed is closely related to the adhesion energy [2], the increase in bonding wave speed with relative humidity indicates an improvement in the adhesion energy.

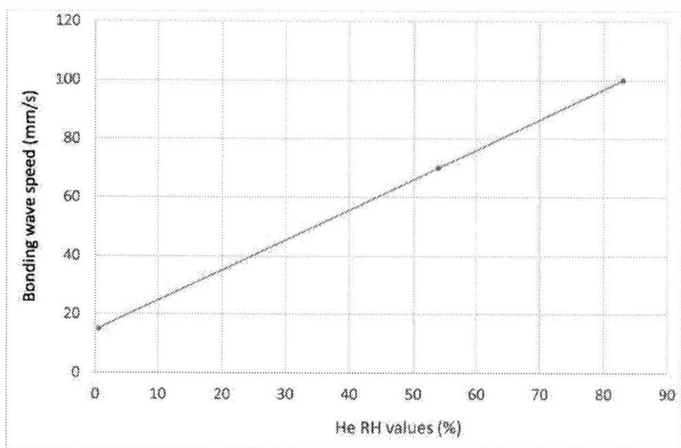

Figure 7 : Bonding wave speed regarding helium RH value.

This result is in line with Radisson findings [8]. According to Radisson, bonding adhesion is influenced by van der Waals forces, hydrogen bonds, and capillary bridges (Figure 8). Increasing the amount of water on the surface leads to the formation of larger capillary bridges, thereby increasing the adhesion energy and the bonding wave speed.

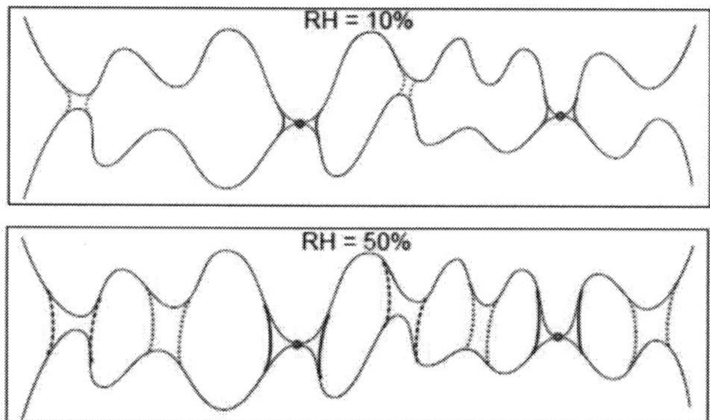

Figure 8 : Adhesion mechanism at the bonding font during adhesion energy measurement depending on the RH value as described by Radisson [8].

Higher adhesion energy, as demonstrated by Turner et al. [9], enables bonding of wafers with higher bow or greater nanotopology. Notably, this means that the bonding limit near the wafer edge becomes less significant, and the bonding area increases, especially for processed wafers where the edge roll-down effect greatly limits the bonding area. Moreover, for a given particle height, the induced bonding defects become less significant. Higher adhesion energy is generally beneficial, except for the occurrence of edge bonding voids. A fast bonding wave results in significant adiabatic expansion, which typically leads to important water nucleation. However, this is not the case with humid helium, as shown in Figure 4. With this specific bonding atmosphere, high adhesion energy can be achieved without edge bonding voids. In addition to its adhesion benefits, a bonding atmosphere with humid helium is also advantageous for adherence. Fournel et al. [10] demonstrated that water plays a key role in the adherence mechanism for $SiO_2//SiO_2$ or $Si//SiO_2$ bonding. Figure 9 illustrates that adherence is primarily influenced by the hydrolysis of roughness asperities.

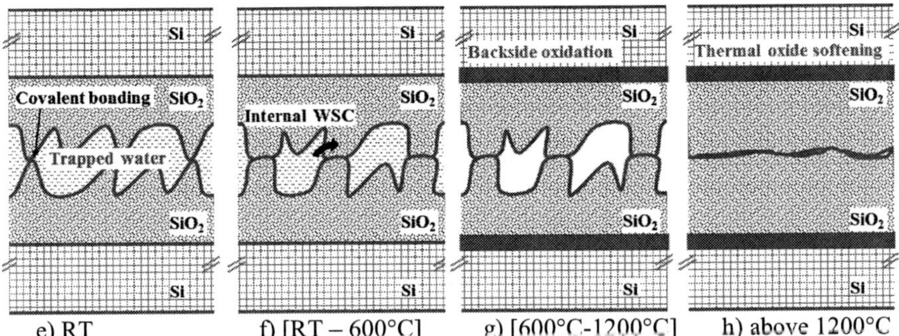

e) RT   f) [RT – 600°C]   g) [600°C-1200°C]   h) above 1200°C

Figure 9 : SiO2/SiO2 adherence mechanism based on roughness asperities hydrolisation by trapped water [**10**].

Increasing the amount of trapped water is expected to enhance hydrolysis and, consequently, increase the adherence energy. TABLE I demonstrates that bonding performed at 54% rh or 80% rh yields higher bonding energy compared to bonding with pure dry helium. Interestingly, there is no significant difference in adherence between bonding performed at 54% RH and 83% RH, despite the significant impact on adhesion. This suggests that beyond a certain water content, without additional surface treatments like plasma treatment [11] or the use of basic molecules [12], further water addition may not substantially increase adherence. In the case of 54% RH, it is possible that a sufficient amount of trapped water already exists at the interface to achieve the highest hydrolysis state of the roughness asperities. Additional water may not provide significant benefits in terms of adherence. However, it is worth noting that if the surface, particularly the sub-surface, is modified, with specific plasma treatments or the addition of catalyzing agents like basic molecules. The impact of water content on adherence may then differ.

TABLE I. Adherence energy of SiO2//SiO2 bonding after a post bonding annealing of 300°C during 2 hours.

He RH(%)	Adherence (J/m²)
0	1.7 +-0.17
54	4.1 +-0.41
83	3.9 +-0.39

Conclusion

In conclusion, utilizing a humid helium bonding atmosphere offers significant benefits in wafer bonding processes. By introducing water vapor into the helium gas, the formation of edge bonding voids can be completely avoided. This is achieved by maintaining a relative humidity (RH) value of up to 83%, which enables the perfect bonding of 300 mm silicon wafers. Moreover, the increase in RH value in the helium atmosphere has a positive impact on the bonding wave speed, leading to higher adhesion energy. This enhancement in adhesion energy improves the bonding force to bring the wafers together. Additionally, the adherence or bonding energy is noticeably improved when water is present in the helium atmosphere during bonding. This is evident in the higher bonding energy observed compared to bonding without water. Therefore, employing a humid helium bonding atmosphere proves to be an excellent approach to eliminate edge bonding voids while achieving high adhesion and adherence energies. This method provides a promising solution for robust and reliable wafer bonding processes.

References

1. F. Rieutord, H. Moriceau, R. Beneyton, L. Capello, C. Morales, and A.-M. Charvet, ECS Trans. 2006, **3**(6), 205–215 (2006)
2. F. Rieutord, B. Bataillou, and H. Moriceau, Physical Review Letter, **94**(23) (2005)
3. V. Larrey, G. Eleouet, C. Bridoux, C. Morales, F. Fournel, F. Rieutord, and D. Landru, Proceeding of The International Conference on Wafer Bonding, WaferBond'19 Trans., p.91 (2019).
4. F. Fournel, B. Rousset, V. Larrey, C. Morales, R. Sachs, L. Sudrie, and C. Morvan. WaferBond'22 Trans. (2022).
5. A. Castex, M. Broekaart, F. Rieutord, K. Landry, and C. Lagahe-Blanchard, ECS Solid State Lett., **2**, p. 47 (2013).
6. W. Kern, D. Puotinen., R.C.A. Review, **31**(2), 187–206 (1970).
7. F. Fournel, L. Continni, C. Morales, J. Da Fonseca, H. Moriceau, F. Rieutord, A. Barthelemy, and I. Radu., Journal of Applied Physics, **111**(10), 104907 (2012)
8. D. Radisson, Direct Bonding of Patterned Surfaces, PhD thesis, Université Grenoble Alpes (2014).
9. K. T. Turner. PhD, MIT (2004)
10. F. Fournel, C. Martin-Cocher, D. Radisson, V. Larrey, E. Beche, C. Morales, P.A. Delean, F. Rieutord, and H. Moriceau, ECS J. Solid State Sci. Technol., **4**, P124 (2015).
11. H. Moriceau, F. Rieutord, C. Morales, S. Sartori, and A. M. Charvet, ECS Trans. 2005, **2**, pp 34–49 (2005)
12. F. Fournel, A. Calvez, V. Larrey, G. Eleouet, C. Morales, and F. Rieutord, ECS Trans. 2020, **98**(4), p. 3 (2020).

ECS Transactions, 112 (3) 23-30 (2023)
10.1149/11203.0023ecst ©The Electrochemical Society

Inline Bondwave Monitoring for Direct Bonding, Process Optimization and Impact on Post-Bond Distortion

L.G. Michaud[a], F. Fournel[b], C.Morales[b], M. Schmidbauer[a], K.Abadie[b], T. Plach[a] and M. Wimplinger[a]

[a] EV Group, DI E. Thallner Straße 1, 4782 St. Florian/Inn, Austria
[b] Univ. Grenoble Alpes, CEA, LETI, F-38000 Grenoble

Direct wafer bonding is essential in semiconductor manufacturing, with bondwave propagation dynamics influencing the overall bond quality. The main factor impacting bondwave velocity dynamics are substrate rigidity, fluid viscosity and adhesion energy between the two surfaces. The latter, which depends on substrates properties and process parameters, is key and should be controlled and monitored for fusion bonding applications. The use of an inline infrared (IR) monitoring within an automated fusion bonding equipment, EVG®850LT, facilitates real-time defect detection, root cause analysis, and bond re-workability. The equipment, which features a sealed bonding chamber equipped with an IR camera and a reflective chuck, together with a plasma chamber for pre-processing enables the assessment of various process conditions. Post-bond distortions are then evaluated using high-resolution metrology. Bondwave monitoring use-cases, a detailed analysis of bondwave speed impact on bonded stack distortion and the influence of diverse process parameters on bondwave propagation are presented or discussed in the current paper.

Introduction

Direct wafer bonding, named also fusion wafer bonding, is based on the formation of molecular bonds between the two surfaces placed in contact. After contact initiation between the two surfaces, the bonding is self-propagating: a bondwave is generated at the initiation point, which propagates freely until the entire surfaces are in contact (e.g. bonded). The dynamic of the bondwave propagation is depending on various material (substrates) and process parameters. As shown by Rieutord et al. (1), and experimentally confirmed in Ref. (2), for a given material and geometry, the speed is function of adhesion energy and fluid viscosity. An analytical formula of bondwave speed v is given by equation [1], introduced by Rieutord et al, where A is a constant, E_a the adhesion energy, η the fluid viscosity, t_w the wafers thickness, E_e the reduced Young's modulus and Λ the mean free path of the fluid particles (or cut-off distance).

$$v = \frac{A^{3/4}}{9} \frac{E_a^{5/4} \, \Lambda^{1/2}}{\eta \, t_w^{3/4} \, E_e^{1/4}} \qquad [1]$$

Evaluating the bondwave speed by inline monitoring is a viable method to monitor the adhesion energy and optimize processes. The adhesion energy enables the two wafer surfaces to join. It is a function of different parameters such as surface roughness, the wet and/or plasma treatment used or the presence of water (2,3). Any variation will have an impact on bondwave speed. Spatial information is also necessary to control surface inhomogeneity in wafer surface properties linked to previous pre-processing steps such as deposition or chemical mechanical polishing.

Inline IR monitoring can be also a practical solution for defect detection. Compared to post bond IR inspection, live information enables easier root cause analysis, e.g., particles, surface inhomogeneities or chuck effect. Inline early detection of defective bonds and process outliers enables bonded pairs to be reworked (separated and re-bonded) without any additional metrology steps such as post bonding IR inspection or Scanning Acoustic Microscopy (SAM). Bond quality can be heavily impacted by the presence of particles (4,5).

In case of fast bondwave, one has to monitor any unwanted effect such as edge voids or increased distortion (6,7). Edge voids are caused by the adiabatic expansion of the fluid compressed at the bonding interface. Cooling results in water nucleation and thus a crown of defects at the wafer edges. Moreover, the deformation induced by the dynamic bond propagation can results in residual stress or wafer distortion. This can be critical for layer transfer processes or 3D integration (8,9).

In this study, we detail the implementation of an IR bondwave observation capability within and EVG®850LT bonding equipment. We provide practical application of this setup, demonstrating its potential for early defect detection and enhancement of process performance. The method can also be applied to monitor change in adhesion energy. Furthermore, we offer an analysis illustrating the correlation between bondwave velocity and post-bond distortion.

Experiment

In an automated EVG®850LT fusion bonding equipment, a bonding chamber has been equipped with an IR camera to record bondwave propagation. The bond chamber set up is shown in Figure 1. The IR source and camera are placed on top of the bonding chamber and can record between 7 and 25 frames per second. The bonding chuck is equipped with a reflective layer. Telecentric lenses are used as the cover of the bonding chamber to reduce top chuck reflection, avoid image distortion and enable atmosphere control inside the bonding chamber. The bonding chamber is equipped with a purge line (nitrogen, air, helium), a turbo pump and a humidifier to control humidity, gas nature and pressure. The bond is initiated with a mobile pin equipped with a load cell, enabling to start the bondwave in a repeatable way at different locations (each bond must be initiated at a single point, but location might vary between center or close to an edge). A dual frequency plasma chamber is also present in the equipment for pre-processing. Plasma activated wafer bonding is used to increase adherence energy compared to standard hydrophilic bonding. Bulk strength can be achieved after low temperature annealing, e.g., 300°C (10,11).

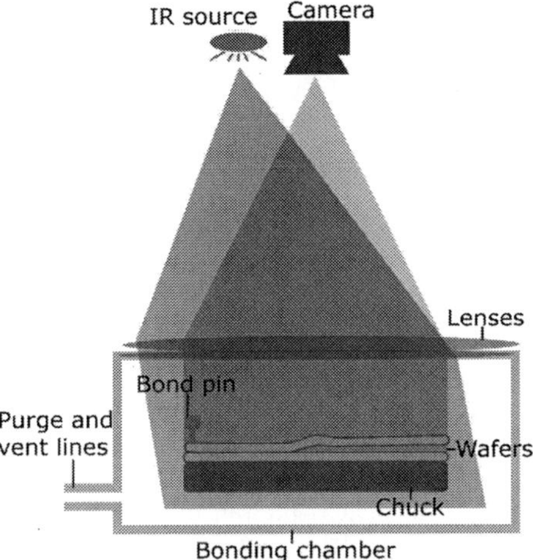

Figure 1. Schematics of the EVG®850LT bonding chamber equipped with an IR source and camera for bondwave observation

Spatial information on bondwave speed is extracted from IR images using a MatLab program developed by Fournel et al, (12). Speed is calculated along radial lines, originating from the bond initiation point. An example of raw IR images is presented in Figure 2(a). Final speed mapping is provided in Figure 2(b). 300 mm (001) silicon wafers covered with 100 nm of thermal oxide were used as top wafers and standard (001) silicon wafers as bottom wafers. Surfaces were prepared using a standard RCA wet cleaning prior to bonding. After bonding, bonded pairs underwent a 2 hours annealing at 300°C. The bonding interface was observed using SAM with a 140 MHz transducer. When applied on the bond pair edge, the pond pin was at the notch location.

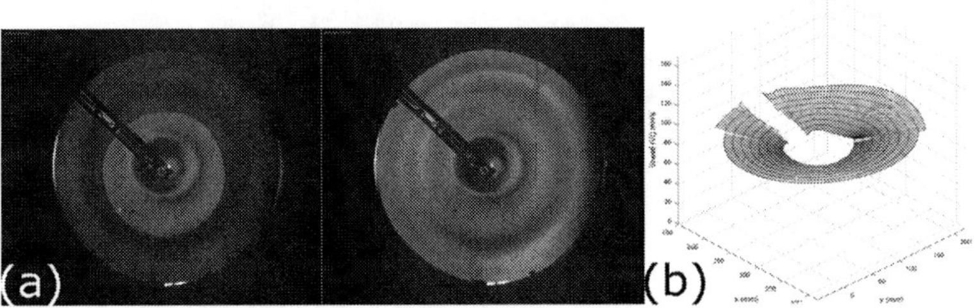

Figure 2. (a) center initiation of a 300 mm Si/SiO$_2$ bonding (b) Corresponding bondwave speed mapping; missing data are due to bond pin and central top wafer reflection

Moreover, a metrology equipment was used for bonded pair shape measurement. Data were used to predict high resolution in-plane distortion (IPD) maps and quantify the impacts of bonding wave speed and bonding parameters. A 4-parameter model was applied to the data to identify contribution (x and y translation, rotation and run-out or scaling). The residual distortion value is the difference between the raw data and total distortion modelized. It is used to predict residual stress that cannot be compensated by simpler correction during bonding steps (i.e. wafer translation, rotation or expansion). It is usually a sign of non linear effect or inhomogeneity in bondwave propagation.

Results

<u>Bonding Wave Observation</u>

Figure 3 shows bondwave propagation after initiation at the wafer edge. The bonding interface was contaminated with particles. Between timestamps t1 and t2, a particle near the initiation impacts bondwave propagation. No voids were observed in a post bond IR image, but Figure 3 SAM image clearly shows a defect. Meanwhile, a bigger particle caused a defect clearly visible with IR between time frames t3 and t4. The SAM image after bond annealing shows a characteristic trail of defects resulting from the impact of defects on dynamic bond interface propagation (13).

Other defects might be linked to particles on the bonding chuck. It will not necessarily result in voids at the interface. Bondwave dynamics will be impacted, however, resulting into local stress or distortion. This can impact subsequent process steps or device performances.

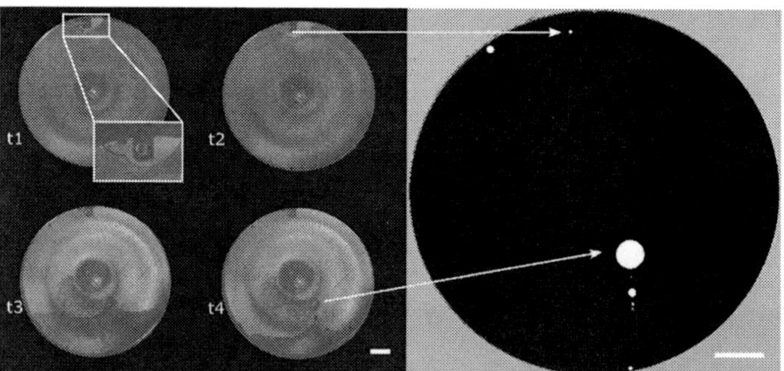

Figure 3. IR bondwave images at different times with t1<t2<t3<t4. The bond pin is visible in the top, above wafers notches Resulting SAM image after Si/SiO$_2$ bonding then a 2h 300°C annealing. The notch is at the top. All white scale bars are 40 mm

Figure 4 shows a bonding with an inhomogeneous surface treatment. This led to a bonding front propagating significantly faster at the wafer edge than in the center. This behavior is expected up to a certain point as fluid can escape at the bond pair edge and offers less resistance to the closing of the interface. However, in this case, the important difference results in a gas bubble being trapped at the opposite edge of the initiation point. As seen in Figure 4(d), it causes a void at the bonding interface, even after annealing.

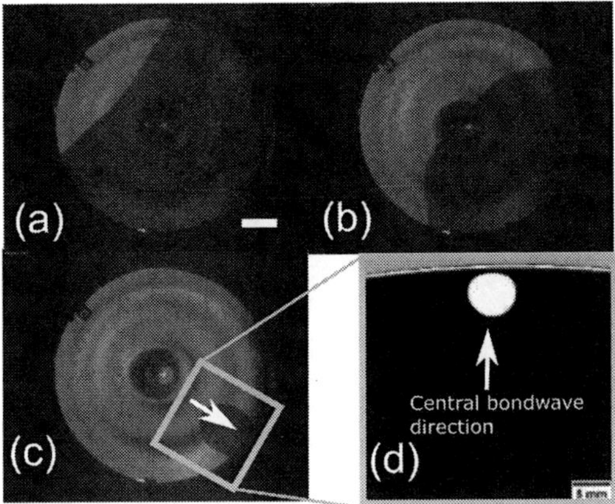

Figure 4. (a,b,c) Bondwave propagation with inhomogeneous bondwave propagation between edge and center. The white scale bar is 50 mm (d) Corresponding SAM image.

Using 2D velocity mapping, we can define regions of interest (ROI) to closely monitor the process and improve the bondwave propagation to avoid void formation. Figure 5(a) display a dataset points coordinates for two batches of wafers with different surface preparation methods. Two ROI are defined, one the edge and one in the center. A 15mm edge exclusion is applied. In Figure 5(b), we show the speed ratio corresponding to the two ROI defined above. Two batch of wafers are presented, one with an initial process leading to defective bond (Figure 4) and one with an improved process for defect free interface. We were able to maintain similar bonding wave speeds while increasing greatly the speed homogeneity, avoiding void formation.

Furthermore, we observe a speed increase when using a pre-bonding plasma treatment. During an atmospheric pressure bonding, the bondwave speed increases from 21 to 38 mm/s and from 27 to 42 mm/s for edge and center initiation, respectively, when using our standard nitrogen plasma process. Plasma activated bonding is not only beneficial for post annealing adherence energy. It can also be used to reduce defect size and unbonded area at wafer edges.

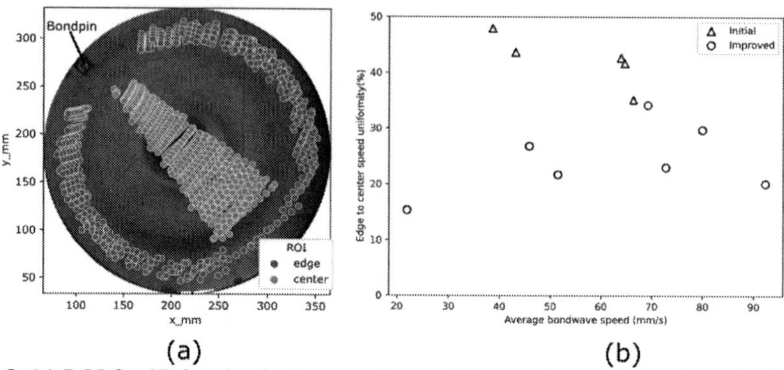

(a)   (b)

Figure 5. (a) ROI for 2D bond velocity mapping. A 15 mm edge exclusion is applied (b) Edge to center velocity ratio as function of average bondwave speed for two processes.

<u>Shape and Distortion Measurements</u>

Figure 6 presents residual distortion values for a wide range of bonding wave speeds. Center initiation gives distortion values which are higher than with edge initiation. Maximum values are achieved at high bondwave speed but wafer to wafer repeatability prevents to see a clear trend. Differences between the two initiations methods can be explained by the more important bond pin signature left in the center, resulting in higher order distortion. Residual distortion differences between two methods remain stable as the bondwave speed increases. Improvement in bonding sequence and chuck design yields significantly lower absolute and residuals distortion (9).

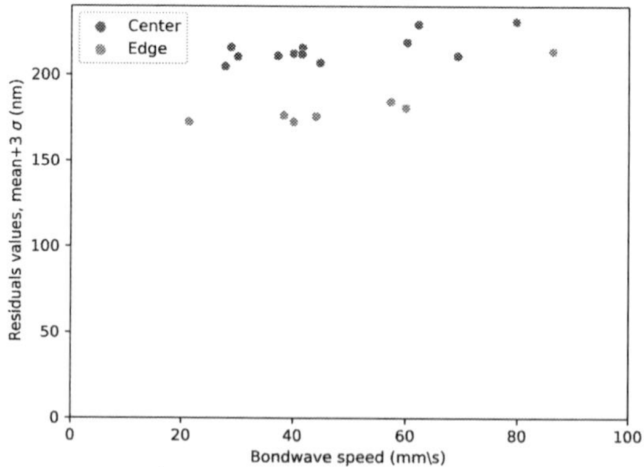

Figure 6. Residual distortion after subtracting 4-parameters model contribution as a function of mean bondwave speed and for different initiation locations. 300 mm Si/SiO$_2$ (100nm) bonded pairs after 2h 300°C annealing step.

In a similar manner, Figure 7 shows run-out or scaling value as a function of mean bondwave velocity for edge and center initiation. There is a linear increase of the run-out with bondwave speed. Trend is similar for both initiation methods. This behavior can be easily explained that the fact that wafers extend when being brought in contact during bonding wave propagation. For 3D integration and layer transfer where absolute distortion and residual value are key and should be minimized, a certain number of strategies are used.

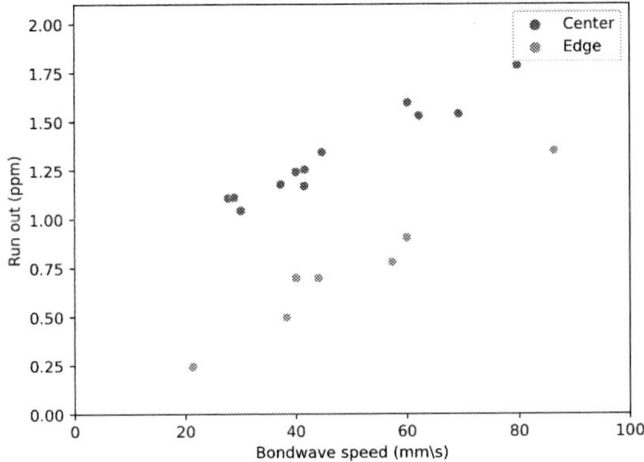

Figure 7. Run out value as a function on mean bonding wave velocity for two different initiation methods. 300 mm Si/SiO$_2$ (100nm) bond pair after 2h 300°C annealing step.

Conclusion

We gave an overview of the possibility offered by inline IR bond wave observation for fusion bonding process monitoring and optimization. We were able to detect defects early-on in the process and optimize processes to avoid post bond defectivity. This opens a lot of possibilities for inline process monitoring and rework capabilities. Furthermore, we showed that bondwave observation is efficient in order to predict adhesion energy changes, as in the case of plasma activated bonding. And finally, we showed that bond pair run out increases linearly with bondwave speed.

References

1. F. Rieutord, B. Bataillou, and H. Moriceau, Phys. Rev. Lett., 94, 236101 (2005).
2. V. Larrey, G. Mauguen, F. Fournel, D. Radisson, F. Rieutord, C. Morales, C. Bridoux, and H. Moriceau, ECS Trans., 75(9), 145 (2016).
3. D. Radisson, thesis, Université de Grenoble (2014).
4. R. Stengl, K. Mitani, V. Lehmann, and U. Gosele, in IEEE SOS/SOI Technology Conference,, p. 123–124 (1989).

5. U. Gösele, Y. Bluhm, G. Kästner, P. Kopperschmidt, G. Kräuter, R. Scholz, A. Schumacher, St. Senz, Q.-Y. Tong, L.-J. Huang, Y.-L. Chao and T. H. Lee, Journal of Vacuum Science & Technology A, 17, 1145–1152 (1999).
6. M. Broekaart, A. Castex, K. Landry, R. Fontaniere, and C. Lagahe-Blanchard, *ECS Trans.*, 50(7), 371 (2013).
7. A. Castex, M. Broekaart, F. Rieutord, K. Landry, and C. Lagahe-Blanchard, *ECS Solid State Lett.*, **2**, P47 (2013).
8. V. Dragoi, A. Filbert, S. Zhu, and G. Mittendorfer, in 2010 11th International Conference on Electronic Packaging Technology & High Density Packaging, p. 27–30 (2010).
9. R. van Haren, S. Li, B. Minghetti, L. van Dijk, K. Brantjes, F. Fournel, G. Mauguen, I. Mendes, C. Lapeyre, M. Pourteau, M. May, L. Pain, K. Abadie, T. Plach and M. Wimplinger, in Metrology, Inspection, and Process Control XXXVII,, vol. 12496, p. 621–634, SPIE (2023)
10. T. Plach, K. Hingerl, S. Tollabimazraehno, G. Hesser, V. Dragoi and M. Wimplinger, Journal of Applied Physics, 113, 094905 (2013).
11. H, Moriceau, F, Rieutord, F, Fournel, Y. Le Tiec, L. Di Cioccio, C. Morales, A. M. Charvet and C. Deguet, Advances in Natural Sciences: Nanoscience and Nanotechnology, 1, 043004 (2011).
12. F. Fournel, B. Rousset, V. Larrey, C. Morales, R. Sachs, L. Sudrie, and C. Morvan, WaferBond'22 Proceeding, 2022.
13. F. Nagano, S. Iacovo, A. Phommahaxay, F. Inoue, F. Chancerel, H. Naser, G. Beyer, E. Beyne and S. De. Gendt., ECS J. Solid State Sci. Technol., 11, 063012 (2022).

ECS Transactions, 112 (3) 31-37 (2023)
10.1149/11203.0031ecst ©The Electrochemical Society

Infrared Spectroscopy Study of Edge Water Penetration at Hydrophilic Bonding Interface

P. Noël[1], V. Larrey[1], C. Morales[1], D. Landru[2], F. Rieutord[2] and F. Fournel[1]

[1] Université Grenoble Alpes, F-38000 Grenoble, France CEA, Leti, Minatec Campus, F-38054 Grenoble, France
[2] SOITEC, Parc Technologique des Fontaines F-38190 Bernin, France

In this article, we report on the use of a new characterization technique to measure the water penetration at the bonding interfaces and to quantify it. This complements previous studies done using X-ray reflectometry and surface acoustic microscopy: Fourier Transform Infra-Red Multiple Internal Reflection (FTIR-MIR) spectroscopy is used here to characterize the evolutions of contributions of silanols, surface bonded water and free liquid water groups.

Introduction

Hydrophilic direct wafer bonding is based on the spontaneous bonding of two surfaces without added materials in-between. This process is used to build structures in microelectronics, optoelectronics or MEMS technologies. Adhesion (bonding wave propagation (1)) and adherence (mechanical strength of the bonding interface (2)) of the structure are directly related to the water amount on surfaces before bonding or at the interface after bonding.

Previous studies showed that, after bonding, the water present in the clean room atmosphere (40% relative humidity) was able to penetrate at the bonding interface increasing the amount of trapped-water at the bonding interface. These studies were based on two types of measurements: hydrogen gas defects (generated by silicon oxidation reaction with water) observed with Scanning Acoustic Microscopy (SAM) and X-Ray-Reflectivity measurements (giving the electron density at the bonding interface)(3,4).

The water quantity found by Tedjini et al. with SAM measurements was 1.6 monolayers as bonded and 3.4 monolayers after water penetration.

Gas defects nucleation was described with a Lucas-Washburn with A the "diffusion" coefficient and l the distance at the wafer edge.

$$l^2 = At \qquad [1]$$

The "diffusion" coefficient for a silicon-silicon bonding found to be was $A_{Si//Si}=1.52 \ 10^{-9}$ m²/s (5)

Calvez et al. showed that the same phenomenon happened for a silicon-oxide bonding. They and found a coefficient $A_{Si//SiO2}=2.7 \ 10^{-9}$ m²/s (6).

For oxide-oxide bonding, the same effect is expected, but no study demonstrated it and quantified it.

In the current study, we measured directly the amount of water by Fourier Transform Infra-Red Multiple Internal Reflection (FTIR-MIR) (7) spectroscopy for silicon-silicon, silicon-oxide and oxide-oxide bonded wafers. However, this measurement of few monolayers of water at bonding interface is quite difficult given the low signal to noise ratio and the environment variability. We report a method to have accurate quantification of water at such bonding interface.

Materials and methods

Silicon-bonded and oxide-bonded samples were 200mm-diameter 725μm-thick (100) silicon wafers. The oxidized wafers were covered with a 100 nm thermal oxide. A chemical treatment has been performed to have hydrophilic surfaces (CARO/SC1/DIO3/IPA Marangoni dryer). Samples were manually bonded after this chemical treatment. A HF-dip of bonded samples was realized conducted prior to FTIR-MIR measurement to remove the water adsorbed on the backside surfaces.

Measurements were performed on a Vertex70V from Bruker with a MIR setup including two silicon prisms, a KBr splitter and a MCT infrared detector. Prisms were 5cm apart. Measurements were performed on integral 200 mm bonded substrates, under a 1 mbar vacuum.

Prisms were located as shown on **Figure 1**. Because of the prisms position and the beam width, concentric circles are plotted to show that multiple radii of water penetration are probed with this technique, as illustrated by concentric circles in the schematics.

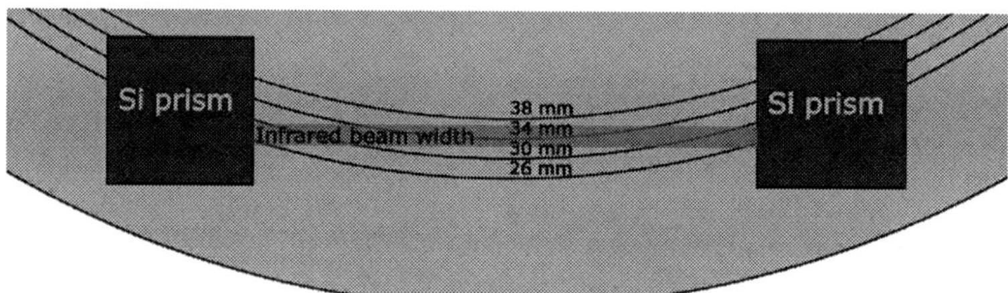

Figure 1. MIR setup: Silicon prisms position, IR beam width, position and concentric circles 26 mm to 38mm from the wafer edge with a 4mm step

The absorbance was calculated using the signal of a silicon bonded reference annealed at high temperature to fully close the interface keeping HF-dipped prior to measurement. A baseline of the signal and a Gaussian decomposition of the OH stretching absorption band signal were performed enabling the identification of silanols, surface bonded water and free liquid water contributions. Values used for the fit were obtained according to the literature and data given in **Table 1** (8–10). C-H absorption bands were added to fully describe the 4000-2500 cm^{-1} wavenumber range.

TABLE I. Infrared absorption wavelengths of hydroxyls compound at bonding interface (8–10)

Chemical	Peak position	Peak FWHM
Isolated Si-OH	3750 cm^{-1}	Thin peak (FWHM $\approx$ 10cm^{-1})
H-bonded Si-OH	3640 cm^{-1}	Thin peak (FWHM $\approx$ 50 cm^{-1})
High H-bonded water	3500 cm^{-1}	Medium peak (FWHM $\approx$ 100 cm^{-1})
Intermediate H-bonded water	3300 cm^{-1}	Large peak (FWHM $\approx$ 200-150 cm^{-1})
Free water	3050 cm^{-1}	Large peak (FWHM $\approx$ 200-150 cm^{-1})

High H-bonded water represents the first molecules that are linked to the surface with hydrogen bonds whereas free water represent the molecules that are not attracted by the surface silanols groups.

The integral of each Gaussian peak is supposed to be proportional to the relative amount of water. A data treatment example is shown on **Figure 2**.

The standard deviation attributed to the measurement was calculated with all the reference signal comparison.

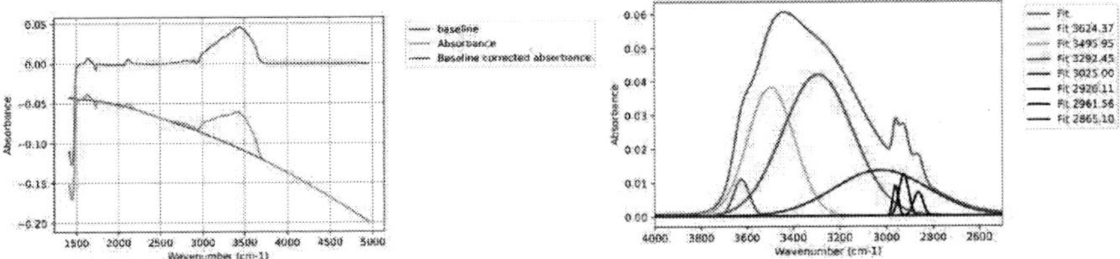

Figure 2. Example of Absorbance data treatment: a) baseline correction b) Gaussian decomposition of OH peaks

Results and discussions

<u>Silicon-silicon bonding</u>

Samples with silicon-silicon bonding interfaces were first investigated. The result of the Gaussian decomposition of the absorption signal versus water vapor exposure time is shown in **Figure 3**.

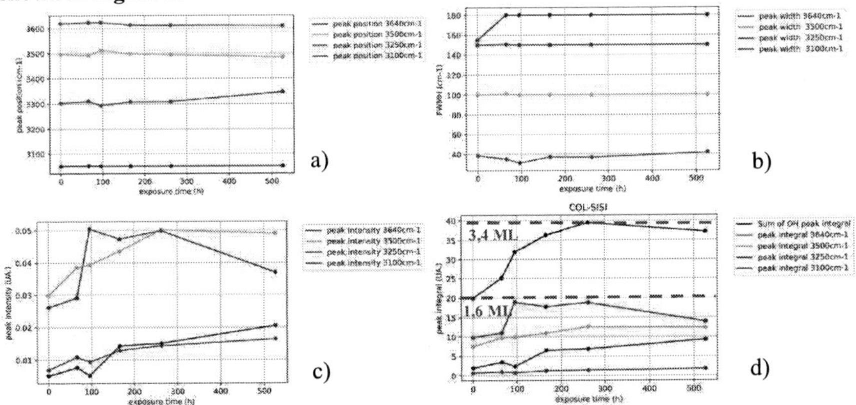

Figure 3. Gaussian decomposition data for silicon-silicon bonding interface for different exposure times a) peak position versus waiting time b) peak width versus waiting time c) peak intensity versus waiting time d) peak integrals versus waiting time

The peak position and Full Width at Half maximum (FWMH) show that the decomposition matches literature values. We can assign the increase of water quantity at the bonding interface mostly to the increase of the peaks integral during the exposure time. The amounts of high H-bonded water, intermediate H-bonded water and free water increase with it, while silanols H-bonded groups during the imbibition time.

This result is consistent with previous studies (5) on water penetration at silicon/silicon bonding interfaces :

- The integral of the peak reaches a plateau at 250 hours. This result is consistent with Tedjini's diffusion coefficient predicting that a 38 mm radius of water penetration (Fig.1.) should be reached 264 hours after bonding.

- The integral increases by a factor 2, which is in line with the expected amount of water at the bonding interface (1,6 monolayers as bonded and 3.4 monolayers after water penetration).

Silicon-Oxide bonding

Samples with silicon-oxide bonding were then investigated. Signal interference oscillations appeared due to the presence of a 100nm oxide. However, the OH absorption band decomposition was still possible. Decomposition results are shown on **Figure 4**.

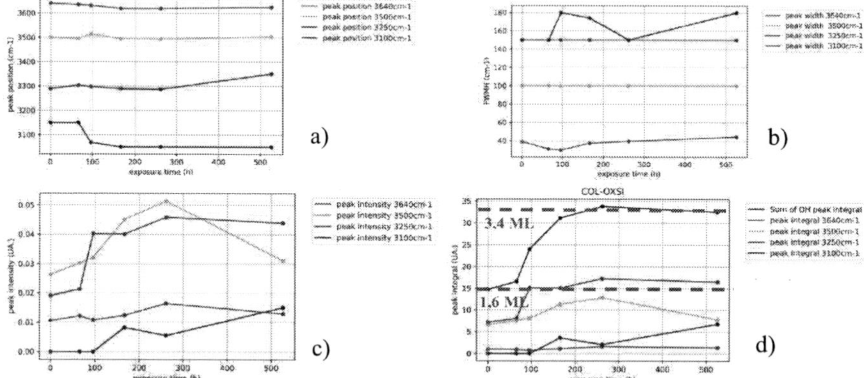

Figure 4. Gaussian decomposition data for silicon-oxide bonding interface for different exposure times a) peak position versus waiting time b) peak width versus exposure time c) peak intensity versus waiting time d) peak integrals versus waiting time

This result is comparable to the previous one: High H-bonded water, intermediate H-bonded water and free water contributions increase over time, as silanols H-bonded groups remain stable.

There are differences with Calvez's work (6) and with silicon-silicon bonding:

- Peak integrals, are lower than those obtained in Figure 3. An explanation could be that the reference used is a silicon-silicon bonding or that the water amount at the interface is lower. However, peak integral variations remain consistent with the previous water quantification as bonded and after water penetration; the value at the plateau is 2 times higher than the as bonded integral.

- The plateau should be reached at 150 hours for a coefficient A $_{Si//SiO2}$=2.7 10^{-9} m²/s based on Calvez et al., while it is reached here at 225 hours, maybe because of spatial resolution limits of the measurements.

Indeed FTIR-MIR seems accurate enough to quantify the amount of water at an interface but lacks spatial and time resolution (due to the prisms position and multiple radii of water penetration taken in account).

Oxide-Oxide bonding

Finally, oxide-oxide bonding samples were studied. Signal oscillations appeared due to the presence of a100nm oxide. However, the OH absorption band decomposition was still possible. Decomposition results are shown on **Figure 5**.

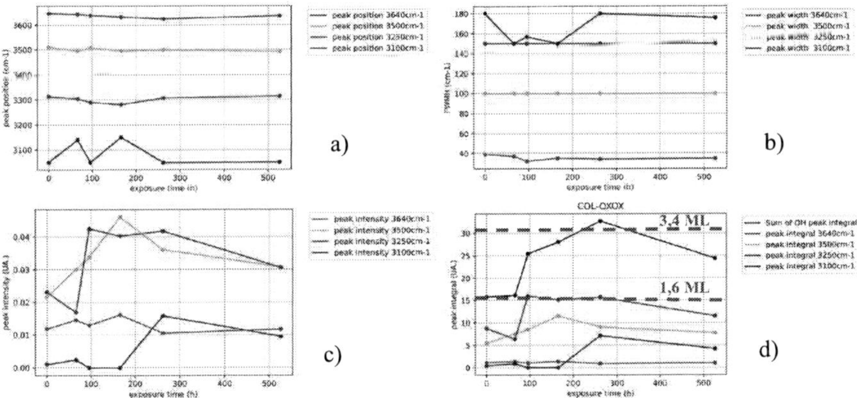

Figure 5. Gaussian decomposition data for oxide-oxide bonding interface for different exposure times a) peak position versus waiting time b) peak width versus waiting time c) peak intensity versus waiting time d) peak integrals versus waiting time

Results are comparable to that of oxide-silicon samples. High H-bonded water, intermediate H-bonded water and free water contributions increase over time, while silanols H-bonded groups remain stable. Peak integral variations remain coherent with the previous water quantification as bonded and after water penetration.

The last point in **Figure 5.d)** is showing that there seems to have a decrease after 520 hours. However, such a point does not seem consistent with previous results, and future experiments will be made to confirm this variation.

There are no values of diffusion coefficient for oxide-oxide bonding exists in the literature. This measurement shows that the water penetration kinetics seem similar to that for a oxide-silicon interface. However, because of low spatial and time resolution, we cannot calculate this coefficient.

<u>Sample comparison</u>

One of the goal of this study was to quantify differences between the different types of bonding interfaces. Peaks integral comparison is plotted in **Figure 6.** to that end.
Previous results showed that interpretations on spatial and temporal dimensions are not feasible. However, the integral increase by a factor of roughly two over time is, whatever the type of interface, in line with the expected variation of water amount at the bonding interface based on literature's data: 1,6 monolayers as bonded up to 3,4 monolayers after water penetration.
Integral values are otherwise higher for silicon-silicon bonding interfaces than for oxide-silicon / oxide-oxide. The likely reason to explain this difference is the use of a closed interface silicon-silicon reference without oxide layer. The presence of thick oxide layers might have lowered the signal in the latter two cases.

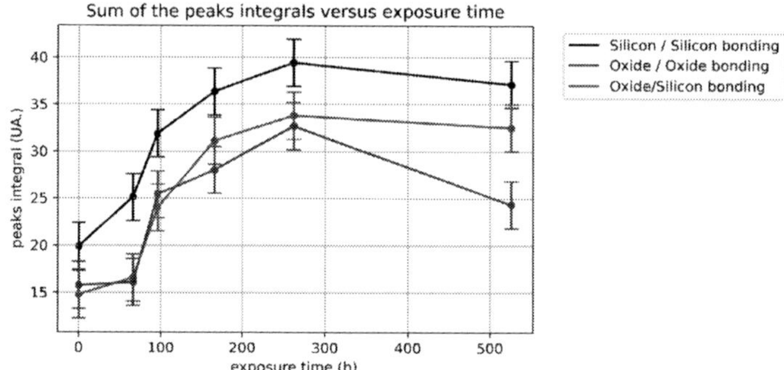

Figure 6. Peak integrals comparison for silicon-silicon / oxide-silicon and oxide-oxide bondings

Conclusion

FTIR-MIR measurements enable us to observe directly the water penetration at the silicon-silicon, oxide-silicon and oxide-oxide bonding interfaces. The evolution of the peak integrals variation were consistent with previous quantifications of water amount at bonding interfaces.
This study enable us to observe water penetration at oxide-oxide bonding interfaces, something not documented in the literature. This phenomenon is similar to silicon-oxide bonding interface but due to low spatial and time resolution no diffusion coefficient could be calculated.
However, this method appears relevant to quantify trapped-water at bonding interface, even if deriving kinetic information from it is not really feasible. However we could imagine setup upgrades to improve spatial resolution (higher samples diameter, thinner infra-red beam, reduce the distance between prisms)
This method could be applied to a wide range of surface treatments to have accurate quantification of the variation in water quantity induced by this treatment. As no other direct measurements of water quantity is possible at the bonding interface, this method is important to show the coherence between water amount and hydrogen production at the bonding interface.

Acknowledgments

The authors would like to thank SOITEC S. A. for financial support.

References

1. Larrey V, Mauguen G, Fournel F, Radisson D, Rieutord F, Morales C, et al. Adhesion Energy and Bonding Wave Velocity Measurements. ECS Transactions. 23 sept 2016;75(9):145-52.

2. Fournel F, Tedjini M, Larrey V, Rieutord F, Morales C, Bridoux C, et al. Impact of Water Edge Absorption on Silicon Oxide Direct Bonding Energy. ECS Transactions. 23 sept 2016;75(9):129-34.

3. Tedjini M, Fournel F, Moriceau H, Larrey V, Landru D, Kononchuk O, et al. Interface water diffusion in silicon direct bonding. Appl Phys Lett. 12 sept 2016;109(11):111603.

4. Rieutord F, Tardif S, Landru D, Kononchuk O, Larrey V, Moriceau H, et al. Edge Water Penetration in Direct Bonding Interface. Meet Abstr. 1 sept 2016;MA2016-02(32):2087.

5. Tedjini M. Gestion de l'eau à l'interface de collage Silicium/Silicium [Thesis]. [CEA Grenoble]: Université Grenoble Alpes; 2017.

6. Calvez A. Gestion de l'eau dans le collage direct [Internet] [These de doctorat]. Université Grenoble Alpes; 2022 [cité 3 juill 2023]. Disponible sur: https://www.theses.fr/2022GRALY096

7. Rochat N, Olivier M, Chabli A, Conne F, Lefeuvre G, Boll-Burdet C. Multiple internal reflection infrared spectroscopy using two-prism coupling geometry: A convenient way for quantitative study of organic contamination on silicon wafers. Appl Phys Lett. 2 oct 2000;77(14):2249-51.

8. Baum M, Rébiscoul D, Juranyi F, Rieutord F. Structural and Dynamical Properties of Water Confined in Highly Ordered Mesoporous Silica in the Presence of Electrolytes. J Phys Chem C. 30 août 2018;122(34):19857-68.

9. Caër SL, Pin S, Esnouf S, Raffy Q, Ph. Renault J, Brubach JB, et al. A trapped water network in nanoporous material: the role of interfaces. Physical Chemistry Chemical Physics. 2011;13(39):17658-66.

10. Davis KM, Tomozawa M. An infrared spectroscopic study of water-related species in silica glasses. Journal of Non-Crystalline Solids. 2 juin 1996;201(3):177-98.

ECS Transactions, 112 (3) 39-49 (2023)
10.1149/11203.0039ecst ©The Electrochemical Society

Nanosecond Laser Irradiation for Interface Bonding Characterization

V. Larrey[a], A. Arribehaute[a], B. Caulfield[a], P. Acosta-Alba[a], C. Morales[a], P. Noël[a], M. Opprecht[a], F. Fournel[a],
F. Rieutord[b], D. Landru[b]
a- Univ. Grenoble Alpes, CEA, LETI, F-38000 Grenoble
b- SOITEC, Parc Technologique des Fontaines, Chemin des Franques, 38190 Bernin

Abstract

In this study, we propose a novel method to quantify the interfacial water trapped at the direct bonding interface. The concept is to intentionally create bonding defects with controlled size and shape, and use them as sensors for the gases generated through the oxidation of a material (in our case, Silicon) by water adsorbed on the surfaces prior to bonding. The evolution of the sensor sizes provides valuable insights into the amount of gas they have trapped, allowing us to analyze the imbibition effect. Analyzing sensors arrays also enables us to quantify the amount of water that was initially present at the bonding interface. Moreover, it opens up the possibility of proposing a novel bonding energy measurement method.

Introduction

Direct bonding processes are increasingly used for the production of substrates and components for nanoelectronics, photonics and micromechanical applications. These processes enable (i) the transfer of layers without additional materials (such as a glue) and (ii) the stacking of components with electrical contacts (1,2). However, this direct bonding process comes with some challenges. It necessitates surfaces that are meticulously controlled in terms of topology, micro-roughness, curvature, particules and hydrocarbon contamination as well as surface chemistry (3,4).

In the case of hydrophilic direct bonding, which is the most commonly employed method, it is widely recognized in the literature that water adsorbed on surfaces becomes trapped at the bonding interface, playing a crucial role in the bonding mechanisms (5). On the one hand, if an excess amount of water is present and oxidizes one of the materials near the bonding interface, this could lead to high defectivity in the form of gas bubbles, e.g. a by-product of the oxidation reaction (6). On the other hand, water also enhances the bonding energy, as previously described in published mechanisms (5,7).

While there have been a few examples in the literature involving FTIR studies (8), the characterization of the amount of water at the bonding interface remains limited. Other works (9) reported that the measurements of native oxide film thickness at the direct bonding interface with XRR analysis could also give valuable insights into the trapped water amount. Tedjini et al. (10) highlighted the imbibition phenomena by observing the defectivity caused by the introduction of additional water. More recently, Yoshioka et al.

(11) showed TDS measurements during the degassing of thin films to compare their water contents prior to bonding.

Experimental details

Nanosecond laser annealing provides the capability to reach exceptionally high temperatures above the melting point of silicon (1414°C) within very short durations (ranging from tens to hundreds of nanoseconds). In our particular case, we are using a SCREEN's LT3100 tool equipped with a UV laser operating at a wavelength of 308 nm and a pulse duration of 160 ns (FWHM). This configuration offers two advantages: first, it facilitates energy absorption at a shallow depth (<30 nm). Second, it limits the thermal diffusion thanks to the short pulse duration. Consequently, under these irradiation conditions, silicon fusion can be achieved on the extreme surface. It has been previously observed that the initiation of this melting phenomenon induced by irradiation is heterogeneous, resulting from the formation and subsequent recrystallization of molten islands during laser annealing (12). Figure 1 depicts AFM characterization of the surface topology of a silicon substrate that underwent nanosecond laser annealing at various energy densities.

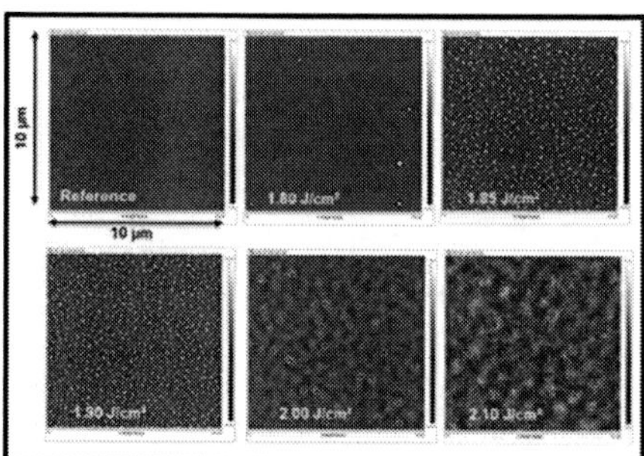

Figure 1: AFM characterization of surfaces irradiated with ns laser

Above an energy density of 1.80 J/cm², surface structures appear as isolated entities with a low density per unit area. As the energy density further increases, these structures become more densely distributed until they eventually cover the entire irradiated surface. Energy densities ranging from 1.8 to 2.0 J/cm² result in root mean square (RMS) roughness values exceeding 1 nm. As surface roughness values exceeding 0.5 nm RMS are generally unsuitable for direct bonding, this presents an opportunity to create controlled bonding defects by manipulating the size of the irradiated zone. Furthermore, the roughened area of the substrate can be spatially controlled. By repeating this local roughening process at multiple points on the substrate, we can generate defect lines or arrays. Following the direct bonding process, the radius of these bonding defects is determined through high-resolution acoustic microscopy (Figure 2a for line sensors and Figure 2b for network sensors). The pixel size in these acoustic images is 10x10 µm². Figure 2c showcases sensors that exhibit precise control in terms of size (60 µm radius) and position.

In this study, we examine the sensor size evolution based on the waiting time after direct bonding, as well as on the post-bonding annealing impact. We investigate direct bonding scenarios involving Silicon to Silicon, Silicon to thermal oxide, and thermal oxide to thermal oxide interfaces.

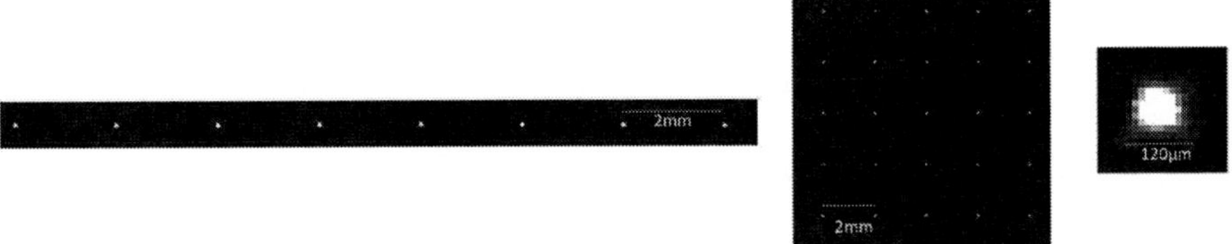

Figure 2: Bonding defects fabrication with controlled size and position

Results and Discussion

<u>Imbibition of the bonding interface by atmospheric water</u>

As a first step, bonding defects are deliberately created along the diameter of a wafer, spaced at a pitch of 2mm. The bonding wave propagates perpendicular to this line of bonding defects. Subsequently, their evolution is measured over time after direct bonding, without any subsequent annealing. High-resolution acoustic microscopy is used for characterization in a SAM Auto Wafer 300 tool developed by TEPLA.

Initial findings, shown in Figure 3 are obtained for Silicon-to-Silicon bonding and cover a time span from the bonding day (D1), 3 days after (D3) and 10 days after (D10). A gradual defect radii increase is evidenced when coming closer and closer to the wafer edge, with defects located at the edge exhibiting faster growth compared to those situated near the wafer center. Similar observations are made with oxide-to-silicon bonding. However, no discernible changes in bonding defects sizes are observed for oxide-to-oxide bonding.

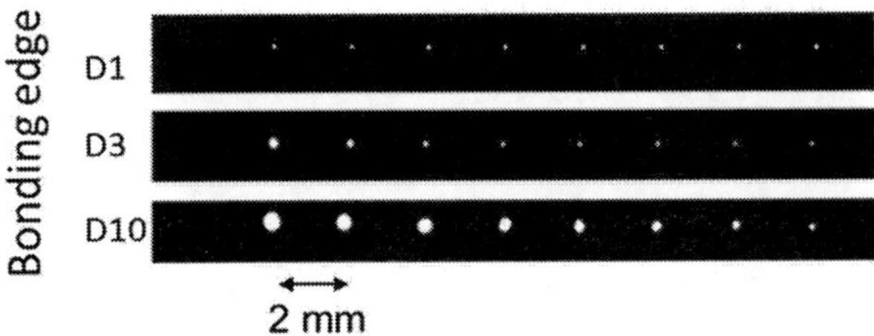

Figure 3: Bonding defects evolution with time, at room temperature

Based on our observations, the presence of additional water from the cleanroom atmosphere due to the bonding interface imbibition is suspected. This water induces silicon oxidation at room temperature. As a consequence, di-hydrogen gas is generated and subsequently trapped by bonding defects. In other words, bonding defects act as humidity sensors. By analyzing consecutive images, we are able to plot the evolution of the defects' radii depending on their positions along the wafer diameter for various waiting times (Figure 4a). For each waiting time, we also record the point at which the defects become sensitive to the water penetration.

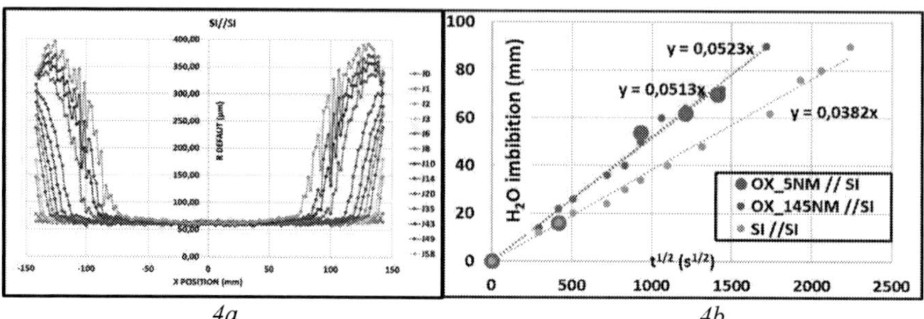

4a   *4b*

Figure 4: (a) Evolution of defects' radii according to their position along a wafer diameter and storage time (in days) (b) Dependence of water penetration distance on the square root of time

The water flow kinetics can be described using macroscopic capillarity models, assuming the propagation of an abrupt capillarity front. Lucas-Washburn model (13) can be used even if we know it is a rough approximation. Indeed a more gradual imbibition was proposed by Rieutord, employing different analytical descriptions based on either the Porous Medium Equation (PME) formalism or the diffusion/heat equation (14).

Similarly to Tedjini's findings, our results demonstrate a dependence of water penetration distance on the square root of time (Figure 4b). Consequently, we derive an observed diffusion parameter, denoted as A, such that $L = \sqrt{At}$. Here, the term "observed diffusion parameter" is used as it is determined for a specific water quantity, which is sufficient to induce the sensor growth. Through linear regression analysis, we obtain $A_{Si//Si}=1,46.10^{-9}$ $m^2.s^{-1}$ for Silicon-to-Silicon bonding. It is worth noting that Tedjini reported higher values ($A_{Si//Si}=9.10^{-9}$ $m^2.s^{-1}$) for liquid water imbibition experiments. Additionally, in his thesis manuscript (15), he mentioned a value of $A_{Si//Si}=1,52.10^{-9}$ $m^2.s^{-1}$ for experiments conducted while waiting in a clean room atmosphere. Remarkably, this value closely matches the one we obtain for the same imbibition conditions, enabling us to conclude that we observe the same water penetration phenomenon.

Importantly, this novel technique allows us to demonstrate imbibition in Oxide to Silicon bonding as well. For such interfaces, we calculate a higher "observed diffusion parameter" $A_{SiO2//Si}=2,7.10^{-9}$ $m^2.s^{-1}$. The reason behind this difference is not entirely clear. One hypothesis could be that the charge states at the bonding interface are modified by the introduction of a silicon oxide layer. As water is a polar molecule, this modification could influence its diffusion at the bonding interface. Another hypothesis might be to consider a larger interface bonding thickness in the case of a Silicon to Oxide bonding. Further investigations are required to fully understand this phenomenon.

<u>Hydration state of surfaces before bonding</u>

In the next step, sensors are arranged into arrays with varying pitches ranging from 2 to 20mm. A nitrogen plasma treatment was used for surface preparation prior to bonding. The radii sensors evolution is then measured as a function of time and annealing temperature after bonding.

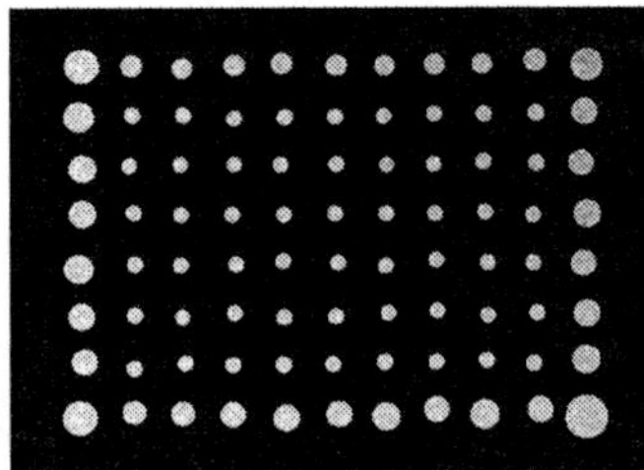

Figure 5: disparity of sensors' radii in a sensor array after thermal annealing

In our study, we emphasize (Figure 5) that the evolution described was highly influenced by the position of sensors within the array. Specifically, we observe that sensors located in the outer corners exhibit larger growth compared to sensors along the outer line, which in turn grow larger than sensors located in the center of the network. This disparity can be attributed to sensors acting as traps capturing dihydrogen generated at the bonding interface during the annealing process, where interfacial water oxidizes the silicon bonded surface. To describe this phenomenon, we formulate a diffusion equation for dihydrogen in the presence of a gas sink at the bonding interface. Naturally, the capture surface for dihydrogen is greater for sensors positioned at the corners of the array, as opposed to those located in the center. For the latter, the amount of dihydrogen captured is finite and evenly distributed among adjacent sensors. Specifically, for a given spacing a, the capture surface for each sensor in the center of the lattice is a^2.

Upon observing the evolution of sensor radii as a function of annealing time, particularly for thermal treatments ranging from 30 minutes to 32 hours at 500°C (Figure 6a), we notice that the sensor radii reach an asymptote for the center sensors with small spacing (a=2 or 5mm). This indicates that the diffusion of gases from the bonding interface to the sensors has reached completion and an equilibrium in pressure and dihydrogen concentration has been achieved between sensors and their surrounding bonding interface. However, for corner sensors or sensors in arrays with larger spacing (a =10 or 20mm), the failure to reach asymptotes after a 32-hour annealing indicates still ongoing diffusion of gaseous species towards the sensors due to the larger capture surface.

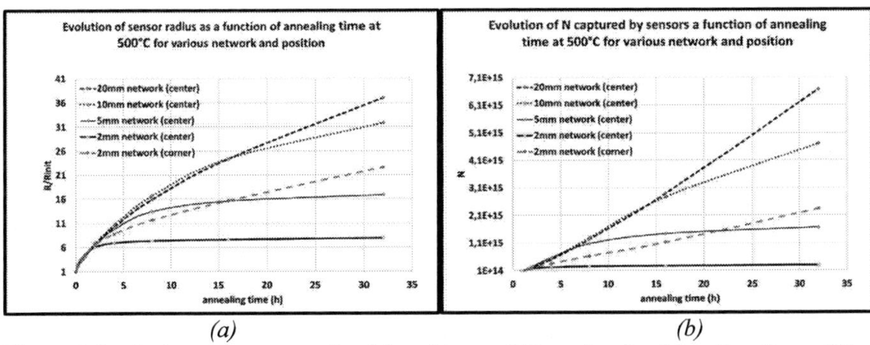

(a)   *(b)*

Figure 6: Evolutions of sensor radius (a) and trapped H_2 molecules (b) as functions of the annealing time

Optical interferometry observations of the bonded back surfaces after annealing (Figure 7) reveal that pressurized sensors generate deformations on the substrates' back surfaces. We characterize that using the Zygo Verfire™ XL tool. In the image, the deformation is depicted as dz/dx, helping in visualizing the substrate's overall scale. The different sensor arrays, ranging from 2 to 20 mm in spacing, are clearly discernible, as well as the two isolated sensors located at the bottom of the image.

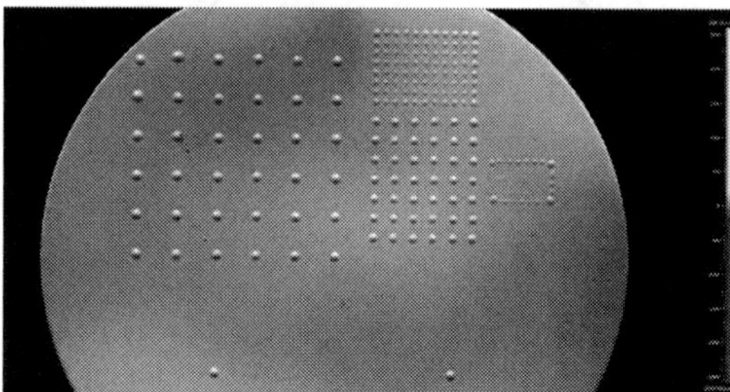

Figure 7: substrate back deformation highlighted with optical interferometry

This information plays a crucial role in determining the appropriate crack model to calculate the equilibrium quantity of dihydrogen molecules present in the collectors. Due to the deformations observed on the rear faces, the Penny Shape model of a circular crack inside an infinite medium cannot be employed. As an alternative, we use a rigid membrane model. With it, the energy equilibrium at constant pressure establishes the relationship between the number N of dihydrogen molecules present in the collector and the collector radius R, the surface energy γ, and the annealing temperature T at which equilibrium was achieved.

$$N = \frac{4\gamma\pi R^2}{3k_B T} \qquad [1]$$

The surface energy γ was determined separately using DCB (double contilever beam) method, where $\gamma = G_c/2$, G_c being the bonding energy. In our specific case, after annealing at 500°C, we measured γ to be 2.5 J/m². Using this value, we plot the evolution of the trapped dihydrogen molecules number in sensors as a function of the annealing time (Figure 6b). The reaching of an asymptote in the center of the closely spaced arrays signs the end of the diffusion process. We have then access to the number of molecules present on a^2 surface area and in equilibrium with the bonding interface. Thus, in the case of the 2mm-spaced network, the collection in a sensor correspond to 2.8 x 10^{14} dihydrogen molecules, considering a surface area of 4 mm². The same calculations performed with the 5mm-spaced network lead to 1.7 x 10^{15} dihydrogen molecules. These two results are then consistent with a collection of 7 x 10^{13} dihydrogen molecules per mm².

We establish a connection between this value and the hydration state of the surfaces before bonding. On a 1 cm² unit surface area, a water monolayer with a height of 0.3 nm corresponds to a quantity of water molecules equal to $\frac{\rho V N_A}{m_{H_2O}} = 10^{15}$, where ρ represents the water density (assuming the adsorbed water density to be equivalent to the liquid one), V the volume of a water monolayer on 1cm², N_A Avogadro's number and m_{H2O} the molar mass of water. During the silicon oxidation, one water molecule produces one dihydrogen molecule:

$$Si+2H_2O \rightarrow SiO_2+2H_2 \quad [2]$$

One water monolayer will result in 4×10^{13} dihydrogen molecules over a surface area of 4 mm^2. Consequently, we determine that the 2.8×10^{14} dihydrogen molecules collected by sensors in the center of the 2 mm array correspond to 7 water monolayers over the 4 mm^2. The equilibrium in dihydrogen concentration between the sensor and the surrounding bonding interface can be expressed as follows:

$$\rho = \rho_{sensor} = (N/V)_{sensor} = \rho_{interface} \sim 1.7 \times 10^{28} \text{ molecules/m}^3$$
$$\rightarrow N_{interface} = \rho\,(hS)_{interface} \sim 2.6 \times 10^{13} \text{ with } h_{interface} = 1nm \text{ et } S_{interface} = 3{,}5mm^2$$

After the completion of the diffusion process, there are still 2.6×10^{13} dihydrogen molecules remaining at the bonding interface surrounding the sensor. In total, 3.1×10^{14} molecules of dihydrogen are produced through the oxidation of silicon, corresponding to approximately 7.7 monolayers of reacted water.

Based on this information, the hydration state of a surface following nitrogen plasma treatment was determined to be approximately 3.85 water monolayers. In comparison, employing the same measurement and calculation protocol, we find a hydration state of 1.6 water monolayers for chemically treated surfaces without plasma. This protocol enabled us to quantitatively assess the hydration states of surfaces prior to bonding and highlighted the enhanced water absorption capability of plasma-treated surfaces at the bonding interface. Noteworthy, as both surfaces has the same hydrophilicity (the same water contact angle), the plasma treatment should not be able to add water on the surface itself. The water excess should be below the surface. Indeed, plasma treatment is known to modify the sub-surface by few nanometer (3 to 5 nm). This sub-surface might then be quite hygroscopic to absorb more than 6 monolayer of water within few nanometers.

A new way of measuring bonding energy

The crack equilibrium according to the rigid membrane model can be described by equations linking its physical characteristics (volume and pressure) to the surface energy of the bonding at the equilibrium temperature. To determine these physical characteristics, acoustic characterization is used to precisely measure the radius of bonding defects (or sensors), while optical interferometric characterization measures the height of its deformation at the rear face. Through COMSOL simulations, we showed that backside deformation and defect height at the bonding interface were remarkably similar for the radii range considered here. As a result, we could accurately approximate the defect height h by measuring the deformation of the substrate's backside.

Acoustic and interferometric measurements are conducted at room temperature, while the membrane was in equilibrium at the annealing temperature of 500°C. It is important to note that a pressurized bonding defect at the annealing temperature would not re-bond when cooled back to room temperature. This is due to the fact that the driving force for bonding is the adhesion energy of the passivated inner surfaces, which is typically on the order of tens of mJ/m^2, significantly lower than the bonding energy (a few J/m^2). Consequently, the edges of a pressurized defect cannot re-bond significantly at pressures around several hundreds of bars. Thanks to acoustic measurement of defects radii at room temperature, we obtain a value for the defect's radius at Griffith equilibrium at the annealing temperature. In other words, R_{amb} is equivalent to R_{eq}.

However, it was necessary to account for the pressure drop experienced by defects between the equilibrium temperature and ambient temperature, as this has an impact of their heights. Therefore, a correction was required for the h value obtained from optical interferometry at room temperature in order to calculate heq at Griffith equilibrium temperature.

For a rigid membrane blister, h_{eq} can be expressed as:

$$h_{eq}(P,R) = \frac{3(1-v^2)}{16}\frac{PR^4}{Et^3} \qquad [3]$$

Where P and R are the pressure and radius of the defect, v and E are the Poisson's ratio and Young's modulus of the Silicon substrate, t is the thickness of the substrate. In addition, the volume of the rigid membrane at equilibrium is given by:

$$V_{eq} = \frac{2}{3}\pi R^2 h_{eq} \qquad [4]$$

V_{eq} therefore varies as PR^6 which implies that $PV=Nk_BT$ varies as P^2R^6. When transitioning from the equilibrium temperature to the ambient temperature, R and N remain unchanged, therefore we can conclude that P^2/T is a constant. It comes:

$$P_{eq} = P_{amb}\sqrt{\frac{T_{eq}}{T_{amb}}} \text{ And } h_{eq} = h_{amb}\sqrt{\frac{T_{eq}}{T_{amb}}} \qquad [5]$$

The height of the bonding defect (sensor) at the equilibrium temperature of 500°C can thus be deduced from optical interferometric measurements at room temperature.

By considering the ideal gas equation $PV=Nk_BT$ along with equations [1,3,4] we get the relationship giving γ as a function of the relevant dimensional and mechanical parameters of the sensors at equilibrium

$$\gamma = \frac{16h_{eq}{}^2Et^3}{6(1-v^2)R^4} \qquad [6]$$

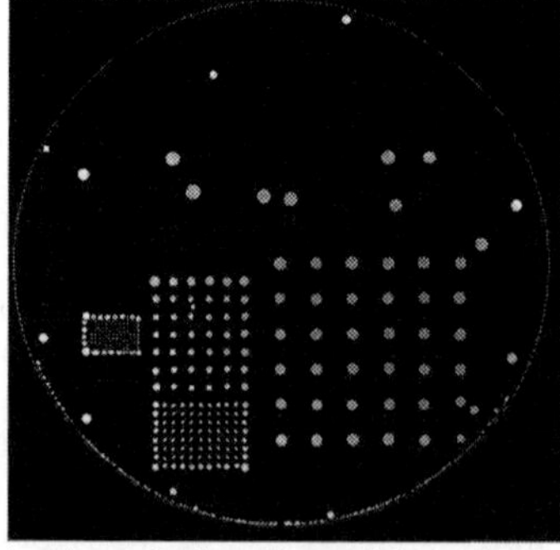

Figure 8: acoustic characterization of a bonding with a wide range of sensor sizes

For this bonding energy study, we use both isolated sensors and sensor arrays. Figure 8 shows an acoustic characterization of one bonding, providing a wide range of sensor sizes. Each sensor radius is associated with a crack height h_{eq} derived from the optical interferometric measurement h_{amb}. These measurements were conducted for two series of bonds. The first series exhibited a bonding energy measured by DCB method of 5 J/m^2, corresponding to γ=2.5 J/m^2. The second series had a bonding energy of 1.9 J/m^2, which translates to γ=0.95 J/m^2. Figure 9 displays the pairs of measurements (h, R) for both series. The square markers represent the series with γ=2.5 J/m^2, while the round markers represent the series with γ=0.95 J/m^2. Additionally, on the same graph, we plot equation [7], which depicts the variation of h as a function of R for a given γ.

$$h_{amb} = h_{eq}\sqrt{\frac{T_{amb}}{T_{eq}}} = \sqrt{\frac{6\gamma(1-v^2)R^4}{16Et^3}}\sqrt{\frac{T_{amb}}{T_{eq}}} \qquad [7]$$

We observe a definite agreement between measurement pairs (h, R) and analytical formulations. This indicates that characterizing the physical dimensions, h and R, of sensors provides an excellent means of calculating the bonding energy. Moreover, this method has potential for the localized characterization of the bonding energy at any point on the substrate. This development opens up the possibility of mapping the bonding interface, which has not been achieved so far.

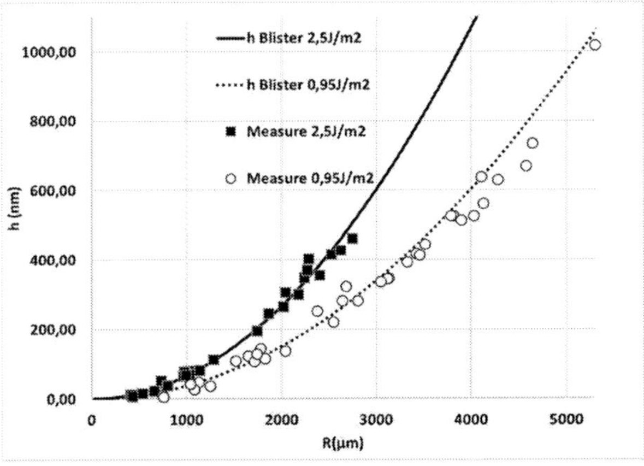

Figure 9: measurements and analytical evolution of sensor's height h according to sensors' radius R for two bonding energies

Conclusions

In this article, we have presented an innovative technique to create bonding defects with precise control over their size and position. These bonding defects were shown to be valuable sensors to detect gases generated at the bonding interface. Through our research, we have achieved several significant findings. First, we successfully demonstrated that these bonding defects served as indicators of water imbibition at the bonding interface.

Additionally, we have conducted a comprehensive quantitative study to assess the hydration state of surfaces prior to bonding. Our investigation revealed that surfaces treated with nitrogen plasma exhibited the ability to retain an excess amount of water. Furthermore, we have introduced a novel technique to quantify the bonding energy. Using bonding defects as sensors, we have devised a method to measure bonding energy and successfully demonstrated its application. This breakthrough paves the way towards the mapping of the bonding energy across various points on the substrate, yielding a deeper understanding of bonding characteristics and facilitating the optimization of bonding techniques.

References

1. JH. Lau, "Recent advances and trends in Cu-Cu Hybrid Bonding" in *IEEE Transctions on Components Packaging and Manufacturing Technology*, Vol.13 N°3, P399-P425 (2023)

2. A. Bond, E. Bourjot, S. Borel, T. Enot, P. Montméat, L. Sanchez, F. Fournel, J. Swan, "Collective die-to-wafer self-assembly for high alignment accuracy and high throughput 3D integration" in *Proc. IEEE 72nd Electron. Compon. Technol. Conf. (ECTC)*, pp. 168–176 (2022)

3. QY. Tong and U. Gösele, "Surface preparation and room temperature wafer bonding", in *Semiconductor Wafer Bonding,* Chapter 4, Wiley-Interscience Publication, P49-P101 (1999)

4. KT. Turner and SM. Spearing, "Mechanics of direct wafer bonding" in *Proc. R. Soc. A* 462, P171–P188 (2006)

5. F. Fournel, C. Martin-Cocher, D. Radisson, V. Larrey, E. Beche, C. Morales, P. A. Delean, F. Rieutord, and H. Moriceau, "Water Stress Corrosion in Bonded Structures" in *ECS Journal of Solid State Science and Technology*, 4 (5) P124-P130 (2015)

6. S. Vincent; I. Radu; D. Landru; F. Letertre; F. Rieutord, "A model of interface defect formation in silicon wafer bonding", *Appl. Phys. Lett. 94*, 101914 (2009)

7. W. Lin, L. Shi, Y. Yao, A. Madan, T. Pinto, N. Zavolas, R. Murphy, S. Skordas, and S. Iyer, "Low-Temperature Oxide Wafer Bonding for 3-D Integration: Chemistry of Bulk Oxide Matters" in *IEEE Transactions on Semiconductor Manufacturing*, Vol.27 n°3, P426-P430 (2014)

8. C. Ventosa, F. Rieutord, L. Libralesso, F. Fournel, C. Morales, and H. Moriceau, "Prebonding Thermal Treatment in Direct Si–Si Hydrophilic Wafer Bonding", *Journal of The Electrochemical Society*, 156 (11) H818-H823 (2009)

9. C. Ventosa, F. Rieutord, L. Libralesso, C. Morales, F. Fournel, and H. Moriceau "Hydrophilic low-temperature direct wafer bonding"in *J. Appl. Phys.* 104, 123524 (2008)

10. Tedjini M, Fournel F, Moriceau H, Larrey V, Landru D, Kononchuk O, et al. "Interface water diffusion in silicon direct bonding" in *Appl Phys Lett.* 12 sept 2016; 109(11):111603.

11. H. Yoshioka et al. "Influence of H2O in bonding interfaces on bonding strength of plasma-activated bonded silicon oxide" in *IEEE 73rd Electronic Components and Technology Conference*, P1119-1123 (2023)

14. L. Dagault, S. Kerdilès, P. Acosta Alba, J.-M. Hartmann, J.-P. Barnes, P. Gergaud, E. Scheid, and F. Cristiano, "Investigation of Recrystallization and Stress Relaxation in Nanosecond Laser Annealed Si1−xGex/Si Epilayers" in *Appl. Surf. Sci.* 527, 146752 (2020).

13. E. W. Washburn, "The dynamics of Capillary Flow" in *Phys. Rev. 17*, 273 (1921)

14. F. Rieutord, S. Tardif, I. Nikitskiy F. Fournel, M. Tedjini, V. Larrey, C. Bridoux, C. Morales, D. Landru, O. Kononchuk, "Water Transport Within Silicon Direct Bonding Gap" in *ECS Transactions, 86 (5)* P39-P47 (2018)

15. Tedjini M, Gestion de l'eau à l'interface de collage, *PhD manuscript* (2016)

ECS Transactions, 112 (3) 51-62 (2023)
10.1149/11203.0051ecst ©The Electrochemical Society

Polymer to Silicon Direct Bonding for Microelectronics

M. Dautriat, P. Montméat and F. Fournel

Univ. Grenoble Alpes, CEA, LETI, F-38000 Grenoble

Direct bonding consists in spontaneously bringing into contact two solid surfaces without any intermediate liquid. We focused on silicon direct bonding with polymer films. Direct bonding was evaluated with two polymers: LOR (MicroChem) and BARC (Rohm & Haas), commonly used in photolithography. Polymer bonding by thermal compression was compared to polymer direct bonding. Adhesion energies and bonding wave velocities of bonding between polymers and silicon surfaces were determined. The bonded stacks exhibited good quality bonding interfaces in terms of defects. High adherence energies up to 10 J/m² were measured.

Introduction

Materials used in microelectronics are generally inorganic. Devices are typically made from complex material stacks with semiconductors, oxides or metals. These materials have specific properties in terms of conduction, insulation, or optical properties.

In general, bonding in microelectronics requires two substrates to be brought into contact. It is possible to add a polymer layer to one or both substrates to act as an adhesive. Today, many polymers can be used for wafer bonding in microelectronics (1). Adhesive bonding is commonly achieved by thermal compression. This involves bringing two wafers into contact under a given force, pressure and temperature, usually under vacuum. Adhesive bonding has various uses in 3D integration (2), thin film transfer for MEMS devices (3), temporary bonding (4) (5) and wafer-level packaging (6).

Direct bonding consists in spontaneously bringing into contact two solid surfaces without any intermediate liquid. A liquid is defined here as a being thick enough to have fluid properties. Silicon direct bonding is widely used in microelectronics, for instance for the production of silicon-on-insulator substrates. Direct bonding can be performed between identical surfaces, for example, two silicon substrates. However, direct bonding is also feasible with two different surfaces such as silicon and metal. Direct bonding of two solid materials requires very strict surface conditions such as planarity, particle cleanliness and low surface roughness. The surface Root Mean Square (RMS) roughness should be lower than 0.5 nm for hydrophilic silicon bonding and 0.3 nm for hydrophobic silicon bonding (7).

In this study, we focused on organic polymer to silicon direct bonding. It is a quite innovative bonding as polymers are materials with very different properties compared to silicon. They are indeed not crystalline, much less rigid and most of the time hydrophobic. A research group has achieved direct bonding of a 3 mm thick PMMA substrate with silicon, glass or a second PMMA substrate. Bonding energies up to 7.8 J/m² were obtained (8) (9). Another direct bonding was performed between Teflon spread on silicon and glass substrates (10). In our study, we will focus on ultra-thin polymer films, e.g. with a thickness of 1 μm or less.

Using a thin polymer film in a direct bonding process could definitely be advantageous. It would be less restrictive in terms of surface conditions and potentially less expensive as chemical-mechanical planarization might not be required. An obstacle to the use of polymers in a direct bonding process is that polymers tend to be hydrophobic, whereas silicon direct bonding is easier and more efficient with hydrophilic substrates. Moreover, the limited thermal resistance of polymers may be a serious limitation to further hot processes.

Experimental

Current processes were performed in a clean room with stabilized temperature (21°C) and humidity (45% of relative humidity).

Process

In this study, 200 and 300 mm silicon (001) wafers 725 and 775 μm thick were used. They were first cleaned to remove particle and organic contamination. After cleaning, standard silicon wafers have a hydrophilic surface with the presence of silanol groups (Si-OH) on a very thin (< 1 nm) chemical oxide film (11). Silicon wafers can be deoxidised and passivated with hydrogen thanks to dips in hydrofluoric acid (HF) (12). In the following, hydrophilic silicon will be designated as SiO_2 and hydrophobic silicon as Si. Then, 200 mm silicon wafers were spin-coated with LOR (MicroChem) and 300 mm silicon wafers with BARC AR26N (Rohm & Haas). The LOR polymer was of two types and thicknesses: LOR 2A with a thickness of 155 nm and LOR 10A with a thickness of 1 μm. Meanwhile, the BARC AR26N polymer was 32 nm thick. Finally, the coated silicon wafers were baked to evaporate solvents.

An EVG520 tool was used for thermal compression bonding of 200 mm wafers and an EVG560 tool for 300 mm wafers. Wafers were then brought into contact in the bonding chamber, under a vacuum atmosphere of 10^{-5} mbar. A thermal stabilization was performed and a force of 6 kN applied to the stack. The resulting stacks were annealed for 3 minutes after 200 mm diameter bonding and 10 minutes after 300 mm diameter bonding.

During direct bonding, wafers were brought into contact on a bonding station in the cleanroom atmosphere. Infrared imaging was used to observe the bonding wave propagation. Then, bonded pairs were annealed in an oven for 10 minutes to consolidate the interfaces.

In order to investigate the bondability limit of polymer to silicon direct bonding, different substrates with increasing roughness were fabricated thanks to various deposition of silicon oxide and silicon nitride. Roughnesses ranging from 0.2 to 3.8 nm RMS were obtained depending on the deposition conditions. Direct bonding of roughened substrates onto SiO_2, Si and AR26N were conducted to evaluate the bondability limit of each material.

Characterization

The polymer thin film was first characterized by Fourier Transformed Infrared (FTIR) spectroscopy using an Accent QS3300 tool. The transmission mode was used to collect spectra with a resolution of 2 cm^{-1} and an average of 64 scans. Tapping mode Atomic Force Microscopy (AFM) in a Fastscan tool (Bruker) was used to evaluate the surface roughness. The water contact angle was measured by a DSA 100 tool (KRUSS). The volume of the drop was 3 μL. The thickness of the polymer films was measured by spectroscopic ellipsometry with an Atlas XP+ tool (Nanometrics). 49 points polar maps were used to that end. Thermogravimetric analysis (TGA) was used to assess polymer degradation by a SETARAM ATG 92.12 model. Measurements were carried out with a ramp of 5°C/min under Argon.

In order to evaluate the adhesion energy, a 205 μm-thick blade was placed between the two wafers. Bonding was then initiated on the opposite side of the blade. During the bonding wave propagation, multiple infra-red pictures of the bonding front were recorded. It was therefore possible to calculate the bonding wave velocity. The bonding wave stopped because of the presence of the blade between the two wafers. It was then possible to measure the length of the non-bonded zone between the blade and the bonding front. The adhesion energy could be estimated using Maszara (13) or El Zein (14) formalism as explained by Larrey et al. (15). The interface of the bonding was observed by an acoustic microscope from PVA-Tepla with a 140 MHz acoustic head frequency. In order to measure the adherence energy, the Double Cantilever Beam (DCB) technique was used in anhydrous atmosphere to avoid any water stress corrosion (16). Bonded pairs were diced in 20 mm wide beams along <110> directions starting from silicon (001) wafers. The DCB technique consists in a blade insertion at the bonding interface. The adherence energy can be calculated with the debonded length using El Zein formula (14) which is the same as that used for the adhesion energy as given by equation 1 in the specific crystallographic direction of the beam:

$$G = \frac{3}{16} \frac{E\, t^3 \delta^2}{(1-v)^2\, a^4} \qquad [1]$$

Where G is the adherence energy (J/m²), E is the silicon Young modulus (= 169.10^9 Pa along <110>), t is the wafer thicknesses, δ is the blade thickness, v is the Poisson's ratio of silicon (= 0.06 between <110> and <1-10>) and a is the debonded length.

Results and Discussion

<u>Polymer thin films</u>

Atomic force microscopy and water contact angle measurements were carried out on the polymers and on the hydrophilic and hydrophobic silicon substrates. AFM images are shown in **Figure 1** and the various measurements summarized in **Table I**. Polymers tend to be hydrophobic, with water contact angles larger than 55°. In the rest of the study, hydrophilic polymer/SiO$_2$ bonding can be compared with Si/SiO$_2$ bonding because of their equivalent water contact angles.

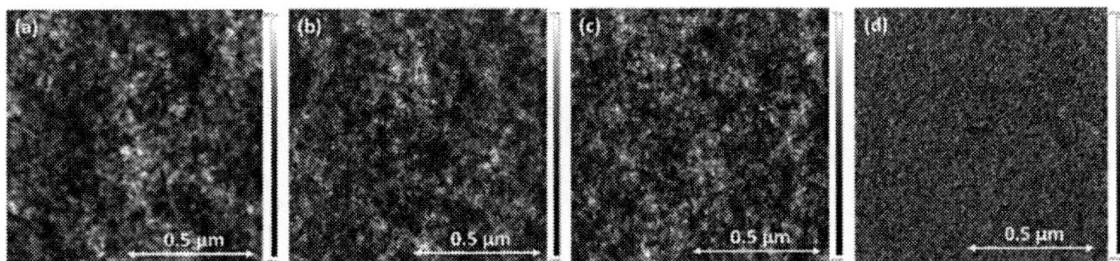

Figure 1. AFM snapshots (1 x 1 µm²) of different substrates: (a) LOR 10A, (b) LOR 2A, (c) AR26N and (d) Silicon

Table I. Water contact angle and RMS roughness of the various materials

Materials	Water contact angle	RMS roughness (nm)
LOR 2A	58°	0.35
LOR 10A	65°	0.29
AR26N	77°	0.31
SiO$_2$	< 5°	< 0.2
Si	78°	< 0.2

Spectroscopic ellipsometry measurements of the polymer films showed a good spin-coating uniformity across the substrates. LOR 2A films were 155 nm thick (min: 153.3 nm; max: 160.8 nm; average: 154.7 nm), LOR 10A films 1 μm thick (min: 1053.8 nm; max: 1098.3 nm; average: 1077.1 nm) and AR26N films 32 nm thick (min: 32.3 nm; max: 32.7 nm; average: 32.4 nm).

Thermogravimetric analyses were carried out on the two polymers. The LOR resin began to degrade at around 210°C and AR26N at around 270°C for a loss of 1% of the initial mass. However, if we consider a loss of 5% of the initial mass, the LOR resin began to degrade at around 337°C and AR26N at around 296°C.

Figure 3 shows the FTIR spectra of the two polymers. The LOR formula is known and shown in **Figure 4**. This polymer has been used for 3D integration and the transfer of thin film materials with a Surface Activated Bonding process (SAB) (17). Moreover, temporary bonding by thermal compression has been realized with LOR resin with a thickness between 4.2 and 7 μm (18). In the FTIR spectrum, the peak at 1693 cm^{-1} is due to the C=O bonds. Bands at 1581 cm^{-1} and 3373 cm^{-1} are due to N-H bonds. Meanwhile, those between 2872 and 2976 and those between 1346 and 1462 cm^{-1} are due to the C-H bonds. We can also see peaks at 1217 cm^{-1} for C-N bonds and at 3240 cm^{-1} for O-H bonds. The chemical composition of AR26N is not completely known, but characteristic bands for C=O bonds at 1724 cm^{-1} and C-H bonds at 2940 cm^{-1} are observed.

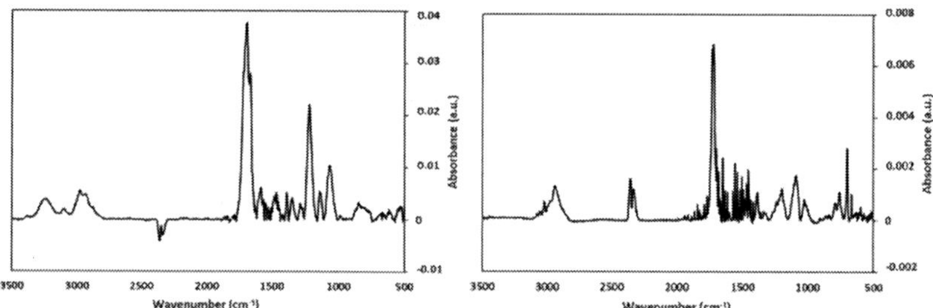

Figure 3. FTIR spectra of LOR (left) and AR26N (right)

Figure 4. The chemical formula of LOR (n = m)

Thermal compression bonding

The impact of the bonding temperature on the quality of the bonding interfaces has been evaluated. Acoustic images of the various stacks are presented in **Figure 5** and **Figure 6**. White areas are unbonded surfaces. In the case of LOR 10A, a change in the interface contrast is observed at 300°C and above, with a degradation of the bonding interface. Meanwhile, the interface starts to degrade at 400°C for BARC AR26N. The adherence energies as a function of the bonding temperature are provided in **Table II**. The adherence of the bonding pairs with LOR10A is quite low up to 100°C. It definitely increases above that threshold temperature, reaching reach 13.7 J/m² at 300°C. It drops to 1.2 J/m² at 400°C. It is well correlated with the bonding degradation evidenced by acoustic microscopy at 400°C. In the case of AR26N, the adherence energy increases up to 300°C where it reaches a maximum of 3.3 J/m². Then, it decreases. Here again, there is a correlation with the degradation of the interface observed by acoustic microscopy. When the bonding temperature increases, there is a rise in the density of covalent bonds, which mechanically strengthens the bonding and thus increases the adherence energy.

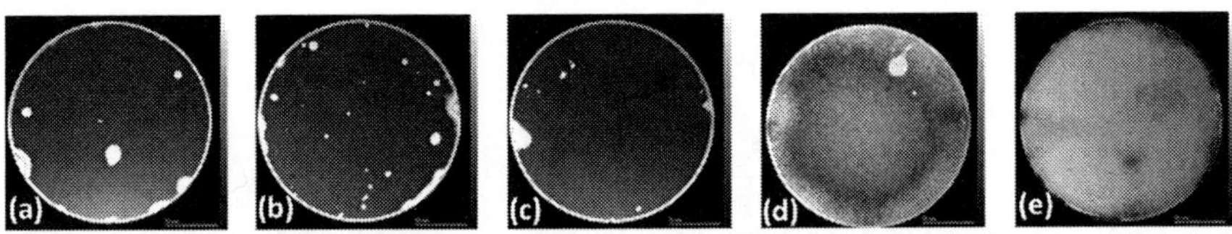

Figure 5. Impact of the bonding temperature on the 200 mm acoustic images of bonded stacks with LOR 10A: (a) RT, (b) 100°C, (c) 200°C, (d) 300°C and (e) 400°C

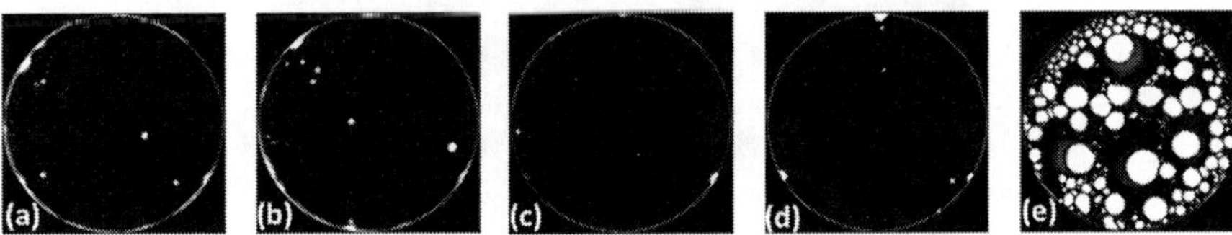

Figure 6. Impact of the bonding temperature on the 300 mm acoustic images of bonded stacks with AR26N: (a) RT, (b) 100°C, (c) 200°C, (d) 300°C and (e) 400°C

Table II. Impact of the temperature on the adherence energy of bonded stacks with LOR 10A and AR26N

Bonding temperature (°C)	Adherence energy of LOR 10A bonded pairs (J/m²)	Adherence energy of AR26N bonded pairs (J/m²)
RT	0.4 ± 0.06	0.1 ± 0.02
100°C	0.4 ± 0.06	0.2 ± 0.02
200°C	8.5 ± 2.9	0.8 ± 0.14
300°C	13.7 ± 5.4	3.3 ± 0.93
400°C	1.2 ± 0.25	0.3 ± 0.04

<u>Polymer to silicon direct bonding</u>

A direct bonding study similar to that of thermal compression bonding was carried out. The roughness limit for hydrophilic direct bonding is 0.5 nm RMS. Our polymers have RMS roughnesses of 0.35 nm (LOR 2A) and 0.31 nm (AR26N), which seems compatible with the direct bonding process. Direct bonding with our two polymer thick films was performed on hydrophilic silicon wafers. Acoustic images of bonded pairs are shown in **Figure 7**. The interface quality is good. The propagation of the bonding wave propagation was investigated. It is shown in **Figure 8** for both polymers. Bonding with LOR2A has been achieved in 15 seconds (200 mm) and bonding with AR26N in 17 seconds (300 mm). It was also possible to achieve bonding with both polymers on hydrophobic silicon substrates. The bonding limit for hydrophobic wafers is around 0.25 nm RMS. It is then quite interesting to note that this limit is overcome using such polymers.

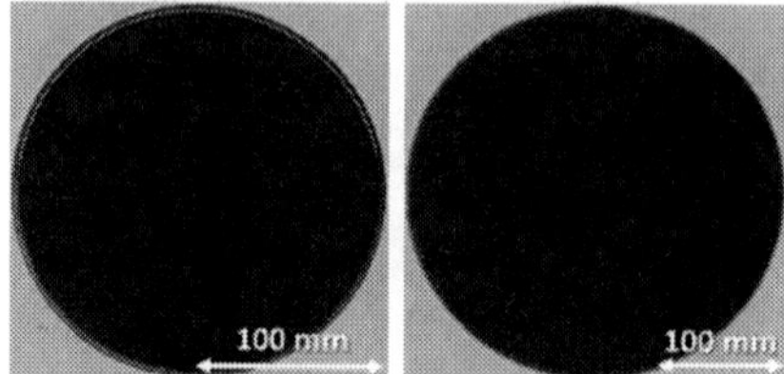

Figure 7. 200 mm acoustic image of direct bonding of SiO_2 wafers with LOR 2A (left) and 300 mm acoustic image with AR26N (right)

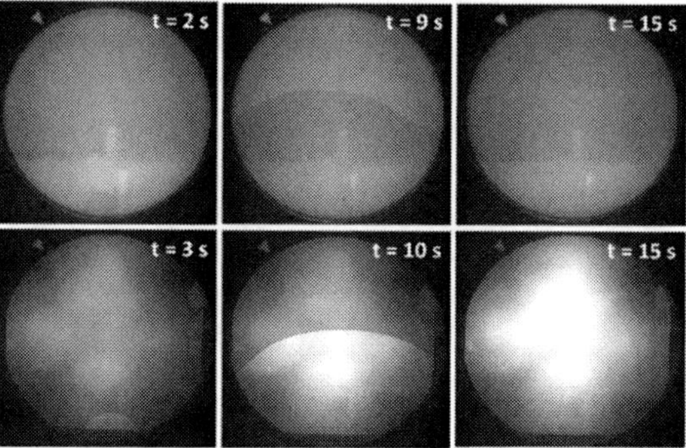

Figure 8. Bonding wave propagation of LOR 2A onto SiO_2 200 mm diameter bonding (top) and AR26N to SiO_2 300 mm diameter bonding (bottom)

The adhesion energy and the bonding wave velocity of these structures were measured. They are provided in **Table III**. Based on the water contact angle values, bonding a polymer surface onto a SiO_2 surface should be equivalent to the bonding of a Si surface onto a SiO_2 surface. Polymer to SiO_2 direct bonding stacks exhibit higher adhesion energies (47 and 52 mJ/m²) and bonding wave velocities (10 and 17 mm/s) than SiO_2 to Si direct bonding (17 mJ/m² and 4 mm/s). Moreover, adhesion energies and bonding wave velocities are lower for polymer direct bonding to Si than to SiO_2. This is likely due to the fact that hydrogen and Van der Waals bonds are involved in the direct bonding mechanism of hydrophilic substrates whereas only Van der Waals bonds are involved in the direct bonding of hydrophobic substrates. Let us now compare polymer/Si and polymer/SiO_2 direct bondings for both types of polymers. The adhesion energy and bonding wave velocity are slightly higher with AR26N (35-52 mJ/m² and 8-17 mm/s) than with LOR (25-47 mJ/m² and 5-10 mm/s). This could be explained by the AR26N polymer ability to form bonds with the silicon substrate.

Table III. Adhesion energy and bonding wave velocity of various bonded pairs

Bonding	Adhesion energy (mJ/m²)	Bonding wave velocity (mm/s)
LOR 2A/SiO_2	47	10
LOR 2A/Si	25	5
AR26N/SiO_2	52	17
AR26N/Si	35	8
SiO_2/SiO_2	47	18
Si/SiO_2	17	4
Si/Si	13	2

Rieutord's analytical model in equation 2 links the adhesion energy to the bonding wave velocity (19):

$$V = A \, \frac{E_a^{5/4} \, z_0^{1/2}}{\eta \, D^{1/4}} \qquad [2]$$

Where V is the bonding wave velocity (m/s), E_a the adhesion energy (J/m²), z_0 is a fluidic cut-off distance, η the air viscosity (= $18.6.10^{-6}$ Pa.s) and D the substrate rigidity (= 5.39 J) linked to the substrate thickness, the silicon Young modulus and the Poisson ratio.

The bonding wave velocity is related to the adhesion energy but also to the fluidic cut-off distance z_0 (which is linked to the mean free path of the expulsed trapped gas). In the literature, the mean free path of the air is equal to 66 nm at 20°C and 50% of relative humidity (20). In the case of direct bonding of hydrophilic silicon, values for the fluidic cut-off distance between 35 and 55 nm can be found in the literature (15) (21) (22). In the model, z_0 is often used as an adjustment variable. If we apply this model to stacks with direct bonding to hydrophilic silicon, the fluidic cut-off distance is about 50 nm for LOR 2A and of 114 nm for AR26N (**Figure 9**). In the case of LOR 2A, the measured z_0 agrees with the model. For AR26N, the value of 114 nm is a higher than literature values, but is still within the same order of magnitude. The specificities of the polymers, such as their stiffness which is lower than in silicon, their surface roughness or their hydrophobicity, may have an impact on the phenomenon. In the case of our bonding, the polymer surface characteristics should be considered in the model.

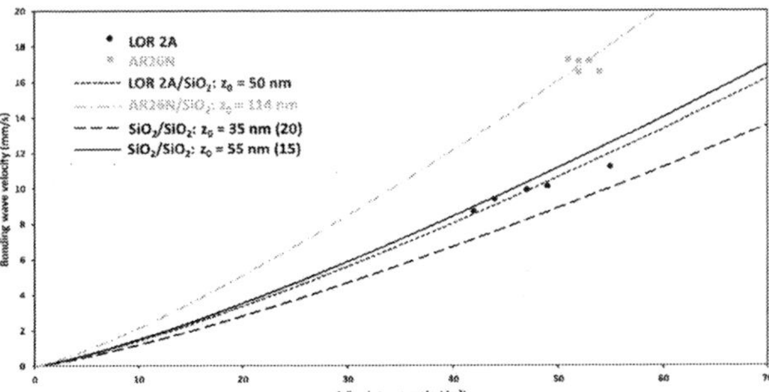

Figure 9. Comparison between bonding wave velocities and adhesion energies values obtained from polymer direct bonding and Rieutord's analytical model

The impact of post-bonding annealing on the quality of the interfaces was also studied. Different anneals lasting 10 minutes for temperatures ranging from 100 to 300°C were performed. **Figure 10** and **Figure 11** show acoustic images of bonded pairs. Grey or white areas at 200°C and above for LOR 2A and at 300°C and above for AR26N are unbonded areas. The acoustic images show that the degradation of the bonding interface with LOR 2A occurs at 250°C and at 300°C for AR26N. The degradation temperature of LOR 2A measured by TGA was about 200°C. The appearance of unbonded areas at 200°C is therefore due to the degradation of the polymer. Meanwhile, the AR26N degradation temperature was around 270°C, in line with the degradation of the interface observed at 300°C with SAM.

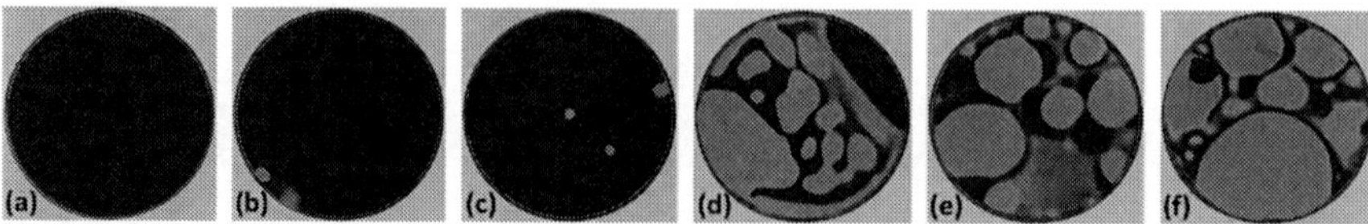

Figure 10. Impact of the 10 min post-bonding annealing temperature on the 200 mm acoustic images of the bonded stacks with LOR 2A: (a) RT, (b) 100°C, (c) 150°C, (d) 200°C, (e) 250°C and (f) 300°C

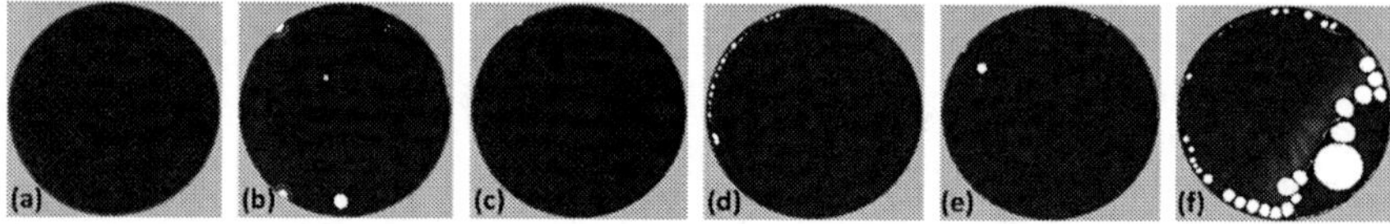

Figure 11. Impact of the 10 min post-bonding annealing temperature on the 300 mm acoustic images of the bonded stacks with AR26N: (a) RT, (b) 100°C, (c) 150°C, (d) 200°C, (e) 250°C and (f) 300°C

The adherence energies of these stacks are provided in **Table IV**. First of all, the adherence energy at Room Temperature (0.14 and 0.20 J/m²) is for those polymers much higher than the adhesion energy (0.047 and 0.052 J/m²). The adhesion energy is the energy used to perform the bonding whereas the adherence energy is the energy required to separate two bonded substrates. As adherence is higher than adhesion at room temperature, this mean that stronger bonds are formed just after the contact. As for hydrophilic silicon bonding, covalent bonds might be formed already at room temperature on the asperity contact points on which more than 100 bar of pressure are expected (23). For LOR 2A, the energy increases up to 150°C. For anneals at higher temperature, it is impossible to measure the adherence energy because of unbonded areas. For AR26N, the adherence increases up to 200-250°C and starts to decrease at 300°C. In both cases, the evolution of the adherence energy is in line with acoustic images and the degradation of the polymers measured by TGA.

Table IV. Impact of the temperature on the adherence energy of bonded stacks with LOR 2A and AR26N

Annealing temperature (°C)	Adherence energy of LOR 2A bonded pairs (J/m²)	Adherence energy of AR26N bonded pairs (J/m²)
RT	0.14 ± 0.01	0.20 ± 0.01
100°C	0.16 ± 0.01	0.30 ± 0.01
150°C	2.2 ± 0.16	4.0 ± 0.33
200°C	Not evaluated	9.5 ± 0.97
250°C	Not evaluated	8.4 ± 0.83
300°C	Not evaluated	4.9 ± 0.42

Bonding with polymer was thus shown to be possible by thermal compression and direct bonding. In both cases, the bonding interface was observed by SAM. For both polymers, the bonding interface started to degrade at a lower temperature by direct bonding (LOR 2A: 200°C and AR26N: 300°C) than during a thermal compression (LOR 2A: 300°C and AR26N: 400°C). This could be explained by the fact that, for direct bonding, the stack was placed in the oven at RT. The anneal was then carried out at the desired temperature and the stack removed from the oven when the temperature came back to RT. For thermal compression bonding, the stack was loaded in the chamber when it was already at the desired temperature. After annealing, it was then removed without waiting for the temperature to decrease. Thermal compression thermal budget was thus lower than with direct bonding. Moreover, thermal compression bonding was conducted under vacuum whereas direct bonding was performed in the cleanroom atmosphere. In that case, water was trapped at the bonding interface, which could have led to a faster degradation. It could be interesting to minimize the amount of water in these kinds of polymer direct bonding. High adherence energies were otherwise observed for both types of bonding. With AR26N, higher energies were obtained by direct bonding. This could be explained by the higher thermal budget and also by the presence of water at the bonding interface, which might help to increase the covalent bonds density between the polymer and the silicon. Minimizing the amount of water might then limit the thermal degradation but could lower the adherence.

The fracture energy of a crystal is typically between 1 and 5 J/m^2 (24). It is around 5 J/m^2 for nanocrystalline silicon (25). Meanwhile, adherence energies above 5 J/m^2 were obtained with our bondings, most likely falsely and because of the presence of polymers in the stack. Indeed, when the blade was inserted during DCB measurements, a fraction of the energy was dissipated inside the polymer itself and not only at the bonding interface. Such a phenomenon was observed even for thicknesses as small as a few tens of nanometres (32 nm for AR26N with an energy of 9.5 J/m^2 reached at 200°C). It seems then that this dissipation occurs in a very small thickness of the polymer.

<u>Study of direct bonding with increasing roughness</u>

In order to investigate if direct bonding with polymer is less restrictive, a study of direct bonding with roughened substrates was conducted on 300 mm wafers. In order to obtain different roughness, deposited SiO_2 was used. Different roughness values can indeed be obtained by varying the layer thickness. All surfaces were then chemically cleaned and were hydrophilic. Different bonding pairs were then studied: hydrophilic/hydrophilic with SiO_2/SiO_2 or hydrophobic/hydrophilic with Si/SiO_2 or $AR26N/SiO_2$. Adhesion energies and bonding wave velocities were measured. The adhesion energies as a function of cumulative roughness are provided in **Table V** and the limits of the bondability of various bonded pairs shown in **Figure 12**. The cumulative roughness is the sum of the roughness of both surfaces.

Table V. Adhesion energy and bonding wave velocity of various materials with roughened substrates made of hydrophilic SiO_2.

Bonding materials	RMS roughness of bonding materials (nm)	RMS roughness of roughened SiO_2 substrates (nm)	Cumulative roughness (nm)	Adhesion energy (mJ/m²)	Bonding wave velocity (mm/s)
AR26N	0.31	0.12	0.43	52	17
		0.19	0.50	45	11
		0.38	0.69	43	9
		0.65	0.96	25	4
		0.72	1.03	4	1
		0.82	1.13	Not bondable	Not bondable
SiO_2	0.12	0.12	0.24	129	48
		0.19	0.31	93	19
		0.38	0.50	50	10
		0.65	0.77	7	1
		0.70	0.82	Not bondable	Not bondable
Si	0.12	0.12	0.24	34	10
		0.34	0.46	10	1
		0.58	0.70	Not bondable	Not bondable

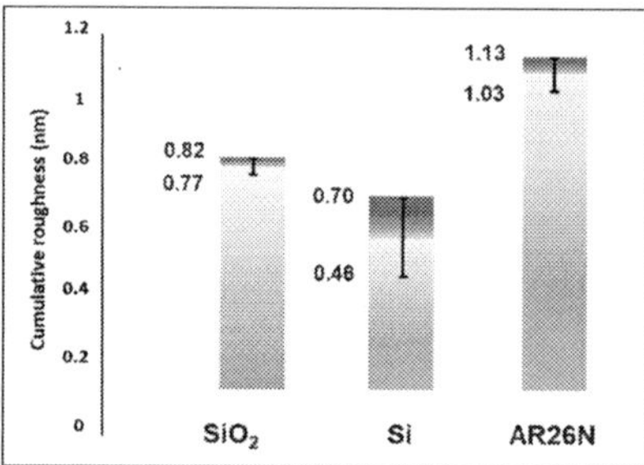

Figure 12. Impact of the substrates roughness on the bondability of different pairs.

The adhesion energy and the bonding wave velocity decrease when the roughness increases. The bondability limit for bonding to SiO_2 substrate is between 0.77 and 0.82 nm and that for bonding to a Si substrate between 0.46 and 0.70 nm. In the case of AR26N, this limit is between 1.03 and 1.13 nm, which is higher than for hydrophilic/hydrophilic and hydrophobic/hydrophilic bonded pairs. The direct bonding limit is therefore extended with AR26N in terms of roughness. This can be explained by the roughness contact adhesion model of Rieutord (26). In this model, the bonding is governed by attractive forces (Van der Waals forces) and repulsive forces given by equation 3. The repulsion force depends on Young's modulus of the material. As the Young's modulus of a polymer is lower than that of silicon, the repulsion force is lower for direct bonding with a polymer thick film. This results in a better crushing of roughness and therefore the possibility of bonding substrates with higher roughness.

$$P = N_0 \, R^{1/2} \, \sigma^{*3/2} \, \frac{4}{3} E^* \, F_{3/2}\left(\frac{d}{\sigma^*}\right) \qquad [3]$$

Where P is the bearing force, N_0 is the number of summits per unit area, R is the radius curvature of the asperities, σ^* is the roughness distribution, E^* is the effective Young modulus and $F_n(d)$ derive from the Gaussian statistics weight function.

Conclusion

Polymer to silicon direct bonding is feasible. Direct bonding using 32 nm and 155 nm thick polymer films was carried out. Bonded pairs show a good interface quality. Adhesion energies and wave velocities were measured. Adherence energies up to 10 J/m² were obtained and some bonding stacks had rather good thermal resistance up to 300°C. Finally, direct bonding with polymer yielded some gains in terms of roughness bondability limit.

References

1. P. Montméat, J. Dechamp, G. Enyedi, F. Fournel, Z. Zavvou, and V. Jousseaume, *Materials Science in Semiconductor Processing*, **148**, 106808 (2022).
2. S. H. Lee, K. N. Chen, and J.J.Q. Lu, *Journal of Microelectromechanical Systems*, **20**(4), 885-898 (2011).
3. V. Dragoi, T. Glinsner, G. Mittendorfer, B. Wieder, and P. Lindner, in *Smart Sensors, Actuators, and MEMS*, Vol 5116, pp. 160-167, Proceedings of SPIE (2003).
4. P. Montméat, T. Enot, G. Enyedi, M. Pellat, J. Thooris, and F. Fournel, *International Journal of Adhesion and Adhesives*, **82**, 100-107 (2018).
5. K. Abadie, P. Montméat, T. Enot, F. Fournel, and M. Wimplinger, *International Journal of Adhesion and Adhesives*, **91**, 123-130 (2019).
6. T. Linz, M. von Krshiwoblozki, and H. Walter, in *2010 International Conference on Body Sensor Networks*, pp. 308-314, IEEE (2010).
7. H. Moriceau, F. Rieutord, F. Fournel, Y. Le Tiec, L. Di Cioccio, C. Morales, A. M. Charvet, and C. Deguet, *Adv. Nat. Sci. Nanosci. Nanotechnol*, **1**, 043004 (2011).
8. G. A. C. M. Spierings and J. Haisma, *Appl. Phys. Lett.*, **64**(24), 3246-3248 (1994).
9. G. A. C. M. Spierings, J. Haisma, and F. J. H. M. Van Der Kruis, *Philips Journal of Research*, **49**(1-2), 139-149 (1995).
10. J. Haisma and G. A. C. M. Spierings, *Materials Science and Engineering: R: Reports*, **37**(1-2), 1-60 (2002).
11. B. Sefsaf, B. Carrière, and J. P. Deville, *Microsc. Microanal. Microstruct.*, **3**, 15-22 (1992).
12. Q.-Y. Tong, E. Schmidt, U. Gösele, and M. Reiche, *App. Phys. Lett.*, **64**, 625-627 (1994).
13. W. P. Maszara, G. Goetz, A. Caviglia, and J. B. McKitterick, *J. Appl. Phys.*, **64**, 4943 (1988).
14. M. S. El-Zein and K. L. Reijsnider, *Journal of Compo. Tech. & Research*, **10**(4), 151-155, (1988).
15. V. Larrey, G. Mauguen, F. Fournel, D. Radisson, F. Rieutord, C. Morales, C. Bridoux, and H. Moriceau, *ECS Transactions*, **75**(9), 145-152 (2016).
16. F. Fournel, L. Continni, C. Morales, J. D. Fonseca, H. Moriceau, C. M. Cocher, F. Rieutord, A. Barthelemy, and I. Radu. *ECS Trans.*, **50**(7), 3–16, (2013).
17. T. Matsumae and T. Suga, in *2016 International Conference on Electronics Packaging*, pp. 310-313, IEEE (2016).
18. T. Matsumae, A. D. Koehler, J. D. Greenlee, T. J. Anderson, H. Baumgart, G. G. Jernigan, K. D. Hobart, and F. J. Kub, *ECS J. Solid State Sci. Technol.* **4**(7), 190-194, (2015).
19. F. Rieutord, B. Bataillou, and H. Moriceau, *Physical Review Letters*, **94**, 236101, (2005).

20. S. G. Jennings, *J. Aerosol Sci.,* **19**(2), 159-166 (1988).
21. E. Navarro, Y. Bréchet, R. Moreau, T. Pardoen, J. P. Raskin, A. Barthelemy, and I. Radu, *Appl. Phys. Lett.,* **103**, 034104 (2013).
22. D. Radisson, PhD Thesis (2013).
23. F. Fournel, C. Martin-Cocher, D. Radisson, V. Larrey, E. Beche, C. Morales, P. A. Delean, F. Rieutord, and H. Moriceau, *ECS J. Solid State Sci. Technol.* **4**(5), 124–130, (2015).
24. B. Lawn, *Fracture of brittle solids, second ed.,* Cambridge Univ. Press, Cambridge (1993).
25. C. St John, *Phil. Mag.,* **32**, 1193 (1975).
26. F. Rieutord, H. Moriceau, R. Beneyton, L. Capello, C. Morales, and A. M. Charvet, *ECS Trans.,* **3**(6), 205 (2006).

ECS Transactions, 112 (3) 63-72 (2023)
10.1149/11203.0063ecst ©The Electrochemical Society

Hybrid Bonding for 3D Applications: Improvements and Limitations

E. Deloffre[a], B. Ayoub[a], S. Lhostis[a], F. Dettoni[a], F. Fournel[b], P. Montmeat[b], S. Mermoz[a]

[a] STMicroelectronics 850 rue Jean Monnet, 38920 Crolles, France
[b] CEA Grenoble 17 Av. des Martyrs, 38000 Grenoble, France

With hybrid bonding pitch reduction, many challenges are arising such as optimized metrology measurement, bonding wave propagation understanding and hybrid surface characterization. By analyzing incoming wafer and how tool setting impacts bonding, overlay values below 110 nm for production wafers can be achieved with 100% electrical yield. Hybrid bonding extends further to IC Logic application or Memory and not only CMOS image sensor. For some of those products, the temperature of usual post bonding thermal annealing (400°C) cannot be applied. Consequently, many studies have been performed on developing low-temperature bonding. To add flexibility to hybrid bonding, new processes such as Surface Activation Bonding (SAB) and Die to Wafer bonding (D2W) have been developed to fit heterogenous integration.

Introduction

Wafer direct bonding has attracted considerable concerns since it takes advantage of the ability to achieve strong adherence between flat, clean, and smooth surfaces without the use of intermediate materials. This technology experienced a consequent rise with the More than Moore's law. With this trend, added value to devices is provided by incorporating functionalities that do not necessarily scale according to "Moore's Law". Indeed, this aims to realize three-dimensional (3D) integration systems by stacking devices and interconnecting them using Through-Silicon-Via (TSV) or Cu-Cu interconnections. Hybrid bonding is preferred to other chip stacking technologies because Cu-Cu hybrid bonding is easily capable of scaling down and presents excellent reliability results.

Overlay: metrology and optimization

Hybrid bonding is a key technology to address several applications, especially CMOS Images Sensor (CIS). Even more specialized applications or better performances could be obtained through hybrid bonding pitch reduction [1]. High quality bonding for 3D technology has been demonstrated using an accurate wafer bonding tool with optimized metrology [2].

Overlay: definition and measurement

Bonding misalignment can be separated into four components: translation, rotation, scaling and distortion (also called residuals). Translation and rotation can be easily suppressed by adding some offsets inside the bonding recipe to compensate bonder's alignment and stage control systems. Scaling and distortion management will be discussed in the next paragraphs.

Overlay measurement specifications depends on pitch size of the product. Indeed, repeatability and accuracy specifications will not be the same for a pitch of 6.9 µm and for ultra-fine pitch as 0.6 µm. Overlay error specifications of Total Measurement Uncertainty (TMU), is usually defined to be 10 % of the overlay budget which leads in our case to TMU target below 6 nm. Thus, to support scaling of bonding pitch, further improvement of bonding accuracy is highly required.

We achieve, with the metrology tool we used today, a TMU of 1 nm on production wafers with a 0.8 nm precision, mean Tool Induced Shift (TIS) of approximately 0.1 nm, and a TIS 3σ value below 1 nm. These results have been obtained thanks to equipment performances but also to alignment marks design [3]. The achieved overlay is fully in line with our specifications for fine pitch products.

<u>Fine pitch</u>

Image Sensors have been the first main driver for the development of 3D integration using hybrid bonding [4]. Smart sensors require ever more demanding interconnexion between the parts embedding the CIS and the Image Sensor Processor (ISP). Products are now available with interconnexion pitch around 1 µm [5]. The integration can be realized using SiN, SiCN or SiO_2 at the bonding interface while copper for pads is the principal bonding metal used [6]. The achievement of a high quality for hybrid bonding requires perfect surface cleanliness, low roughness and low topography of the surfaces to be bonded. With pitch reduction requiring metal pads width below submicrometric dimensions, the management of the copper pads recess is key. As shown by Ayoub [7] the copper pads can be monocrystalline below for submicrometric dimensions. The recess conditions must then be adapted to the grain orientation with the lowest dilatation coefficient, that is [111] orientation. Adapting the surface preparation conditions has allows us to demonstrate 0.6 µm pitch hybrid stack with no void at the bonding interface [8] as shown on Figure 1 below.

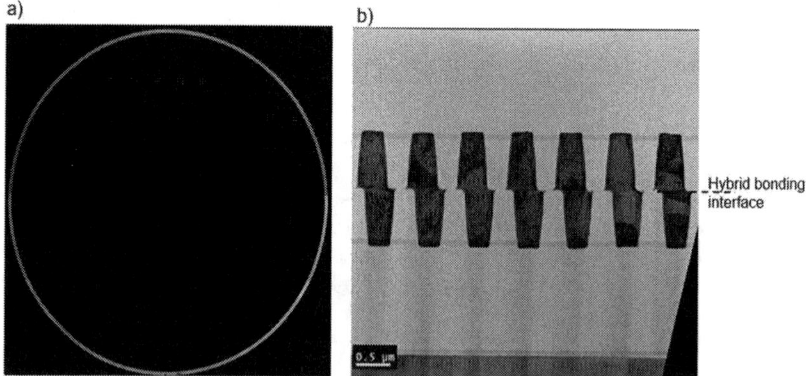

Figure 1: a). Scanning Acoustic Microscopy image of bonded wafers with 300 nm wide Hybrid Bond Metal pads and b) the corresponding TEM cross section.

The optimization conditions for surface preparation were applied to a 3D stacked CMOS Image Sensor (cf. Figure 1a). The ISP part is composed of 7 metal layers with specific via and metal levels for hybrid bonding. The CIS part is made of 4 metal layers with also a specific via and metal levels. Four hybrid bonding pitches are demonstrated, from 1.44 µm down to 0.81 µm. After bonding at room temperature, bonding annealing at 400 °C for 2 h is performed. The top substrate is then thinned down to 6 µm and the backside steps are performed until color resists and microlens. The Scanning Acoustic Microscopy (SAM) images show perfect bonding for the multi-pitch test vehicle after bonding anneal [9] (cf. Figure 2b). Excellent bonding interface is confirmed by TEM cross sections as shown on Figure 2 (c to f).

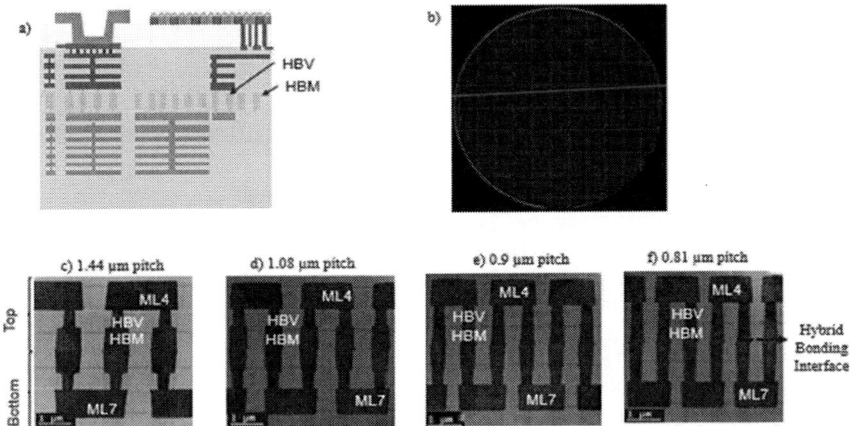

Figure 2: a). Test vehicle scheme with multi-pitchs from 1.44 µm down to 0.81 µm, b) Corresponding Scanning Acoustic Microscopy image after bonding anneal and TEM cross sections of daisy chains with electrical pitch c) 1.44 µm, d) 1.08 µm, e) 0.9 µm, f) 0.81 µm.

High robustness is obtained checked with deep studies on the stability of the bonding interface in case of misaligned pads [10].

The total overlay values reached for these wafers is below 110 nm 3σ with residuals values below 80 nm and scaling inferior to 0.5 ppm for interconnect pitches from 6.9 µm down to 0.8 µm. To be able to easily repeat these results in high volume production mode, Advanced Process Control (APC) loops can be introduced to correct translation and rotation. APC loops not only guarantee overlay within specifications but also monitor and control bonding tools.
When translation and rotation are annihilated, most of the overlay is coming from scaling. Thanks to a bottom bending chuck, scaling values can be drastically reduced. However, using a bending chuck leads to an increase of distortion. For example, similar product wafers have been bonded with and without using bending chuck. Scaling suppression led to distortion increase of 37 %. A tradeoff can be found between scaling and distortion decrease depending on products specifications.

Overlay results post bonding have been compared to the ones measured after back-side thinning using standard box-in-box structures (Figure 3b). This measurement is performed in the visible wavelength range. As shown in Figure 4, raw measurements are matched. This indicates that the marks have been well designed for overlay measurements of bonded wafers and that no specific residual is added to the stack post-bonding. It also means that distortion implied by the bonding process is totally transferred to imager sensor wafer.

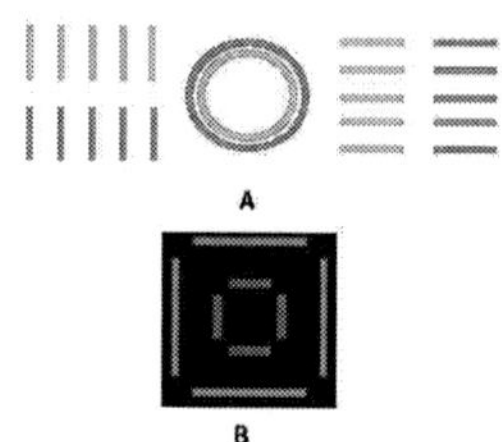

Figure 3: a) Specific alignment marks used for bonding.
b) Standard BEOL overlay marks used after thinning.

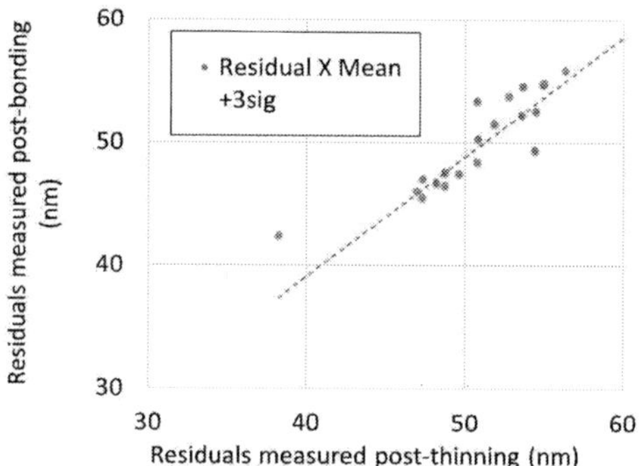

Figure 4: Correlation between residual values post bonding and post thinning.

<u>Distortion optimization</u>

The latest process and hardware developments have made it possible to greatly reduce scaling. However, distortion remains the most complicated parameter to optimize. It is strongly linked to the design of the chip (number of metal levels, stress...). Today, a minimum critical dimension design rule should be respected to avoid shorts between front side and backside layers and this, is preventing pixel shrink. To reduce pixel size, distortion value needs to be decreased.

For that purpose, in situ monitoring of the bonding wave is necessary as well as bonding chucks multiple vacuum zones to achieve homogenous bonding wave propagation.

Bonding recipes can be tuned to time to release off specific vacuum zones in such a way that bonding wave is forced to propagate homogeneously. [11]

Wafer shape, distortion and nano topology measurement can also be analyzed on wafers prior to bonding. Thanks to these measurements, the right vacuum bonding zone to use can be predicted [12] and distortion value below 65 nm 3σ can be achieved on production wafers.

Electrical results

The work on metrology improvement allows to decrease even more the bonding pad width. The image on Figure 5 (a) shows a cross section using STEM of a daisy chain with 350 nm wide bonding pads with 1.44 μm pitch. 100% electrical yield is obtained for mean overlay between top and bottom parts ranging from 20 to 60 nm depending on the wafers (cf. Figure 5, b).

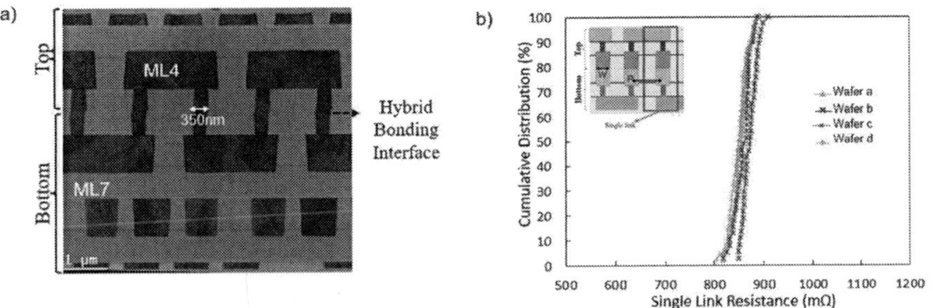

Figure 5: a). TEM cross section of a daisy chains with HBM width 350nm and electrical pitch 1.44μm and b) Corresponding cumulative distribution of a single element of the daisy chains for different wafers with mean overlay ranging from 20 nm to 60 nm.

Even if significant improvements have been performed on overlay, some misalignment between pads can remain and have an impact on contact resistivity. That is why a specific methodology was developed to extract the resistivity of the bonding interface using intentionally misaligned daisy chains (cf. Figure 6a) [13].

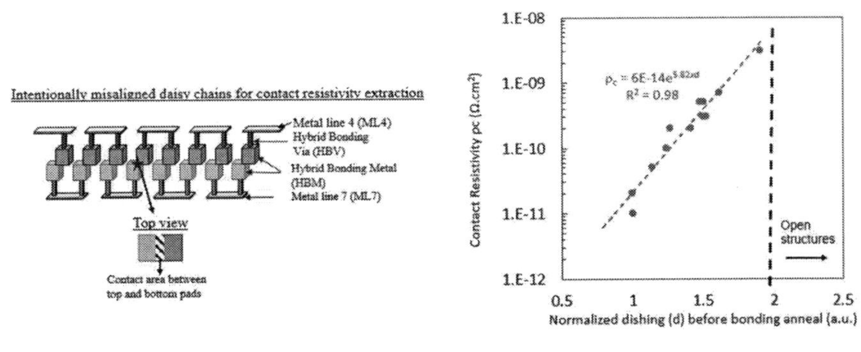

a)   b)

Figure 6: a). Structure of intentionally misaligned daisy chains used to extract contact resistivity b) Contact resistivity extracted for different dishing in HBM before bonding, normalized to our process of record.

We pointed out that the electrical resistivity can vary from 5.10^{-11} Ω.cm-2 up to 10^{-9} Ω.cm-2 when the copper recess is increased [8] (cf. Figure 6b).

This result clearly highlights a major impact of dishing on the Cu-Cu interface reconstruction after thermal annealing. It also permits to define dishing specifications at the wafer level to eliminate open circuits and yield loss.

Low temperature bonding

Even if hybrid bonding integration and performance have been considerably improved, we can notice that thermal budget is a main limitation for this technology. Indeed, to reach strong bonding energy which is mandatory for subsequent mechanical manufacturing; a bonding anneal of 800°C is required. By using plasma treatment prior bonding, anneal temperature can be decreased to 400°C. However, some devices cannot withstand such thermal budget because of thermosensitive materials integration (GST or quantum dots for example). To overcome this limitation, many studies have been performed on developing low temperature direct bonding process. Surface activated bonding (SAB) is a promising method to achieve high bonding energy at room temperature, but chemical surface treatments (as amino-alcohol organic molecule for example [14]) are easier to implement for mass volume production and allows highly strong bonding at 200°C that can stand high stress process steps (grinding, CMP and dicing).
Although specific plasma or surface preparation could decrease the required annealing temperature, the copper oxide will limit electrical performances with annealing below 250°C for standard hydrophilic bonding. That is why, new ECD Cu deposition like oriented nanotwinned Cu is very promising to facilitate oxygen diffusion. [15]

SiO$_2$ bonding energy

Bonding energy is a key parameter to ensure that our products will withstand packaging that can be a source of high stress. Commonly, bonding energy is measured between two silicon wafers with thermal oxide by double cantilever beam (DCB) under prescribed displacement. As already described in literature [16], to avoid water stress corrosion effect, bonding energy has to be measured in an anhydrous atmosphere. In this case, process shift can more easily detected contrary to standard DCB method in cleanroom atmosphere.
Thanks to specific NaOH pre-treatment, high bonding energy (> 4.5 J/m²) could be achieved for SiO$_2$/SiO$_2$ with annealing temperature of 200°C during 2h.

Optimized hybrid bonding stack

Reducing bonding anneal is critical for 3D stacked including memories. However, bonding anneal is not the only parameter to be considered. The materials deposited after the memory integration also need to be grown at low temperature. We've studied the impact of the dielectric properties grown at low temperature placed at the hybrid bonding level (Figure 7a). We present on Figure 7b to d the scanning acoustic microscopy images of wafers bonded at 200°C. A specific dielectric material with deposition temperature below 300°C were identified that allows not outgazing on the wafer edge after bonding anneal.

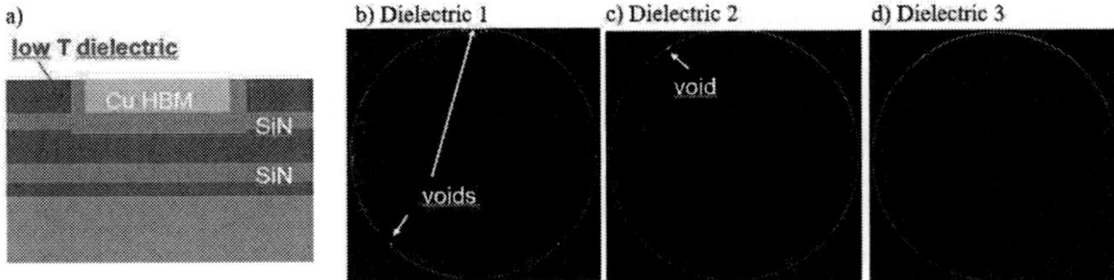

Figure 7: a). Test vehicle scheme for the dielectric properties at the bonding interface. b) to d) SAM images after bonding anneal at 200°C for 3 different dielectrics at the bonding interface, grown at low temperature.

As low temperature dielectric combined with NaOH pre-treatment has been tested and is compatible with direct bonding, NaOH pre-treatment impact has also been verified on Cu roughness as shown on Figure 8 below. The roughness (Rq) obtained after CMP is around 0.2 nm and is not affected by the basic treatment. The resulting surface is compatible with hybrid direct bonding. Indeed, roughness less than 0.5 - 0.6 nm is acceptable for direct bonding. We can note that the roughness is slightly increasing after a long air storage period. This behavior is a well-known oxidation of the copper under air and is not overstated by the NaOH treatment.

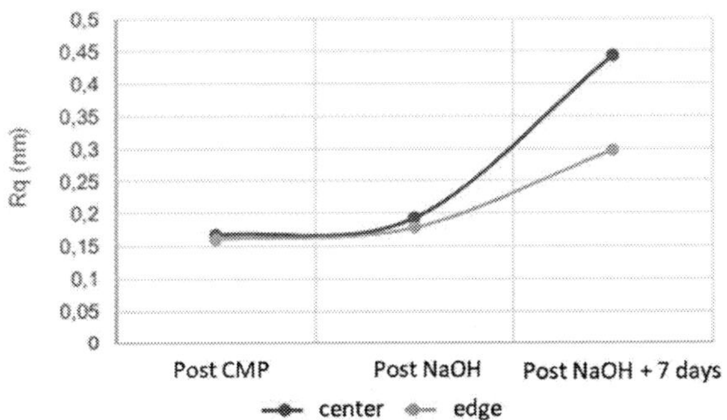

Figure 8: SiO_2 roughness post CMP and with NaOH surface treatment.

Thanks to bonding dielectric with deposition temperature below 300°C, combined with specific pre-treatment (NaOH and N_2 plasma), hybrid bonding can be compatible with 3D Phase Change Memory product.

Heterogenous integration

To expand the possibilities in terms of integration, new bonding processes have been studied. To be in line with market' requests, focus is mainly on two kinds of processes: bonding under high vacuum to avoid any annealing temperature limitation and die to wafer to be able to propose heterogenous integration.

Bonding under vacuum

To reach strong bonding energy which is mandatory for subsequent mechanical manufacturing; a bonding anneal of 800°C is required. By using plasma treatment prior bonding, anneal temperature can be decreased to 400°C. However, some devices cannot withstand such thermal budget. Even if specific plasma or surface preparation could even decrease the required annealing temperature, if substrate with different thermal expansion coefficient must be bonded, any anneal temperature could lead to delamination. That's why, to overcome this limitation, many studies have been performed on developing bonding process without thermal budget. Surface activated bonding (SAB) is a promising method to achieve high bonding energy at room temperature. The SAB method removes surface oxides and contaminants thanks to surface activation by Ar atom beam bombardment in ultra-high vacuum (UHV) prior to bonding.[17]
However, even if this technology gives very interesting results with metal layers, SiO_2 bonding energy obtained with SAB bonding is comparable to the one obtained with conventional direct bonding (close to 0.3 J/m²). Amorphous silicon deposition could be a solution to use SAB technology for hybrid bonding below 150°C.

Die to Wafer Bonding

As hybrid bonding is now well mastered from an industrial point of view, Die to Wafer (D2W) hybrid bonding is an enabling process to accelerate deployment of 3D/heterogeneous integration. Surface preparation processes are key points to ensure good bonding quality and yield in line with industrial requirements.
Conventional D2W assemblies are currently based on pick & place processes, whereby high alignment accuracy and good assembly throughput seem hardly reconcilable. To solve this issue, different techniques have been proposed. The self-assembly assisted by capillarity appears as a promising technology. [18]

Conclusion

The transition of hybrid bonding pitch from 6.9 µm to 0.6 µm is possible thanks to a dedicated metrology and a strong understanding of bonding wave behavior. To extend hybrid bonding to new products such as phase change memory, surface pre-treatment has been developed. In order to build new heterogeneous structures in three-dimensional (3D) integration circuits, many works have been done on new bonding technologies such as surface activation bonding or die to wafer bonding.
Further studies will continue to make these processes more robust and compatible with high volume manufacturing.

References

1. Ayoub, B., Lhostis, S., Moreau, S., Perez, E. L., Jourdon, J., Lamontagne, P., ... & Frémont, H. (2020, December). Impact of Process Variations on the Capacitance and Electrical Resistance down to 1.44 µm Hybrid Bonding Interconnects. In *2020 IEEE 22nd Electronics Packaging Technology Conference (EPTC)* (pp. 453-458). IEEE.
2. Grauer, Y., Eisenbach, S., Penia, M., Elka, D., Simkin, A., Safrani, A., & Megged, E. (2023, April). Advanced overlay metrology for 3D NAND bonding applications. In *Metrology, Inspection, and Process Control XXXVII* (Vol. 12496, pp. 886-902). SPIE.
3. Dettoni, F., Deloffre, E., Grauer Y., et al. Advanced overlay metrology for CIS bonding applications. ECTC 2023 to be published.
4. Oike, Y. (2021). Evolution of image sensor architectures with stacked device technologies. *IEEE Transactions on Electron Devices*, 69(6), 2757-2765.
5. TechInsight 23- https://www.techinsights.com/blog/sony-2-layer-transistor-pixel-stacked-cmos-image-sensor-early-findings
6. Moreau, S., Jourdon, J., Lhostis, S., Bouchu, D., Ayoub, B., Arnaud, L., & Fremont, H. (2022). Hybrid bonding-based interconnects: A status on the last robustness and reliability achievements. *ECS Journal of Solid State Science and Technology*, 11(2), 024001.
7. Ayoub, B., Moreau, S., Lhostis, S., Frémont, H., Mermoz, S., Souchier, E., ... & Thomas, O. (2022). In-situ characterization of thermomechanical behavior of copper nano-interconnect for 3D integration. *Microelectronic Engineering*, 261, 111809.
8. Ayoub, B., Lhostis, S., Moreau, S., Souchier, E., Deloffre, E., Mermoz, S., ... & Frémont, H. (2022, December). Sub 1 µm Pitch Achievement for Cu/SiO 2 Hybrid Bonding. In *2022 IEEE 24th Electronics Packaging Technology Conference (EPTC)* (pp. 418-424). IEEE.
9. Ayoub, B., Lhostis, S., Moreau, S., Souchier, E., Deloffre, E., Mermoz, S., ... & Fremont, H. (2022, December). Sub 1 µm Pitch Achievement for Cu/SiO2 Hybrid Bonding. In *24th Electronics Packaging Technology Conference*. IEEE
10. Ayoub, B., Lhostis, S., Moreau, S., Mattei, J. G., Mukhtarov, A., & Frémont, H. (2023). Investigation into Cu diffusion at the Cu/SiO2 hybrid bonding interface of 3D stacked integrated circuits. *Microelectronics Reliability*, 143, 114934.
11. Netzband,C., Ryan, K., Mimura, Y., Ilseok, S., Aizawa, H., (2023, May). 0.5 µm Pitch Next Generation Hybrid Bonding with High Alignment Accuracy for 3D Integration, *Electronics Packaging Technology Conference (EPTC)*, to be published.
12. Mitsuishi, H., Mori, H., Maeda, H., Ushijima, M., Kamshita, A. et al. (2023, May). 50 nm Overlay Accuracy for Wafer-tiwafer Bonding by High-precision Alignment Technologies, *Electronics Packaging Technology Conference (EPTC)*, to be published.
13. Ayoub, B., Lhostis, S., Moreau, S., Perez, E. L., Jourdon, J., Lamontagne, P., ... & Frémont, H. (2020, December). Impact of Process Variations on the Capacitance and Electrical Resistance down to $1.44\,\mu\mathrm{m}$ Hybrid Bonding Interconnects. In *2020 IEEE 22nd Electronics Packaging Technology Conference (EPTC)* (pp. 453-458). IEEE.

14. Fournel, F., Calvez, A., Larrey, V., Eleouet, G., Morales, C., & Rieutord, F. (2020). Impact of an Amino-Alcohol Organic Molecule on SiO2 and Si Bonding Energy. *ECS Transactions, 98*(4), 3.
15. Chen, C., Juang, J. Y., Chang, S. Y., Shie, K. C., Li, Y. J., & Tu, K. N. (2019, May). Low-temperature Cu-to-Cu direct bonding enabled by highly (111)-oriented and nanotwinned Cu. In *2019 6th International Workshop on Low Temperature Bonding for 3D Integration (LTB-3D)* (pp. 38-38). IEEE.
16. Fournel, F., Martin-Cocher, C., Radisson, D., Larrey, V., Beche, E., Morales, C., ... & Moriceau, H. (2015). Water stress corrosion in bonded structures. *ECS Journal of Solid State Science and Technology, 4*(5), P124.
17. Suga, T., He, R., Vakanas, G., & La Manna, A. (2021). Direct Cu to Cu bonding and alternative bonding techniques in 3D packaging. *3D Microelectronic Packaging: From Architectures to Applications*, 201-231.
18. Amandine, J., Sanchez, L., Castan, C., Laugier, M., Rolland, E., Montmayeul, B., ... & Cheramy, S. (2019, May). Self-Assembly process for 3D Die-to-Wafer using direct bonding: A step forward toward process automatisation. In *2019 IEEE 69th Electronic Components and Technology Conference (ECTC)* (pp. 225-234). IEEE.

ECS Transactions, 112 (3) 73-81 (2023)
10.1149/11203.0073ecst ©The Electrochemical Society

Process and Design Challenges for Hybrid Bonding

Vikas Dubey[a], Dirk Wünsch[a], Knut Gottfried[a], Tobias Fischer[a, b], Anke Hanisch[a],
Sebastian Schermer[a], Christian Helke[a,b], Micha Haase[a, b], Sanghamitra Ghosal[a], Lutz
Hofmann[a], Danny Reuter[a], Maik Wiemer[a] and Stefan E.Schulz[a,b]

[a] Fraunhofer ENAS, Technologie Campus 3, 09126 Chemnitz, Germany
[b] TU-Chemnitz, Center for Microtechnologies, Reichenhainer Str. 70, 09126 Chemnitz,
Germany

Achieving high-quality interconnect interfaces for fine pitch integration is crucial in today's advanced electronic systems. Among various interconnect options, hybrid bonding stands out as a superior choice due to its ability to accommodate a high input/output (I/O) count, enabling high-density memory integration, increased power delivery, and improved signal speed. To ensure the utmost quality in hybrid bonding, embedding Cu interconnects within the dielectric layer has proven effective. Furthermore, the surface planarization process, accomplished through chemical mechanical polishing (CMP), plays a pivotal role. In this regard, the final CMP process typically involves a meticulous two-step procedure involving copper bulk CMP followed by barrier CMP. The latter yields the desired surface finish crucial for successful hybrid bonding. Several key surface properties, including copper recess (referred to as dishing) in the vias, erosion and roughness of the dielectric layer, and surface topography changes from high-density to low-density copper vias, significantly impact the overall bond yield. To optimize these parameters, a comprehensive understanding of the design of the interconnect layer for the CMP process is essential. In this study, we explore the impact of via scaling and via density for interconnect pitches from 5 μm to 1 μm and the surface topography due to dummy vias of the final bonding surface.

Keywords: Hybrid bonding, fine pitch integration, interconnect interfaces, high-density memory, power delivery, signal speed, chemical mechanical polishing (CMP), copper recess, erosion, roughness, profile change, atomic force microscopy (AFM).

Introduction

The advent of 3D integration has revolutionized semiconductor packaging, enabling its application in diverse fields such as the Internet of Things (IoT) (1), image sensors (2), and high-bandwidth memory (HBM) (3). Hybrid bonding technology (4, 5) has emerged as a crucial development, facilitating high-density interconnect packaging across various applications. Notably, this technology has been employed in the creation of cutting-edge devices such as image sensors (6), micro light-emitting diodes (micro-LEDs) (7), and stacked memory for server applications (8). The proliferation of mobile computing devices like smartphones and tablets has been made possible by the implementation of heterogeneous 3D integration, enabling seamless integration of systems-in-package (SiP) while enhancing signal integrity and power efficiency. Hybrid bonding technology serves as an assembly approach for achieving high-density interconnect assembly in 3D integration scenarios.

Hybrid bonding technology integrates direct bonding techniques with embedded interconnect vias, enabling precise copper (Cu)/dielectric bonding. Unlike solid-liquid interdiffusion (SLID) bonding, hybrid bonding surpasses the limits of interconnect technology scaling by achieving sub-10 μm pitch dimensions. This breakthrough empowers CMOS back-end-of-line (BEOL) processes with enhanced alignment tolerances, facilitating pitch scaling. Hybrid bonding manifests in three distinct stacking approaches: wafer-to-wafer (W2W), die-to-wafer (D2W), and die-to-die (D2D). Among these approaches, wafer-level bonding stands out as the more feasible option, benefitting from the availability of specialized equipment for comprehensive wafer-level cleaning and handling. Conversely, the die-level hybrid bonding approach presents formidable challenges, as it is susceptible to particle contamination during dicing and arm movement in the bonding process. D2W and D2D techniques also introduce additional hurdles, including meticulous handling during surface cleaning, plasma activation, and bonding, all of which contribute to potential yield losses. Nonetheless, D2D and D2W bonding offer the promising advantage of achieving high yields by leveraging pre-electrically tested known-good-dies (KGD).

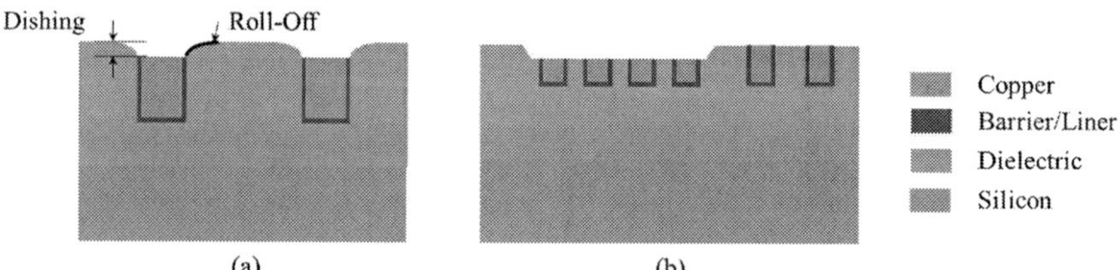

Figure 1. The cross-section view of the surface profile of the hybrid bonding surface. a) shows the "dishing" and "roll-off" around the metal vias and (b) shows the surface topography generated due to difference in the metal via density after the metal chemical mechanical polishing step.

The preparation of the bonding surface in the CMOS damascene process follows a standard procedure. Achieving a high bonding yield heavily relies on surface topography. Varying via density across interconnect pitches can result in different behaviors such as copper via dishing, roll-off of the oxide and the topography of the surface. In Figure 1 (a), "dishing" refers to the separation between the copper via surface and the dielectric surface when the copper surface is situated below the dielectric surface. Conversely, if the copper via surface is above the dielectric surface, it is referred to as "protrusion." The occurrence of dishing or protrusion depends on the relative selectivity of the copper and barrier/liner layer during the metal chemical mechanical polishing (CMP) process. CMP is a crucial technology for hybrid bonding, ensuring the creation of ultra-smooth and flat surfaces at the nanometer scale to facilitate effective bond propagation during low-temperature bonding. Furthermore, different dielectric materials can affect the rate at which the dielectric is removed during the CMP process. Another significant parameter is the "roll-off" of the dielectric surrounding the copper vias, which measures the slope of the dielectric in nm/μm. The "roll-off" will guide the bonding of the dielectric layer around the metal via. Lastly, surface topography (shown in Figure 1 (b)) is a key factor that defines the flatness of the bonding surface for successful bonding. The surface topography may vary when the density of the copper via pattern changes and this can sometimes lead to bonding voids as the bond wave is not able to travel around the high topographical surface leading to possible voiding between the bonding interface.

The paper presents the work done with a bond dielectric describing the impact on the via dishing and dielectric roll-off with respect to scaling via diameter. However, the bonding surface topography is directly impacted by the following factors, a) via density, b) via size and c) density variation, due to the presence of "dummy vias" which basically regulates the copper and dielectric density variation and its impact on the bonding quality. The dummy vias herein refer to the via structures which are not intended for electrical interconnect connections and are only present to assist the CMP process optimization for better process control. Hence, the dummy vias are not connected to the underlying routing metal layers.

Experiments

The reticle has been meticulously crafted to ensure precise alignment tolerances of up to 200 nm during the wafer's alignment process. Within the test array, the copper density exhibits a range of 12.57% to 16%. The test chip incorporates a combination of square and circular vias, featuring various pitch sizes. These pitch sizes span from 5 μm (with a via diameter of 2.25 μm) to 1 μm (with a via diameter of 450 nm). The size of the via array adjusts proportionately to the pitch size. There are two variations designed, firstly without dummy vias and secondly with the dummy vias.

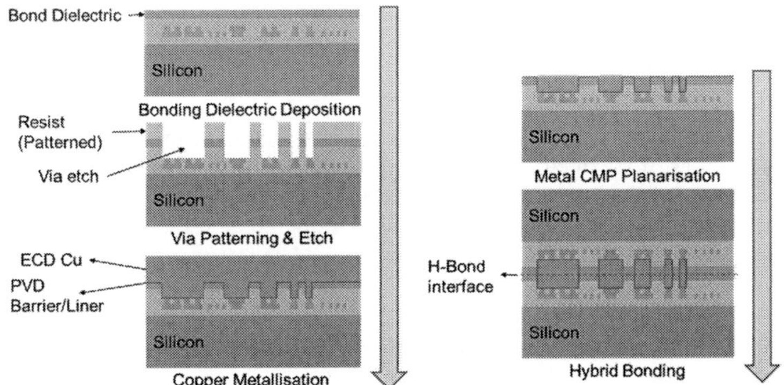

Figure 2. The schematic shows the damascene fabrication of the bond layer for hybrid bonding.

The process flow for wafer fabrication is illustrated in Figure 2. Initially, the wafers undergo preparation, where SiO_2 is deposited through PECVD at 300 °C, followed by annealing at 350 °C. To achieve smoothness, the bond dielectric is polished with the assistance of the dielectric CMP process utilizing IPEC472 by Axus Technology. The roughness of the polished surface is measured employing Agilent 5600LS atomic force microscopy.

For patterning the wafer, the i-line stepper lithography NSR2205i11D is employed, and the etching process is performed in an Oxford Plasmalab System 100 by Oxford Instruments, utilizing reactive ion plasma etching. The barrier/liner/seed layer is then deposited through physical vapour deposition (PVD), and a 1500 nm copper layer is electroplated using the ClassOne Solstice system. Finally, the wafer is polished for metal planarization utilizing the Surface CMP tool by Axus Technology.

Metal CMP technology involves two steps. The first step is copper CMP, which removes the excess bulk copper until reaching the desired endpoint with a specific overpolish duration. The second step, known as barrier CMP, eliminates the barrier/liner layer and serves as the final polishing step to adjust the via dishing. Each dielectric type requires two wafers to undergo the polishing process.

The bonding process takes place in the EVG Gemini wafer bonder. During bonding, the wafers undergo treatment with low-nitrogen plasma and are subsequently rinsed with DIW to generate hydroxyl groups on the bonding surfaces. Precise alignment of the wafers is achieved using the wafer aligner in the EVG Gemini system. The pre-bonding itself occurs at room temperature without the application of pressure, leading to the formation of bond between the dielectrics and the wafers can be subsequently bonded leading to hybrid bonding.

Prior to bonding and following the metal CMP process, the wafers undergo characterization for dishing, roll-off, and long scan using the Bruker Automated AFM, Insight Cap. The scanning is conducted with a resolution of 2048 points per line and 128 lines. The size of the scan depends on the pitch being examined. For a 1μm pitch, the scan size is 6 μm x 6 μm, for a 2 μm pitch it is 12 μm x 12 μm, for a 3 μm pitch it is 18 μm x 18 μm, and for a 5 μm pitch it is 30 μm x 30 μm. This scan size is chosen to capture a 5 x 5 via array for statistical analysis.

Automated dishing/roll-off analysis is performed using custom software that incorporates artificial intelligence for automated via detection and data evaluation (9, 10). For the long scan data, a similar script is utilized. It first levels the profile using a line and then applies a spline curve. The profile is then filtered, and the maximum and minimum peaks are extracted. Statistically, the slope is calculated.

After bonding, the wafers are subjected to characterization using an infrared camera and scanning acoustic microscopy (SAM300) by PVA Tepla. The SAM300 employs a 110 MHz transducer with a focal length of 3.2 mm.

Results & Discussions

In this segment, we provide an elaborate examination of the variation in dielectric roughness subsequent to each step in the process, namely dielectric deposition, dielectric CMP, and barrier CMP. Following the metal CMP process, we delve into the behavior of the bonding surface, encompassing aspects like via dishing, dielectric roll-off, and surface topography. Ultimately, section on hybrid bonding presents the analysis of the bonded wafer pair using scanning acoustic microscopy.

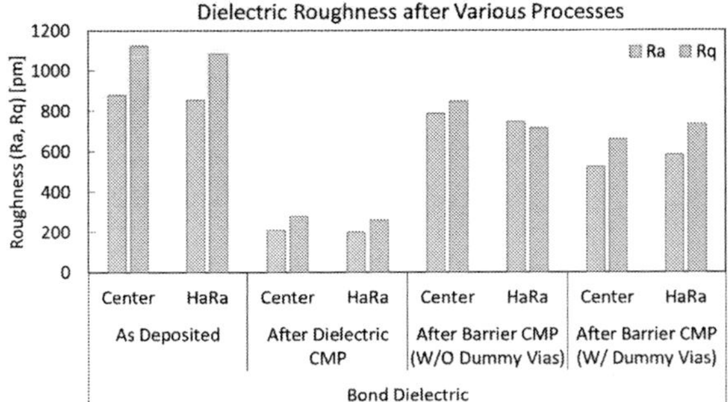

Figure 3. The roughness of the dielectric surface as deposited, after dielectric CMP and after Barrier CMP (without dummy via wafers and with dummy via wafers). "HaRa" in the above graph is a short form of "Half-Radius".

<u>Dielectric Roughness:</u> In order to assess surface roughness, dummy wafers are also coated with the corresponding dielectric, alongside the actual wafers. The roughness is measured both before and after dielectric chemical mechanical polishing, as these surfaces are involved in dielectric bonding. Initially, the deposited dielectric exhibits a roughness (Ra) of less than 1 nm. However, after dielectric CMP, the roughness decreases to below 300 pm. This low roughness value indicates reduced mechanical irregularities and an increased likelyhood of successful bond formation. Nonetheless, it is important to note that the dielectric surface may experience roughening during barrier CMP, as the roughness depends on the size of the slurry particles utilized for the barrier polishing. It has been observed that the roughness increases to approximately 800 pm following barrier CMP for wafers without dummy vias and to 600 pm for wafers with dummy vias. The roughness is consistent across the wafers.

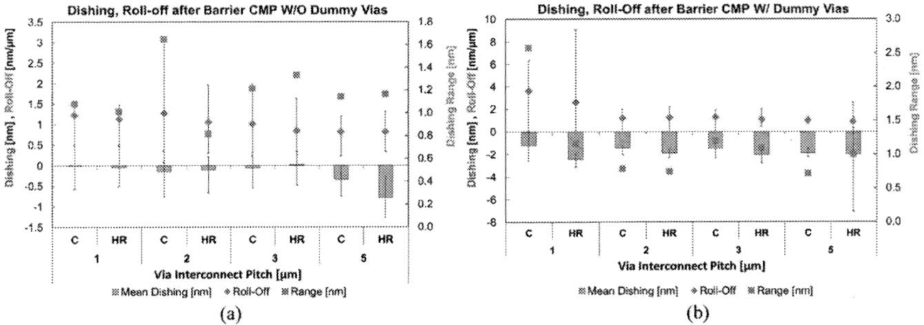

Figure 4. Dishing, dielectric roll-off and the dishing range for 5x5 via array for 1 μm, 2 μm, 3 μm and 5 μm via pitch respectively for wafers (a) without dummy vias and for wafers (b) with dummy vias. ("C" stands for measurement at the center of the wafer and "HR" stands for the measurement at the half-radius of the wafer).

<u>Dishing and Roll-off of the via after metal CMP:</u> After performing hard pad barrier CMP, it is observed that all via pitches (1 µm, 2 µm, 3 µm, and 5 µm) exhibit low dishing. The results demonstrate excellent control over the dishing phenomenon across all via diameters. The dishing behaviour of vias remains consistent both at the center and halfway radius of the wafer, indicating uniform CMP control throughout the wafer. For wafers without dummy vias, the 5 µm pitch vias exhibit greater dishing compared to the 3 µm, 2 µm, and 1 µm pitch vias, this can be compensated by the expansion of copper within the larger vias, denoted as $\delta l \propto V(Cu)$, where δl represents the copper expansion in the via and $V(Cu)$ denotes the volume of copper within the via. For wafers with dummy vias, all via diameters exhibit similar dishing across all pitch sizes.

When comparing the roll-off measurements of the bond dielectric material, for wafer without dummy vias it stays consistently 1 nm/µm for all via pitches, indicating a uniformly flat dielectric layer between the vias. While for wafer with dummy vias, the roll-off stays close to 1.3 nm/µm with better variance control for 2 µm, 3 µm and 5 µm pitch sizes. The roll-off measurement and the variance increases for 1 µm via pitch. Typically, as the pitch size increases, the roll-off also tends to increase. The roll-off behavior is similar at both the center and halfway radius of the wafer. Lower roll-off values contribute to improved bond propagation, thereby increasing bonding yield.

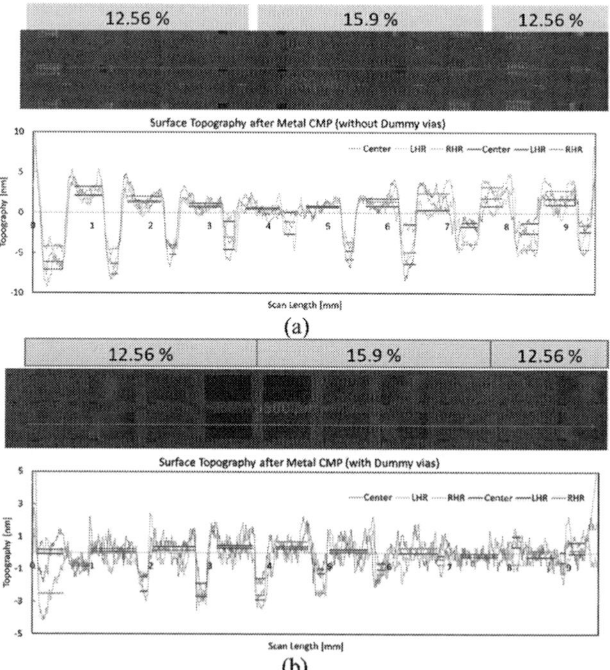

Figure 5. AFM topography scan for via arrays a) without dummy vias and b) with dummy vias. The scan length is 9500 µm and covers all the pitch sizes. The image shows the surface scanned under the AFM. The via array pitch from the left side is in the

following order, 5 µm, 3 µm, 2 µm, 1 µm and then 1 µm, 2 µm, 3 µm, 5 µm and then 5 µm and 3 µm.

<u>Surface Topography after metal CMP</u>: Long scan measurements were employed, and the results were analyzed using atomic force microscopy (AFM). Figure 5 shows the images of the surface scanned without (in figure 5(a)) and with (in figure 5(b)) dummy vias. Scan length is 9500 µm. It is evident that the bond surface topography changes with changing copper density. For our experiment two different copper density is used, firstly 12.56 % and secondly 15.9 %. The surrounding copper dummy via has a density of 16.62 %.

From figure 5, it is observed that the via size affects the topography inspite of having the same density. When comparing the impact of the via diameter as the factor, it is observed that with decreasing size of the via diameter the topography increasing inspite of having the same density (see figure 5(a)). Also, for higher copper density the topographical recess is larger compared to lower copper density via array.

The topography increases for the copper via array when the array is surrounded by a higher copper density vias (see figure 5(b)). The topographical recess improves as the copper density of the via array (15.9 %) is similar to the surrounding dummy vias (density of 16.62%). Hence, it also becomes difficult to observe the difference between the interconnect via and the surrounding vias.

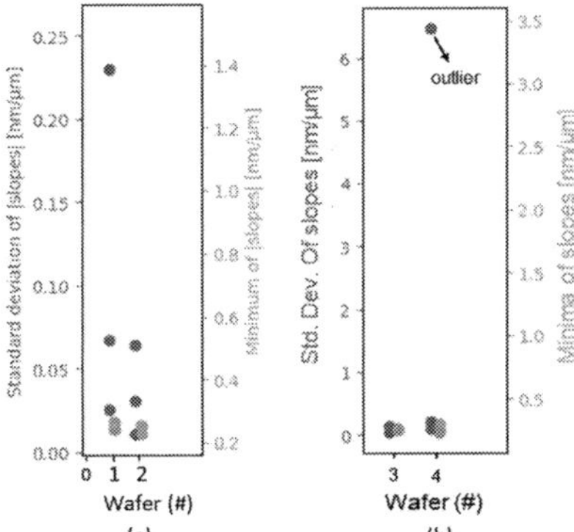

Figure 6. The statistical value of the slopes obtained from the long scan topography measurement for the top (wafer 1, 3) and the bottom (wafer 2, 4) wafer. (a) wafer 1, 2 are the wafers with surrounding dummy vias and (b) wafer 3, 4 are the wafer pairs without the surrounding dummy vias.

Figure 6 displays a comparison of the standard deviation and minima of topographical slope. The bond dielectric used in this study exhibits a slope of less than 1 nm/µm.

<u>Hybrid Bonding</u>: The wafers after surface inspection are bonded after nitrogen plasma treatment and cleaning and the bond interface is inspected using scanning acoustic microscopy. The bond interface shows a clear impact of the bond surface topography. It can be seen in figure 7(a) that with large topographical via arrays is not bonded and appears as a white region. While the region that is well bonded appears as black. The

bonding across various via structure is better with the dummy vias (see figure 7(b)). The edge of the wafer is not bonded due to CMP non-uniformity. With long scan it was also observed that the topography is unexpectedly higher at the edges.

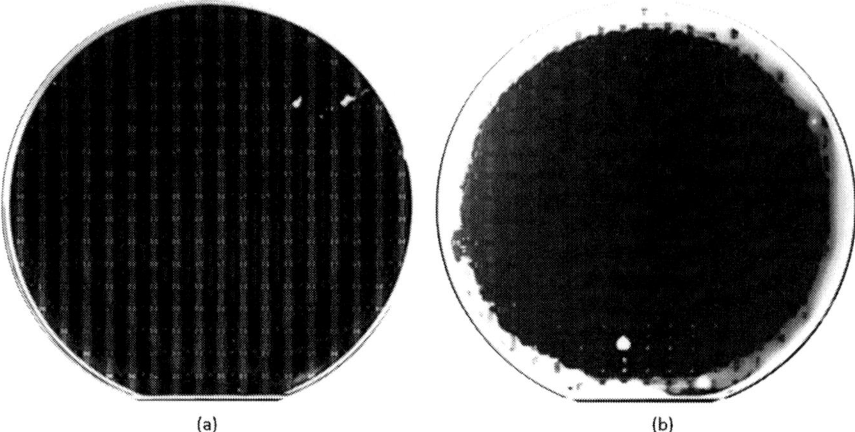

(a)   (b)

Figure 7. Scanning acoustic microscopy images of the bonded wafer pair, a) wafer pair without dummy vias, b) wafer pair with dummy vias.

Conclusion

In conclusion, we understand the via diameter impact and the aspects related to presence of dummy vias on the hybrid bonding using the bond dielectric.

- Roughness of the bond dielectric is higher after barrier metal CMP. This may affect the bonding quality at the bond interface.
- For bond surface without dummy vias, the via dishing is directly affected by the via diameter and it increases with increasing size of the via. On the contrary, the via dishing remains same across all via diameter when the bond surface is filled with dummy vias.
- Topography is a directly affected by the copper via density and size of the vias in the array.
- Topography improves when the via array is surrounded by the dummy via having similar via density.
- The topography recess is less when the via diameter is small in the via array.
- The bonding across the various via diameter improves when the bond surface is filled with dummy vias. Although the consideration regarding the via dishing must be made with respect to the smallest via as the effective copper volume available for the interconnect formation is lowest and the copper expansion will be less for smaller via when compared to larger vias.

Hence, in this work we demonstrate the impact of via scaling, via array size, density with respect to the presence of dummy vias and compared it without the dummy vias. The bonding is heavily dependent on the surface topography. Hence, the via design can be key deciding factor for enablement of high-density interconnect formation using hybrid bonding technology.

Acknowledgments

The author would like to extend their appreciation to all those involved in supporting the fabrication process, including lithography, etching, deposition, process control, and fab management, at Fraunhofer ENAS and ZfM in Chemnitz. A special acknowledgement goes to the teams at Fraunhofer ENAS, specifically the inline metrology and artificial intelligence groups (Doreen Hensel, Andreas Zienert, Max Huber, and Jan Langer), for their valuable contribution in developing the automated AFM data evaluation software.

References

1. M. Koyanagi, "Heterogenous 3D Integration for Internet of Things," 12th IEEE Int. conf. on Solid-State and Integration Technology (ICSICT), Guilin, China, Oct 2014.
2. Y. Kagawa, H.Iwamoto, "3D Integration Technologies for the Stacked CMOS Image Sensors", IEEE 3DIC, Sendai, Japan, Oct 2019.
3. K. Abe et. al., "Ultra-high bandwidth memory with 3D stacked emerging memory cells", IEEE ICICDTT, Grenoble, France, June 2008.
4. S. Kühne and C. Hierold, "Wafer level packaging and direct interconnection technology based on hybrid bonding and through silicon vias", J of micromach. microeng., 21 085032, July 2011.
5. V. Dubey, D. Wünsch, K. Gottfried, "Impact of Dielectric and Copper Via Design on Wafer-to-Wafer Hybrid Bonding", IEEE Proc. of 73rd ECTC, May 2023.
6. C. Cavaco et. al, "On the Fabrication of Backside Illuminated Image Sensors: Bonding Oxide, Edge Trimming and CMP Rework Routes", ECS Trans. 64 123, 2015.
7. K. Yadavalli, C-L Chuang, H.S. El-Ghoroury, "Monolithic and heterogeneous integration of RGB micro-LED arrays with pixel-level optics array and CMOS image processor to enable small form-factor display applications", SPIE Proc. of AR,VR,MR, vol. 11310, San Francisco, California, USA, Feb 2020.
8. J. Wuu et. al, "3D V-Cache: The Implementation of a Hybrid-Bonded 64MB Stacked Cache for a 7nm x86-64 CPU", IEEE ISSCC, San Francisco, CA, USA, Feb 2022.
9. A. Zienert et. al, "Automatic Detection of Via Arrays in AFM Images for CMP Dishing Evaluation", Materials for advanced metallization conference proceedings, 2023.
10. J. Langer, A. Zienert, D. Hensel, L. Hofmann, K. Gottfried and T. Rothe, "Automatic Analysis of CMP Dishing in Via Arrays from AFM Images", International Conference on Planarization Technology, Portland, OR, USA, Sept. 2022.

ECS Transactions, 112 (3) 83-94 (2023)
10.1149/11203.0083ecst ©The Electrochemical Society

SAB-Enabled Room Temperature Hybrid Bonding

P. Renaud[a], K. Abadie [a], F. Fournel [a], C. Dubarry [a], F. Baudin [a] and A. Tauzin [a]

[a] Univ. Grenoble Alpes, CEA, LETI, 38000 Grenoble, France

On the one hand, direct hybrid bonding is foreseen to revolutionize semiconductor device integration, allowing the seamless 3D interconnection of diverse materials with distinct properties. On the other hand, Surface Activation Bonding (SAB) is a powerful technique within the field of low-temperature bonding, offering enhanced bonding strength and compatibility with a wide range of materials. By dealing with the possibilities of SAB, this paper demonstrates the possibility of realizing a Cu-oxide direct hybrid bonding with a 5 μm pitch interconnections at ambient temperature. This success highlights the potential of SAB as a critical enabler for low-temperature hybrid bonding and its potential impact on next-generation semiconductor devices.

Introduction

The need of advanced semiconductor technologies scaling has driven the current growing interest in 3D integration, which offers a multitude of benefits for various applications including CMOS image sensors, high-performance computing, DRAM, and displays. Among these applications, hybrid bonding-based 3D stacking has emerged as the cutting-edge solution in the field of imaging [1]. By employing copper-oxide direct bonding, this technology achieves high integration densities with micron-sized pixels, pushing the boundaries of imaging performance. Notably, recent achievements have demonstrated exceptional reliability in functional imagers with sub micrometer pitch [2], promoting the potential of hybrid bonding in enabling next-generation imaging applications.

Quite early in 2000's, Suga et al [3] introduced the concept of bump-less interconnections based on direct bonding of mixed surfaces made of metal pads surrounded by a dielectric material. This concept is now known as direct hybrid bonding. Hydrophilic direct bonding involves surface topography and cleanliness control, chemical and/or plasma activation before contacting the surfaces, and then sufficient annealing, typically done at 400°C, in order to get rid of the copper oxide at the bonding interface and ensure good electrical connection. However, the semiconductor industry increasingly demands low-temperature integration methods (< 250°C) to minimize thermal stress and preserve the functionality of sensitive chips, such as image sensors, displays, and memory devices. Surface Activation Bonding (SAB) is a promising well known technique that enables low-temperature direct bonding[3]. SAB could then offer a path to achieve robust and reliable hybrid bonding at significantly reduced temperatures, thus addressing the thermal budget concerns of sensitive devices. However, up to now, SAB hybrid bondings have been mainly performed using modified SAB technology [4] or modified bonding mechanisms [5]. Indeed, hybrid bonding usually starts with Cu recess and oxide surface bonding, yet it is well known that SAB can not bond with high adhesion and adherence the silicon di-oxide material. Some tricks have then been tested in order to enable low-temperature hybrid bonding processes on both surface materials. Modified SAB technology is based on a Si ultrathin film deposition to make the entire surface reactive and bond the Cu and the dielectric at the same time. On the other hand, oxide recess approach uses a process which puts copper pads in protrusion instead of recess after CMP to allow the contact of the Cu pads and support the poor SAB oxide bonding. Both processes have some disadvantages. The first one modifies the dielectric function between the cooper pads and the second one induces gaps at the bonding interface, which could be an issue for the post processing.

The aim of this publication is to provide a first step in exploring the possibilities of standard SAB in the context of very low temperature hybrid bonding. Our first objective is to gain a better understanding of surface modification during SAB activation, in order to enhance our control over the process. Various characterization methods such as acoustic microscopy (C-SAM), TEM (Transmission Electron Microscopy), and EDX (Energy-Dispersive X-ray Spectroscopy) were employed to assess the quality of the interface. Through our investigations, we have successfully demonstrated the viability of SAB hybrid bonding at low temperatures, and even at room temperature. Finally, the integration of SAB into low-temperature hybrid bonding processes holds great promise for advancing semiconductor technologies and driving innovation in a wide range of applications.

Experimental procedure

This study uses 200 mm silicon wafers with 2.5 µm-diameter copper pads spaced 2.5 µm apart (5 µm pitch) in a silicon oxide matrix, as presented on Figure 1. Copper pads are fully uniformly spread across the wafers. The silicon nitride and the silicon oxide are both deposited at 400°C by PECVD. The copper pads are then fabricated using a damascene process incorporating a Ti/TiN bilayer as diffusion barrier. As this study focuses on morphological and mechanical characterizations, only one damascene layer is made on wafers to be bonded. Noteworthy, copper pads are left in a slight recess induced by the CMP process prior to bonding.

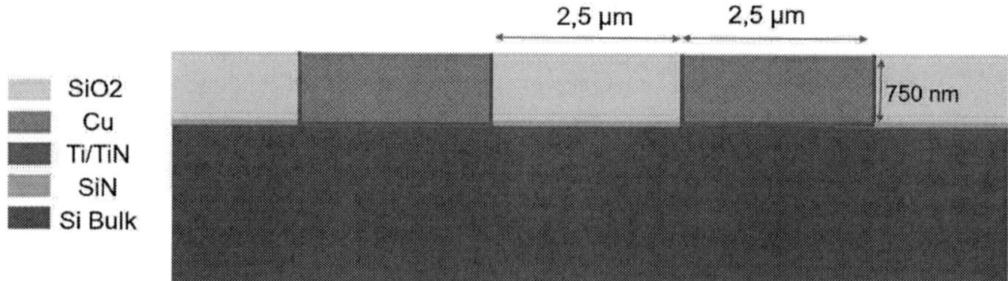

Figure 1 : Integration scheme

In this study, a hydrophilic direct hybrid Bonding sample without anneal or annealed at 150°C for 2 hours has been performed in order to compare with SAB hybrid bondings.

Hydrophilic hybrid bonding

Hydrophilic direct bonding mechanisms are based on spontaneous adhesion phenomena when surfaces are brought into contact. The creation of weak intermolecular bonds (hydrogen, van der Walls, and capillarity bridges) at the point of contact initiates a bonding wave that spreads along the surface [6]. Thus, this technic requires completely flat and smooth surfaces on both copper and oxide parts. This task is ensured by a specific Chemical Mechanical Polishing (CMP) that provides excellent bonding specifications. Bonding is carried out less than 24 hours after the CMP to limit copper oxidation and global organic contamination. The wafers are placed face to face, aligned, and contact is initiated at the center of the surface. There is no addition of any material (polymer, metal, etc.) or chemical preparation during the bonding, and all the process takes place under ambient temperature and pressure conditions.

Afterwards, bonded wafers are annealed in order to strengthen the bonding by improving the Cu/Cu contact, increasing copper diffusion at the interface and along grain boundaries, and increasing covalent bonds density (already present for SiO2-SiO2 interface at room temperature [7]). The creation of covalent bonds at the interface depends on the materials, the surface conditions (flatness, roughness, and cleanliness) and the thermal budget applied during annealing.

SAB

(Surface Activation Bonding) employs argon atom bombardment as a surface preparation technique. This bombardment takes place in an ultra-high vacuum (UHV) environment at room temperature for several tens of seconds. By doing so, the bombardment eliminates the copper oxide on the surface, leaving behind exposed metallic bonds on the copper pads. These bonds remain intact throughout the process, thanks to the UHV environment, until the bonding occurs. While the conventional SAB method is effective for Cu-Cu bonding at room temperature, it has been proven ineffective for SiO_2-SiO_2 bonding [6]. Although the argon atom bombardment still has an etching effect on the SiO_2 surface, it does not enhance the bonding strength for this material. Consequently, to ensure high-adherence bonding at low temperatures, it is crucial for the copper pads to ensure the contact during the SAB bonding. Otherwise, the strength of the bonding at low temperature will be no better than that of a traditional direct SiO_2-SiO_2 direct bonding under vacuum, which is quite low [7].

In the UHV environment, just after the Argon bombardment, two identical hybrid wafers are immediately bonded at room temperature under a low pressure of 0.3 MPa. It is important to note that the tool used for this process lacks alignment methods apart from rough mechanical one using the wafer notches. As a result, the copper pads are randomly brought into contact with other copper pads or with the oxide matrix. However, this randomness does not affect the morphological studies, as numerous pads align statistically. Regarding annealing treatment, the SAB bonded wafers are either left unannealed or subjected to annealing at temperatures of 150°C for a duration of 2 hours. This enables to see the evolution of the copper-copper and SiO2-SiO2 interfaces after annealing.

Mechanical thinning/removing of silicon bulk

After bonding and annealing (if applied), the bonded pairs encounter a fine grinding process to thin one the bonded wafers (namely 'top wafer' down to 30 μm of silicon. The success of this step depends on the bonding adherence, as many stresses are applied during the grinding. There is a risk of delamination of the thinned wafers if the bonding interface is not strengthened enough. After grinding, the remaining 30 μm-thick Si is removed using dry etching. A 1 μm damascene layer is then successfully been transferred from the top wafer to the bottom one.

Experimental plan

Before the bonding process, two different queue times are implemented between the hybrid surface CMP and the SAB bonding. Some samples are activated and bonded within 24 hours after CMP, while others are allowed to wait for 7 days before activation and bonding. This study enables us to evaluate the necessity of a specific sequencing, such as in the hydrophilic hybrid bonding.

Results and discussions

Etching effect of SAB activation – AFM

SAB activation has an etching effect on the surface due to the argon atoms bombardment. In the case of a hybrid Cu/SiO_2 surface with TiN barrier the three materials can react differently, inducing a potential different etching rate. Understanding this phenomenon is important because, as explained in the last section, to ensure a high enough adherence to the SAB bonded pair, a Cu-Cu contact at room temperature is essential. The copper pads, which are already in recess after CMP, must not be too deepened by the argon bombardment. Otherwise, the low temperature anneals will not be sufficient to bring them into contact by thermal expansion and to allow diffusion.

An AFM (Atomic Force Microscopy) study is therefore set up here to determine the abrasion effects during activation, such as etching rates depending on the materials, possible edge/center effects or repeatability. The study is carried out on wafers that underwent the CMP/activation sequence either over 24 hours or 7-days. In both cases, a post-CMP wafer and a post activation wafer are compared. In addition, 12 spots are measured on each wafer (4 in the center, 4 at the edge, 4 mid-radius) as represented on Figure 2 (only the mid-radius scan).
On Figure 2, AFM measurements are conducted on two wafers derived from a 24-hour CMP/activation sequence, with one wafer examined immediately after CMP and the other following surface activation. The scans show an evident increase in copper dishing after Ar activation. However, it is worth noting that the increase in dishing appears to be uniform on the different pads and relatively slight under these activation conditions. Results presented in Figure 3 allow going further in the analysis.

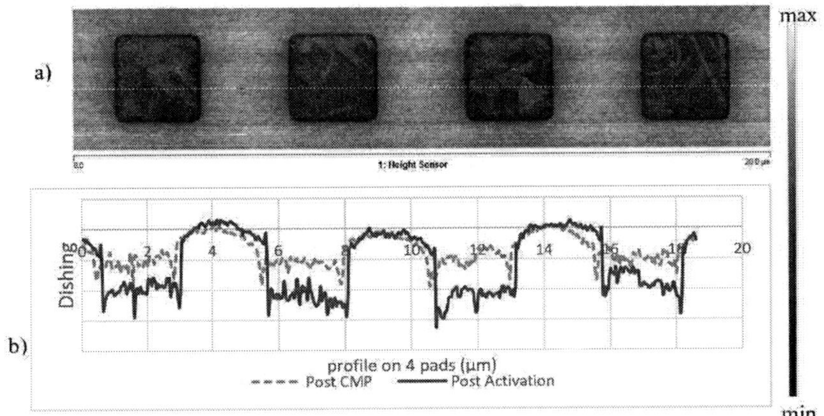

Figure 2: a) 20μmx4μm AFM scan of 4 Cu pads after CMP b) height profiles across 4 copper studs after CMP (dashed line) and after SAB surface activation (solid line)

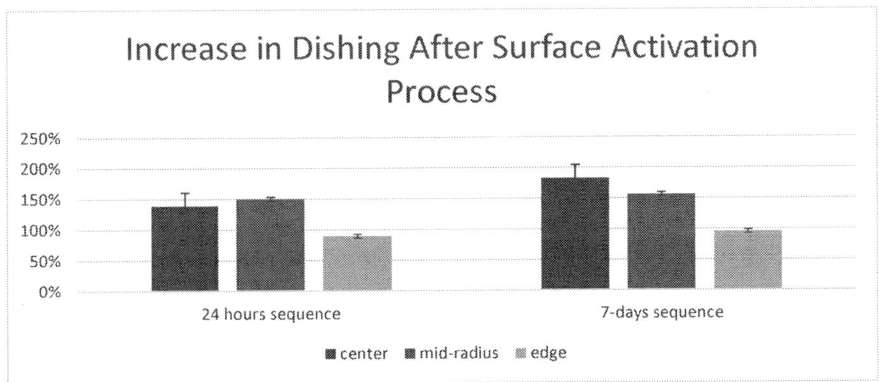

Figure 3: Increase in Dishing after Surface Activation Process (calculated with formula [1])

The increase in dishing was determined by the formula [1]:

$$\text{Increase in Dishing (\%)} = \qquad\qquad [1]$$
$$(\text{Dishing Value after activation} - \text{Dishing Value after CMP})/\text{Dishing Value after CMP}$$

Firstly, it is observed that the increase is quite repeatable, with no wide disparity, and values between +90% and +180%. While the center and mid-radius values are in the 140-180% of increase range, we can observe a less pronounced effect of the SAB activation at the wafer edges, with values of 90-100% of dishing increase, which can be attributed to a slightly non-uniform Ar bombardment during the process.
Another interesting observation to note is that the overall increase in dishing for the wafer

subjected to the 7-days sequence is slightly higher than the 24-hours processed one (+145% compared to +126%). The mechanisms that can be suggested is that the copper oxide present on the surface of the pads after the 7-days sequence etches more rapidly than the copper present for the 24-hours process under the Ar bombardment. Indeed, copper oxide develops over time as the pads are exposed to the air, thus requiring a careful control of the queue time between CMP and bonding in a classical hydrophilic bonding process. Nevertheless, all wafers, independently of this queue time, ultimately reach a nearly identical state after SAB. This indicated that Surface Activated hybrid bonding does not necessitate a specific sequence between CMP and bonding which is an interesting advantage compared to the hydrophilic hybrid bonding.

Overall, it is worth noting that despite the observed increase in dishing, the values remain within a range that does not affect significantly the bonding at room temperature as shown by the acoustic microscopy characterization presented in Figure 4. It means that despite the increase in dishing values after the SAB surface preparation, there is no need to adjust the nominal CMP process, and SAB bonding can be applied without extra developments.

An additional concern to SAB surface activation is the potential impact on copper roughness, a crucial factor for achieving optimal bonding. Consequently, multiple measurements are conducted on the wafers subsequent to CMP and activation processes. The results revealed a slight ten percent increase in the RMS roughness (0.47 nm RMS after CMP compared to 0.53 nm RMS after activation). However, this disparity did not reach statistical significance, as it is within the range of standard deviation for the measured values. Moreover, the recorded roughness values remained within the specifications for direct hybrid bonding.

<u>Acoustic characterization</u>

C-SAM (C-mode Scanning Acoustic Microscopy) serves as the first characterization step carried out immediately after bonding, providing an initial assessment of the bonding defectivity. This technique employs an ultrasonic beam to scan and image the bonding interface, offering a non-destructive means of detecting voids (or air gaps in atmospheric bonding). In HR (High Resolution) mode, the pixel size reaches 4μm per side. In the case of hybrid bonding, SAM is employed primarily to identify macro bonding defects, such as particles, and subsequently evaluate the closure quality of the bonding interface by comparing different shades of gray within the bond. It is important to note that immediately after bonding, the interface is never entirely bonded due to factors like copper dishing or copper roughness resulting from CMP. Since these voids are smaller than the pixel resolution, the grayscale shading provides qualitative information regarding their concentration relative to other areas on the wafer. C-SAM is typically performed before and after annealing to highlight improvements in interface quality or identify any potential issues such as degassing or delamination.

Figure 4 **a and b** show the result for a non-aligned SAB Hybrid Bonding sample together with a non-annealed aligned hydrophilic bonding sample (**c**) for comparison.

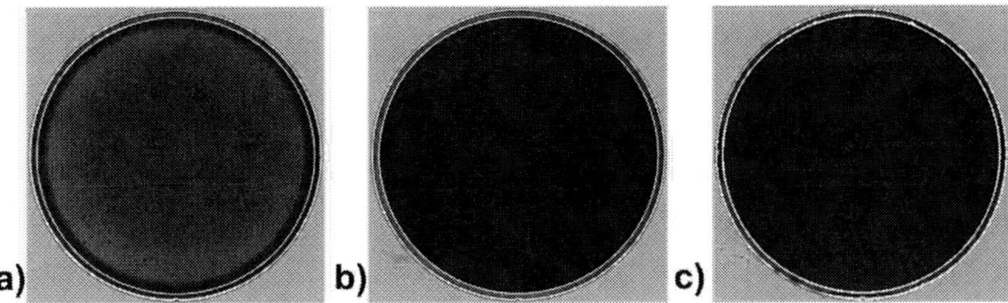

Figure 4: High Resolution-Acoustic Images of a non-aligned SAB Hybrid Bonding interface **a)** before annealing, **b)** after annealing at 150°C during 2 h and **c)** Acoustic Image of an aligned hydrophilic direct Hybrid Bonding before annealing

For the SAB bonding of Figure **5a**, the as-bonded scan is composed of shades of gray, which means that the interface is partially closed. As expected, the Acoustic image gets darker after annealing (see Figure 5b), which confirms that the annealing assures an obvious reinforcement of the interface. The copper pads have undergone expansion due to temperature, resulting in closer contact with the opposing surface. Furthermore, the interfaces between copper and oxide, as well as oxide and oxide, exhibit also heightened closure through increasing covalent bond formation.
Nevertheless, it is important to remember that despite the fact that this bonding is patterned, there is no control over alignment. Indeed, the presence of a linear and angular offset in the overlay produces a moiré effect. Consequently, the bonding process gives rise to distinct regions characterized by precise alignment between the pads (pads facing the pads) but also regions where misalignment occurs (pads facing the oxide matrix). These well-aligned and misaligned areas are consistently repeated across the entire wafer.

As a result, the misaligned areas show a high density of copper pad facing oxide region. Due to low adhesion energy between the SiO_2 surface and the copper one, the wafer are not enough attracting to each other to overcome the copper dishing. Consequently, non-bonded pads remain at the bonding interface making the SAM image brighter in these areas. Figure 5 offers a compelling visual representation of this phenomenon comparing Figures **a** and **b**, which depict a zoomed-in view captured by HR C-SAM and an optical microscope, respectively. Remarkably, both images exhibit the emergence of the same moiré effect in the examined area, underscoring its relevance. The patterns exhibited in terms of shapes and sizes are identical, enabling us to confirm that the well-aligned zones manifest as darker regions on the scan. This indicates a substantial proportion of bonded areas with a properly established interface. It is also conceivable that a SAB-aligned bonding would be promising with a dark SAM scan across the entire wafer. Additionally, this is supported by Figure **4c**, which displays a dark acoustic image of a well-aligned hydrophilic bond without annealing. It is important to note that in this case where the adhesion is sufficiently strong, a slight dishing does not pose a problem, and full bonding can still be achieved.

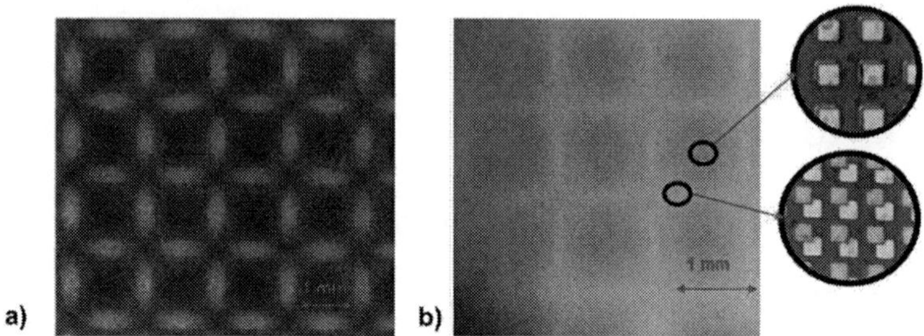

Figure 5: a) Zoom on a HR C-SAM and b) Optical Microscope images of a non-aligned SAB Hybrid Bonding sample after Si bulk removing

In summary, the Scanning Acoustic Microscopy (SAM) results reveal that the unannealed SAB Hybrid Bonding samples exhibit a considerable presence of regions where the interface is expected to be robust. These regions correspond to areas where the pads are well aligned with each other, suggesting a promising bonding outcome in terms of interface strength.

As a matter of fact, the successful removal of bulk silicon by mechanical grinding serves as an initial confirmation of the bonding interface high adherence. SAB bonded wafers not annealed, annealed at 150°C during 2 hours and the hydrophilic bonded ones annealed at 150°C during 2 hours undergo effective grinding and dry etching, leaving behind only the damascene structure, with a thickness of around 1 μm, above the bonding interface. Despite the inherent weakness of the oxide/oxide and copper/oxide interfaces without annealing, the success of the thinning process indicates the presence of strong and numerous copper/copper metal bonds formed through SAB activation. These bonds appear to be sufficiently numerous and strong to provide favorable mechanical properties to the bonding interface.

<u>Morphology and composition of bonding interfaces (TEM and EDX)</u>

Ultimately, TEM (Transmission Electron Microscopy) observations, complemented by EDX (Energy-Dispersive X-ray Spectroscopy), are conducted to assess the quality of bonding interfaces across different cases. Various criteria are employed to evaluate hybrid bonding at the copper-copper interface. These include a well-sealed interface, minimal interface defects, absence of copper oxide at the interface or well-reconstructed grain boundaries. In addition, it is important to evaluate the oxide-oxide interface to ensure its high quality.

In this respect, three samples with different bonding and annealing conditions were analyzed through TEM cross-sections of the bonded pads as shown on Figure 6. These cross sectional images of bonding pads correspond to a SAB hybrid bonding (**a** and **b**) or to a hydrophilic one (**c**) in order to compare them. Bonding **a** is not annealed and is bonded and thinned out at room temperature, when **b** and **c** are annealed both at 150°C during 2 hours before being thinned out.

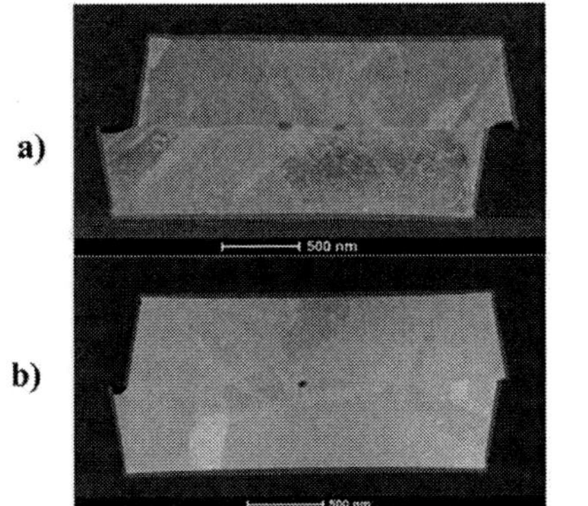

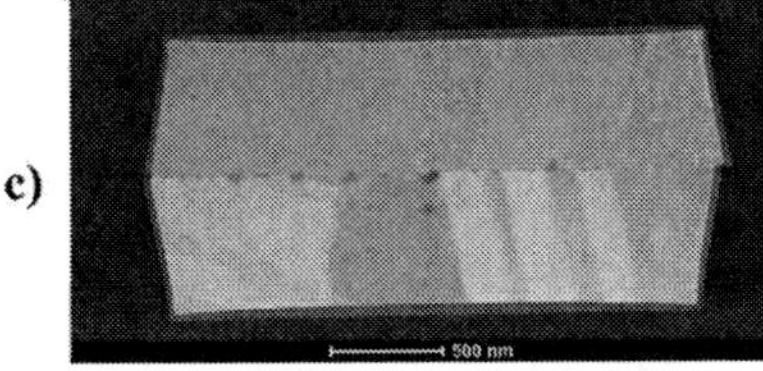

Figure 6: TEM cross sectional images of bonding pads a) Bonded with SAB - non-annealed, b) bonded with SAB and annealed at 150°C - 2h and c) hydrophilic bonding annealed at 150°C - 2h

Primarily, it is worth noting that all pads bondings show a sealed interface with an established contact between top and bottom pads. The difference between the three samples is mainly in the reconstruction of the interface. While the boundary line of the pad bonded under hydrophilic conditions remains straight (cf. Figure 7c), the other ones (Figure 7a and b) clearly reveal a fragmented line corresponding to triple grain boundaries at the interface. The hydrophilic bonding annealed at 150°C has kept mainly its copper oxide layer signature. In contrary, the SAB fragmented interfaces sign the copper to copper metallic contact and interdiffusion between the pads. This phenomenon becomes even more pronounced in the case of SAB bonding subjected to annealing at 150°C for two hours. In fact, the bonding interface becomes indistinguishable in the latter scenario (Figure 7b). The distinction between the annealed one and the non-annealed one can be attributed to the increased diffusion of copper atoms along the grain boundaries, facilitated by the energy provided during the annealing process.

Another clear distinction between SAB and hydrophilic bonding methods lies in the number of defects, particularly at the interface and within the pads. Defects in hybrid bonding originate from two main sources[8]. Firstly, surface imperfections such as roughness and small trenches resulting from the CMP process can lead to the formation of voids with the atomic diffusion of copper during further annealing. Those kind of defects can affect both SAB and hydrophilic bondings. Secondly, as elucidated by L. Di Cioccio et al. in their 2014 study [9], the Cu_2O layer is naturally present on the copper during hydrophilic bonding and first annealing stage due to copper oxidation by the interfacial water. This oxide layer acts as a source for vacancies formation into the Cu pads, as it undergoes a dewetting phenomenon during the annealing process. These vacancies can aggregate and appear as voids in the TEM cross sections. At temperatures around 150°C, as explained by Di Cioccio et al., due to copper plastic deformation, the Cu_2O layer turns into nodules at the interface, which constitutes vacancies traps. Subsequently, these nodules evolve into voids as oxygen diffuses into the Cu pad. Since the copper oxide is removed during argon ions bombardment, SAB bondings are not subjected to this second kind of defects. Figure 6 clearly highlights the distinction between the two processes, SAB vs hydrophilic, regarding interface defects presence and evolution. In image **c** (corresponding to hydrophilic bonding), there are numerous defects observed within the pads and at the interface, whereas images **a** and **b** (corresponding to SAB bondings) only show one or two defects at the interface. Figure 7 confirms it, comparing the non-annealed SAB bonding with the hydrophilic one annealed at 150°C, using TEM combined with EDX analysis.

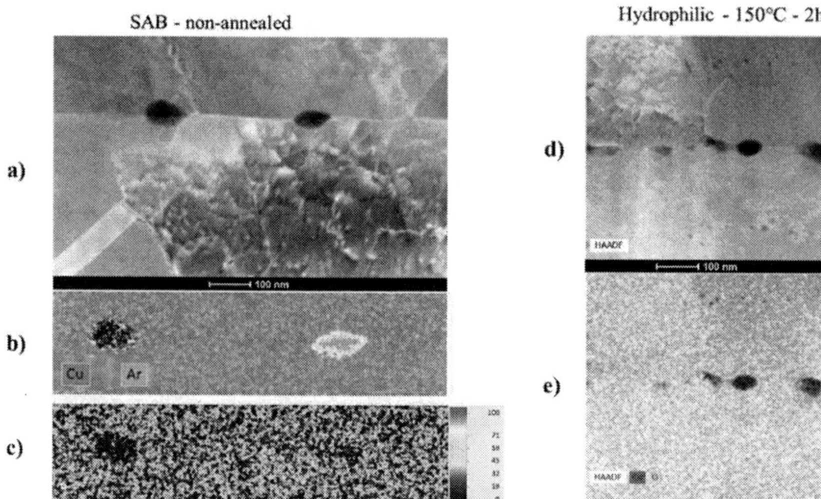

Figure 7: TEM combined with EDX zoom on copper-copper interfaces: a) High-Angle Annular Dark-field Imaging (HAADF) TEM, b) EDX revealing Cu and Ar presence (orange and blue areas respectively), c) EDXMap in low-concentration mode revealing Oxygen presence only, d) HAADF TEM and e) EDX revealing Cu and O presence (orange and green respectively) – a, b, c : SAB bonding, d, e : hydrophilic bonding

EDX analysis of defects allows a better understanding of their origins. In the case of the hydrophilic bonding (Figure 7 **d** and **e**), EDX image **e** exhibits indeed the presence of oxygen in some cavities, whereas it does not detect any trace of oxygen in the SAB metallic bonding **c**. Indeed, **c** image is an EDX map that reveals only oxygen in low-detection mode. As the highest oxygen concentration on this map is located within the copper pad (actually corresponding to background noise) and not the cavities, it means that there is absolutely no oxygen in these cavities. As explained earlier, this is due to the non-presence of the copper oxide layer on the top of the pad in SAB before the bonding. Noteworthy, Figure 7 **b** indicates the presence of argon in some cavities. They can be attributed as residues from the activation bombardment. Nevertheless, their quantity seems not significant to cause any issue.

Not shown here, SiO_2-SiO_2 interfaces out of the pads have also been analyzed and have shown no sign of any defects.

To conclude this TEM-EDX analysis, all the samples demonstrate a well-formed bonding interface, even in the non-annealed SAB case. Indeed, despite exhibiting some dishing and lacking subsequent annealing, the copper pads are in contact and show a successfully reconstructed interface.

Conclusion

For the first time, we have demonstrated the successful achievement of low-temperature (150°C) and even room-temperature hybrid bonding, and the potential of Surface Activated Bonding in enabling high quality 3D connection at this very low thermal budget. All bonded samples showed a high macroscopic quality (SAM defect-free, grinding resistant). Moreover, we have shown thanks our TEM-EDX study that SAB hybrid bonding offers a better interface reconstruction, a decrease in defects and the removing of the Cu_2O layer. In addition, we also identified the ease of processing in that SAB bonding requires no sequencing constraints, nor development of a new CMP. In the wake of these encouraging results, new vehicles including electric test structures are to be bonded with alignment in a SAB system. This new study will allow not only to validate the process on aligned bonded structures but also to qualify the electrical performances of hybrid SAB.

The integration of SAB into low-temperature hybrid bonding processes holds significant promise for advancing semiconductor technologies across various applications.

Acknowledgments

We would like to thank François Aussenac, Adeline Grenier and Hugo Dansas for the TEM preparation and observation, and Christophe Lecouvey for the AFM measures.

References

[1] B. Ayoub *et al.*, « Sub 1 µm Pitch Achievement for Cu/SiO₂ Hybrid Bonding », in *2022 IEEE 24th Electronics Packaging Technology Conference (EPTC)*, Singapore, Singapore: IEEE, déc. 2022, p. 418-424. doi: 10.1109/EPTC56328.2022.10013180.

[2] J. Jourdon, S. Lhostis, S. Moreau, N. Bresson, P. Salomé, et H. Frémont, « Evaluation of Hybrid Bonding Interface Quality by Contact Resistivity Measurement », *IEEE Trans. Electron Devices*, vol. 66, n° 6, p. 2699-2703, juin 2019, doi: 10.1109/TED.2019.2910528.

[3] T. Suga, « Feasibility of surface activated bonding for ultra-fine pitch interconnection- a new concept of bump-less direct bonding for system level packaging », in *2000 Proceedings. 50th Electronic Components and Technology Conference (Cat. No.00CH37070)*, Las Vegas, NV, USA: IEEE, 2000, p. 702-705. doi: 10.1109/ECTC.2000.853235.

[4] J. Utsumi, K. Ide, et Y. Ichiyanagi, « Cu/SiO2 hybrid bonding obtained by surface-activated bonding method at room temperature using Si ultrathin films », *Micro Nano Eng.*, vol. 2, p. 1-6, mars 2019, doi: 10.1016/j.mne.2018.11.004.

[5] A. Shigetou, T. Itoh, M. Matsuo, N. Hayasaka, K. Okumura, et T. Suga, « Bumpless Interconnect Through Ultrafine Cu Electrodes by Means of Surface-Activated Bonding (SAB) Method », *IEEE Trans. Adv. Packag.*, vol. 29, n° 2, p. 218-226, mai 2006, doi: 10.1109/TADVP.2006.873138.

[6] Damien Radisson. Direct bonding of patterned surfaces. Fluid mechanics. Université de Grenoble, 2014. English. NNT : 2014GRENY086 - tel-01362940.

[7] F. Fournel *et al.*, « Water Stress Corrosion in Bonded Structures », *ECS J. Solid State Sci. Technol.*, vol. 4, n° 5, p. P124-P130, 2015, doi: 10.1149/2.0031505jss.

[8] Y. Beilliard *et al.*, « Advances toward reliable high density Cu-Cu interconnects by Cu-SiO $_2$ direct hybrid bonding », in *2014 International 3D Systems Integration Conference (3DIC)*, Kinsdale: IEEE, déc. 2014, p. 1-8. doi: 10.1109/3DIC.2014.7274306.

[9] L. Di Cioccio *et al.*, « Modeling and Integration Phenomena of metal-metal direct bonding technology », *ECS Trans.*, vol. 64, n° 5, p. 339-355, août 2014, doi: 10.1149/06405.0339ecst.

ECS Transactions, 112 (3) 95-101 (2023)
10.1149/11203.0095ecst ©The Electrochemical Society

Hydrophilic Bonding of SiO₂/SiO₂ and Cu/Cu using Sequential Plasma Activation

K. Takeuchi[a,b*], T. Ninomiya[a,b], M. Kubota[a,b], M. Kawano[a,b],
T. Takagi[a,b], M. Niwa[a,b], T. Kuroda[a,b], and T. Suga[a,b,c]

[a] Systems Design Lab, the University of Tokyo, Tokyo 113-0032, Japan
[b] Research Association for Advanced Systems, Tokyo 113-0032, Japan
[c] Collaborative Research Center, Meisei University, Tokyo 191-8506, Japan
* Currently at Tohoku University, Sendai 980-8579, Japan

Hybrid bonding is an indispensable technique for the 3D integration of electronic systems. Cu-to-Cu interconnections and SiO_2-to-SiO_2 dielectric layers should be bonded simultaneously in the wafer-to-wafer bonding process. In this study, sequential plasma activation (SPA) including O_2 plasma, N_2 plasma, and N radical is investigated for low-temperature bonding of Cu and TEOS SiO_2 at 200°C. The SPA bonding improves the bond strength to more than 1 J/m² compared to the conventional single gas plasma activation bonding. The surface analysis indicates that SPA forms oxynitrides on TEOS SiO_2 surface and Cu oxide with adsorbed water on the Cu surface, facilitating the bonding interface formation. The presented technique will contribute to the hybrid bonding applications at lower temperatures.

Introduction

To meet the increasing market demand for next-generation electronic devices, 3D system integration is getting greater and greater attention. However, traditional methods such as soldering or bump bonding cannot handle high density interconnection. Therefore, hybrid bonding technology, which simultaneously bonds Cu wiring layers and SiO_2 dielectric layers, is indispensable (1). In the hybrid bonding process, hydrophilic bonding is commonly used to bond SiO_2 to SiO_2. This technique involves bonding of hydrophilic surfaces, followed by post-bonding annealing to achieve a reliable bonding interface. For Cu bonding, it is necessary to break the oxide layer at the Cu bonding interface and allow Cu atoms to diffuse into each other to achieve electrical connections (2).

However, since post-bonding annealing at high temperatures can damage the device or induce residual stress at the bonding interface, low temperature process below 200°C is preferable. Currently, the most widely adopted process is hydrophilic bonding using N_2 plasma, which also achieves hybrid bonding through heating at around 350°C to 400°C. For this reason, numerous studies focus on various approaches to lower the process temperature of hybrid bonding.

In order to lower the post-bonding annealing temperature, sequential plasma activation (SPA), which activates the bonding surface with O_2 plasma, N_2 plasma, and N radicals subsequently, has been reported to improve the wafer bond strength of SiO_2 materials with the post-bonding annealing at 200°C (3,4). It has been shown that the SPA process forms reactive and unstable oxynitrides on the SiO_2 surface, followed by the replacement of the oxynitrides by OH groups. Therefore, SPA improves the bond strength of SiO_2 to 2.5 J/m^2. On the other hand, it is also reported that the nitridation of Cu surface by plasma is effective for low temperature bonding due to the suppression of the oxide growth on the Cu surface (5). Therefore, the SPA bonding is expected to be effective for Cu as well.

In this study, we investigate the effect of the SPA technique on the low temperature hydrophilic bonding of TEOS SiO_2 and Cu. In order to clarify the effect of SPA technique for TEOS SiO_2 and Cu, we utilized blanket wafers with TEOS SiO_2 and Cu layers without patterning for the bonding experiments.

Method

We prepared the TEOS SiO_2 and Cu blanket wafers by deposition on Si wafers. Cu layers were deposited on 4 inch, 525 μm thick Si wafers, and TEOS SiO_2 layers on 6 inch, 625 μm thick Si wafers. The Cu layers were deposited by sputtering with a 1 μm thickness on 25 nm thick Ti layers, while the SiO_2 layers were deposited using plasma-enhanced TEOS process for 1 μm thickness. Both types of deposited layers were planarized by chemical-mechanical polishing (CMP) to achieve a smooth surface with a surface roughness of Ra <0.5 nm. The SPA bonding process was carried out using RIE plasma and microwave radicals of N_2 and O_2 gas. The bonding surfaces were activated by O_2 plasma, N_2 plasma, and N radicals sequentially. The plasma and radical powers were 250 W. The plasma irradiation time was varied from 15 to 60 s and radical irradiation time was 15 s for the investigation. For comparison, the surface activation was also performed using single gas plasmas (O_2 and N_2) and a combination of the plasmas. After the surface activation, the wafers were exposed to ambient air to adsorb water on the surface, followed by bonding in air and post-bonding annealing at 200°C for 7 hours.

The bonding quality was evaluated by the bond strength. In order to analyze the effect of the SPA process, the TEOS SiO_2 and Cu surfaces were analyzed by x-ray photoelectron spectroscopy (XPS) after the SPA treatment and after the debonding of the bonded wafers.

Result and Discussion

Figure 1 shows the atomic force microscopy (AFM) images of the TEOS SiO_2 and Cu surfaces after CMP. The surface roughness is RMS 0.41 nm for TEOS SiO_2 and 0.40 nm for Cu, which are sufficiently smooth for low temperature bonding.

The bond strength of the SPA bonding for TEOS SiO_2 and Cu is shown in Fig. 2. The bond strength without surface activation is 0.49 J/m^2 for TEOS SiO_2 and 0.04 J/m^2 for Cu. The SPA treatment improves the bond strength of TEOS SiO_2 and Cu to 1.13 J/m^2 and 1.03 J/m^2, respectively. The bond strength decreases with the plasma irradiation time, resulting in a bond strength of 0.59 J/m^2 for both TEOS SiO_2 and Cu when the O_2 plasma and N_2 plasma activation are carried out for 60 s. This is attributed to the surface damage by the longer plasma activation. It is also worth noting that the bond strength of Cu

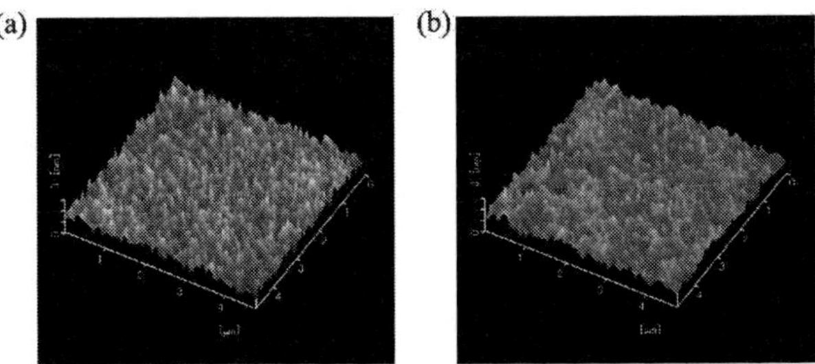

Fig. 1. AFM images of (a) TEOS SiO$_2$ and (b) Cu surface after CMP

decreases when the N$_2$ plasma activation is longer than the O$_2$ plasma. This will be discussed later.

Next, we show the comparison of the effect of the plasma combination, as presented in Fig. 3. The bond strength of each condition is compared. The plasma irradiation time is fixed at 30 s. In the case of only O$_2$ plasma activation, the bond strength is 0.57 J/m^2 and 0.98 J/m^2 for TEOS SiO$_2$ and Cu, respectively. Meanwhile, the N$_2$ plasma activation achieves the bond strength of 0.75 J/m^2 and 0.33 J/m^2 for TEOS SiO$_2$ and Cu, respectively. This suggests that the O$_2$ plasma activation is effective for the hydrophilic bonding of not TEOS SiO$_2$ but Cu, while the N$_2$ plasma is effective for not Cu but TEOS SiO$_2$. This also agrees with the results that the bond strength of Cu is decreased when the N$_2$ plasma is longer than the O$_2$ plasma, as shown in Fig. 3.

On the other hand, the combination of O$_2$ plasma and N$_2$ plasma shows the middle bond strength between that of O$_2$ single plasma and N$_2$ single plasma activation. The bond strength is 0.69 J/m^2 and 0.71 J/m^2 for TEOS SiO$_2$ and Cu, respectively. Furthermore, when the N radical is applied for the combination of O$_2$ plasma and N$_2$ plasma, the bond strength

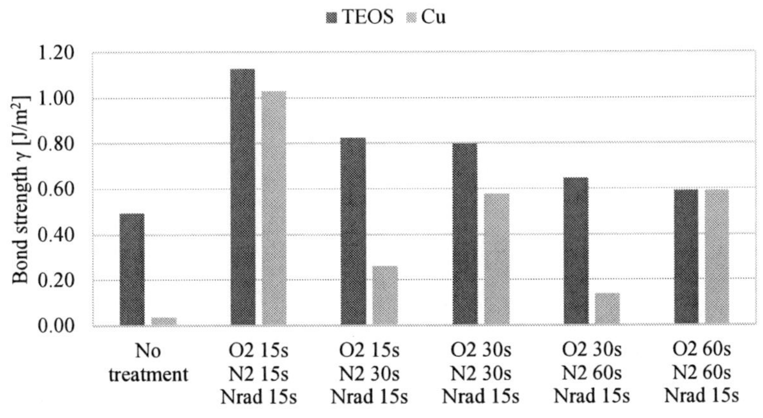

Fig. 2. Bond strength of TEOS SiO2 and Cu by SPA bonding

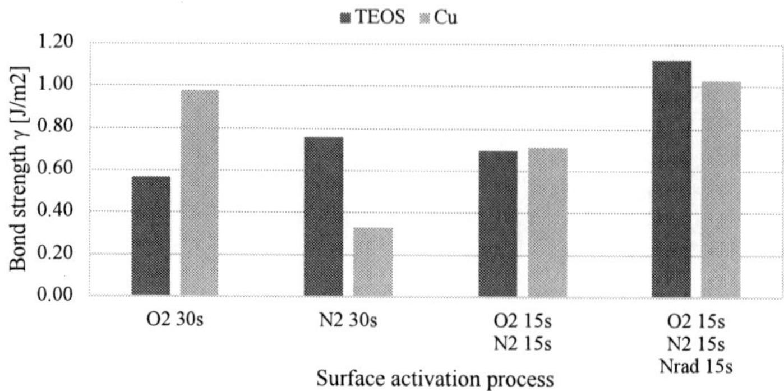

Fig. 3. Bond strength of TEOS SiO$_2$ and Cu with varied plasma combination

improved. Therefore, it can be said that the SPA process including N radical treatment improves the bond strength for both TEOS SiO$_2$ and Cu.

To understand the effect of plasma on Cu hydrophilic bonding, the XPS analysis is conducted for each condition. Figure 4 shows the typical XPS result for Cu2p core spectrum of the SPA-treated Cu surface. The Cu2p peak for each condition is deconvoluted to the Cu, Cu$_2$O, CuO, and Cu(OH)$_2$ peaks at 913.8 eV, 932.7 eV, 934.3 eV, and 936 eV, respectively (6-8). It is notable that the CuN peak is not detected, as well as from the N1s core spectrum. Furthermore, the O1s peak that can be separated to Cu oxides, Cu(OH)$_2$, and H$_2$O is also analyzed for each condition. Based on these results, the peak area ratio of Cu, Cu$_2$O, CuO, Cu(OH)$_2$, and H$_2$O is calculated and shown in Fig. 5.

The comparison between the peak area ratio before and after bonding shows that the Cu peak area ratio decreases after the bonding and post-bonding annealing for all

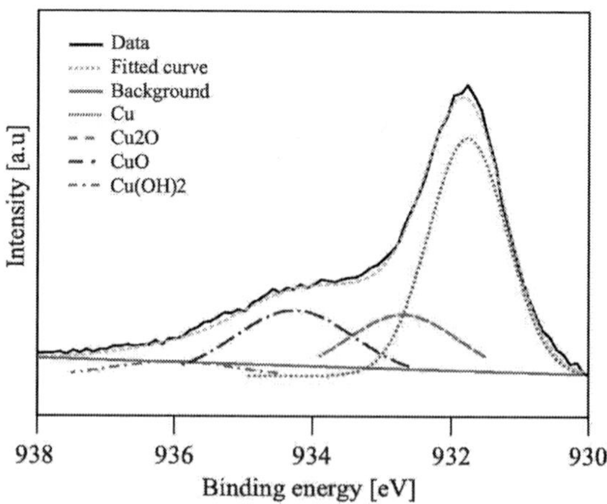

Fig. 4. Typical XPS Cu2p peak of the Cu surface and its curve fitting

conditions except the bonding without surface activation. This indicates that the oxide interface is formed at the bonding interface of Cu during the bonding and annealing step, which is a typical reaction of the hydrophilic bonding of Cu. In particular, the O_2 plasma surface activation oxidizes the Cu surface, resulting in 4.5 % of Cu, while 43.6 %, 43.1 %, 52.9 % Cu are detected for N_2 plasma, O_2 and N_2 plasma, and SPA treatment, respectively. Therefore, it is also suggested that, in the case of $O_2 + N_2$ plasma and SPA treatment, the O_2 plasma first oxidizes the Cu surface, followed by the physical etching of the outermost layer of the oxide layer by N_2 plasma.

From the perspective of the bond strength, the N_2 plasma and $O_2 + N_2$ plasma treatment, by which lower bond strength is achieved, the post-bonding annealing increases the peak area ratio of Cu_2O, but decreases CuO. On the contrary, in the case of stronger bonding by O_2 plasma and SPA, the peak area ratio of CuO increases after the post-bonding annealing. This suggests that the formation of CuO at the bonding interface is crucial for high bond strength of Cu/Cu interface.

In the previous studies, it is indicated that the hydrophilic bonding of Cu requires the adsorbed water on the Cu oxides (9,10). The adsorbed water forms hydrogen bonds and intermolecular bonds at the bonding interface. Additionally, the growth of Cu oxides contributes to the formation of the bonding interface by closing the micro gaps between bonding surfaces (11,12). In the case of N_2 plasma and $O_2 + N_2$ plasma, the oxide Cu surface is etched, resulting in a lack of sufficient adsorbed water. Therefore, the post-bonding annealing does not form the gap-closing oxides at the bonding interface. This also supports that the bond strength of Cu decreases when the N_2 plasma irradiation time is longer than that of O_2 plasma. In contrast, the SPA treatment renders a hydrophilic surface with adsorbed water by utilizing the N radicals. Therefore, the post-bonding annealing forms CuO at the bonding interface, which results in higher bond strength.

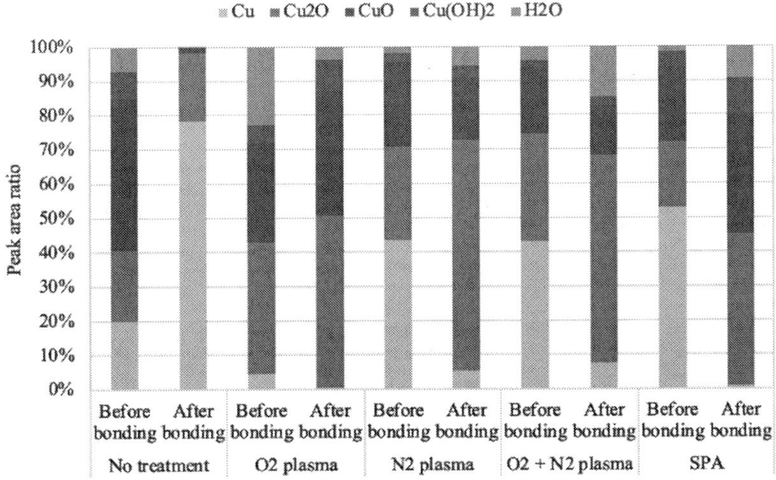

Fig. 5. XPS Peak area ratio of Cu, Cu_2O, CuO, $Cu(OH)_2$, and H_2O of the Cu surface before and after bonding with varied plasma activation

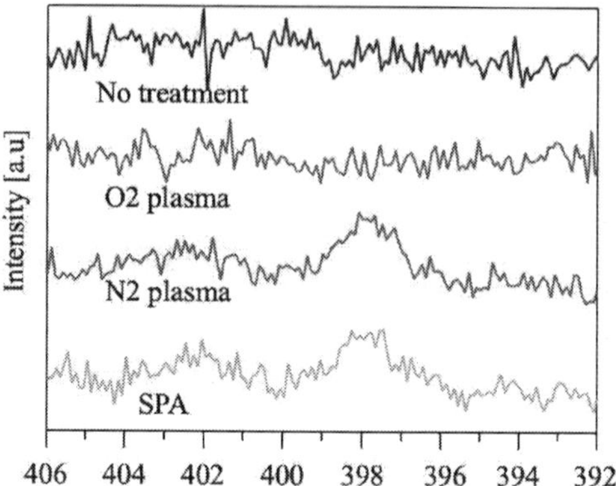

Fig. 6. XPS N1s peak of the debonded surface of TEOS SiO$_2$ with varied plasma condition

For the bonding of TEOS SiO$_2$, the XPS analysis is conducted for the debonded surface. Figure 6 shows the N1s peak of the debonded surface for each condition. When the TEOS SiO$_2$ surface is not treated or treated with O$_2$ plasma, no N1s peak is detected from the debonded surface. On the other hand, the N$_2$ plasma and SPA treatment form the oxynitrides at the bonding interface, as detected in the N1s peak. Since the oxynitrides improve the bond strength of SiO$_2$ due to its reactivity, the bond strength of TEOS SiO$_2$ is also improved when the surface is activated by N$_2$ plasma or SPA treatment.

Conclusion

In this study, we investigated the SPA technique for the hydrophilic bonding of TEOS SiO$_2$. The bond strength is improved to over 1 J/m^2 by the SPA technique for both TEOS SiO$_2$ and Cu under the same process condition. XPS analysis indicates that the O$_2$ plasma is effective not for TEOS SiO$_2$ but for Cu hydrophilic bonding, while N$_2$ plasma is effective not for Cu but for TEOS SiO$_2$ bonding. The SPA treatment enhances the bonding of Cu by forming the Cu oxides at the bonding interface, and the bonding of TEOS SiO$_2$ by forming oxynitrides at the bonding interface. This technique will contribute to the hybrid bonding application at lower process temperature.

Acknowledgments

This work is based on results obtained from a project, JPNP20017, subsidized by the New Energy and Industrial Technology Development Organization (NEDO).

References

1. S. Moreau, J. Jourdon, S. Lhostis, D. Bouchu, B. Ayoub, L. Arnaud, and H. Frémont, *ECS Journal of Solid State Science and Technology*, **11**(2), 024001 (2022).
2. Han-Wen Hu and Kuan-Neng Chen, *Microelectronics Reliability*, **127**, 114412 (2021).
3. Ran He, Akira Yamauchi, and Tadatomo Suga, *Japanese Journal of Applied Physics*, **57**, 2S1, 02BD03 (2018).
4. Kai Takeuchi, Fengwen Mu, Akira Yamauchi, and Tadatomo Suga, *ECS Journal of Solid State Science and Technology*, **10**(5), 054007 (2021).
5. Haesung Park and Sarah Eunkyung Kim, *IEEE Transactions on Components, Packaging and Manufacturing Technology*, **10**(2), 332-338, (2020).
6. Xiaoxia Wang, Baoqin Zhang, Wei Zhang, Mingxun Yu, Liang Cui, Xueying Cao, and Jingquan Liu, *Scientific Reports*, **7**(1), 1584 (2017).
7. G. Lavareda, C. Nunes de Carvalho, A. M. Ferraria, A. M. Botelho do Rego, and A. Amaral, *Journal of Nanoscience and Nanotechnology*, **12**(8), 6754-6757 (2012).
8. Zhenhua Dan, Yulin Yang, Fengxiang Qin, Hao Wang, and Hui Chang, *Materials*, **11**(3), 446 (2018).
9. Ran He, Masahisa Fujino, Akira Yamauchi, Yinghui Wang, and Tadatomo Suga, *ECS Journal of Solid State Science and Technology*, **5**(7), 419-424 (2016).
10. Akitsu Shigetou and Tadatomo Suga, 2009 59th Electronic Components and Technology Conference, 365-369, 2009.
11. Akitsu Shigetou and Tadatomo Suga, *Journal of Electronic Materials*, **41**(8), 2274--2280 (2012).
12. Juan J. Diaz Leon, David M. Fryauf, Robert D. Cormia, Min-Xian Max Zhang, Kathryn Samuels, R. Stanley Williams, and Nobuhiko P. Kobayashi, *ACS Applied Materials & Interfaces*, **8**(34), 22337--22344 (2016).

ECS Transactions, 112 (3) 103-109 (2023)
10.1149/11203.0103ecst ©The Electrochemical Society

Modified SAB Methods for Hybrid and
All-Cu Bonding for 3D Integration below 200°C

T. Suga, K. Otsuka

Collaborative Research Center, Meisei University, Hino-shi, Tokyo 191-8506, Japan

Two Surface Activated Bonding (SAB) methods will be proposed to enable low-temperature hybrid bonding for 3D integration. A modified one involves surface activation processes using Ar fast-atom-beam bombardment with simultaneous co-sputtering of Si nano-adhesion layer, followed by sequential plasma irradiation with N2 radicals.

In the other one, we will connect two device wafers not in a hybrid but all-Cu bonding. A small insulation area surrounds the Cu pads on the wafer, while the rest is covered with Cu solid layers. These solid layers constitute the ground plane, power plane, or their paired layers and may contribute to heat dissipation when connected to thermal vias. The two wafers are connected only by bonding on the Cu electrodes and solid layers. Cu-Cu direct bonding is possible at room temperature by applying the standard SAB directly. Room-temperature bonding is overwhelmingly advantageous for bonding heterogeneous devices and wafers.

Introduction

Current hybrid bonding technology generally requires heating or post-annealing to at least 350°C. Therefore, usable materials are limited, and the integration of heterogeneous semiconductors is severely restricted. Only a few layers of 3D stacking have been realized, but what if this becomes a stack of tens or even hundreds of tiers in the future? Who says it's not realistic? If this becomes necessary, the integration technology that requires heating cannot be said to be the final solution. At least, even in the current situation, heating at 350°C is unbearable, and bonding at 200°C or lower is required.

Why do current hybrid bonding techniques require 350°C heating and post-annealing? The history of wafer bonding tells us. Wafer bonding has roots in glass-to-glass optical contacts beginning in the 18th century. It is called fusion bonding because the bonded interfaces of the glasses become invisible when heated, and the bonding technology was later developed to fabricate silicon-on-insulator (SOI) wafers. It was clarified that the mechanism is the formation of a hydrogen bond by the -OH group and then of a Si-O covalent bond by subsequent condensation reaction by heating and post-annealing at high temperature, and it came to be called oxide bonding or hydrophilic bonding. 3D stacked devices began with a method in which insulating surfaces are bonded by this hydrophilic bonding method. Then, metal vias are formed to connect the upper and lower devices (so-called via-last).

However, as the density of connected signal lines increases, and the size and pitch of electrodes become smaller, it becomes difficult to form through vias after bonding. Therefore, hybrid bonding, in which vias and Cud electrodes are formed first. Then the insulator surfaces and the Cu electrodes are bonded on the same plane, which is currently the mainstream of 3D integration.

However, the bonding mechanism of Cu is entirely different from that of insulating SiO_2. Atomic diffusion is required because the Cu-Cu bond is metallic. In addition, since the surface of Cu is oxidized under normal conditions, high-temperature bonding is required to diffuse it beyond the oxide layer.

Therefore, various hybrid bonding methods, including Cu-Cu low-temperature bonding, are being investigated. But the essence of the problem lies in simultaneously bonding two materials with different bonding mechanisms on the same plane. But think about it. Why can't 3D integration be achieved without bonding Cu and SiO_2 simultaneously? It is simply a result of the technology's history that wafer bonding evolved with SiO_2-SiO_2 bonding. The real purpose of 3D integration is to interconnect the signal lines of the top and bottom devices and provide sufficient strength and reliability, not the SiO_2-SiO_2 bonding.

The Surface Activated Bonding (SAB) method using Ar beam bombardment was initially successfully developed for metal-to-metal, metal-to-ceramics, and later for Si–Si and heterogeneous semiconductors bonding in vacuum [1][2]. In this case, the native oxide on metals and semiconductors is completely removed by Ar beam bombardment, and bonding of activated surfaces can be formed only by contact at room temperature.

According to the SAB method, Cu-Cu can be directly bonded at room temperature. In the present paper, we propose an All-Cu 3D interconnect, where all bonding is performed only with Cu, as an alternative to hybrid bonding. The Cu signal lines are connected to each other, the insulating layer is covered with Cu plane electrodes, and the plane electrodes are bonded to each other. This method can perform all bonding between Cu and Cu, and a single bonding mechanism can complete all processes at room temperature. If there is a drawback with this method, it is that it requires a high vacuum. SAB is an ideal method for Cu-Cu bonding but might reduce throughput. This problem with equipment development will be improved in the future. However, SAB can also contribute to lowering the process temperature of hybrid bonding not in a high vacuum, which is currently developing. A method that combines the SAB technique and hydrophilic bonding for that purpose is reported in the next session.

Modified SAB combined with hydrophilic treatment

A modified SAB involves surface activation processes using Ar fast-atom-beam bombardment with simultaneous co-sputtering of Si nano-adhesion layer, followed by sequential plasma irradiation with N_2 radicals. A thin Si nano-layer became to be known to enhance hydrophilicity and expected to effective in reducing the bonding temperature [3][4]. These processes combine hydrophilic treatment and bonding in a low-vacuum chamber.

A concern when using a Si nano-adhesion layer is that there may be current leakage due to Si on the insulating layer. However, according to the results of application to Cu-SiO_2 hybrid bonding, depending on the conditions, Si is partially oxidized, which is thought to contribute to the isolation between Cu-pads [5]. In addition, the electrical resistance of amorphous Si is eight orders of magnitude higher than that of metals, and when the film thickness is 0.5 nm or less, it is considered to have substantially insulating properties [6]. In fact, CMOS image sensors have been put to practical use by Au-SiO2 hybrid bonding using a Si nano-adhesion layer, and no Si-induced dielectric breakdown problems have been observed [7].

The Si nano-adhesion layer and the sequential plasma treatment [8] enhance hydrophilicity, enabling low-temperature bonding of both Si oxides and Cu pads as hybrid bonding. Bonding in a low-vacuum environment helps remove excess H_2O molecules adsorbed on the wafers and prevent gas-trapping void generation caused by air entrainment. Ar or N_2 atom beam irradiation is also promising as an alternative to plasma irradiation [9]. In particular, when the Cu pad becomes finer, plasma may form CuN on Cu, or Cu contamination may form on SiO_2. Still, there is no such concern in unidirectional atom beam irradiation.

A wafer bonder system for mass production that integrates these processes for a low-temperature wafer bonding below 200°C is currently under development as a project subsidized by the Japanese government.

All-Cu 3D (AC3D) interconnect as an alternative to hybrid bonding

Figure 1 shows the concept of the All-Cu 3D (AC3D) interconnect, and Figure 2 shows an example of the surface of devices or wafers designed for AC3D bonding. A small insulation layer surrounds the area around the Cu electrode on the wafers, while the rest is covered with Cu solid layers. These solid layers constitute the ground plane, power plane, or their paired layers and may contribute to heat dissipation when connected to thermal vias. The two wafers are connected only by bonding on the Cu electrodes and solid layers. The insulating parts around the Cu electrodes do not necessarily have to be bonded, and the gaps may be kept in a vacuum. Of course, the bonded surfaces must be flattened, and the plane electrode's new division and layout design will be required.

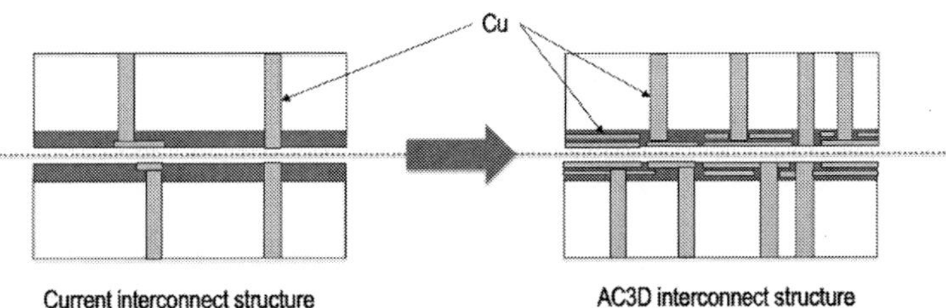

Figure 1. The concept of the All-Cu 3D (AC3D) interconnect.

We are currently conducting simulations to investigate how the plane electrode affects the signal transmission characteristics. Figure 3 compares an electrode configuration for hybrid bonding with 1 μm electrodes of 2 μm pitch and an All-Cu 3D interconnect. Cu occupies 25% of the bonding area in the former, while it is 69% in the latter.

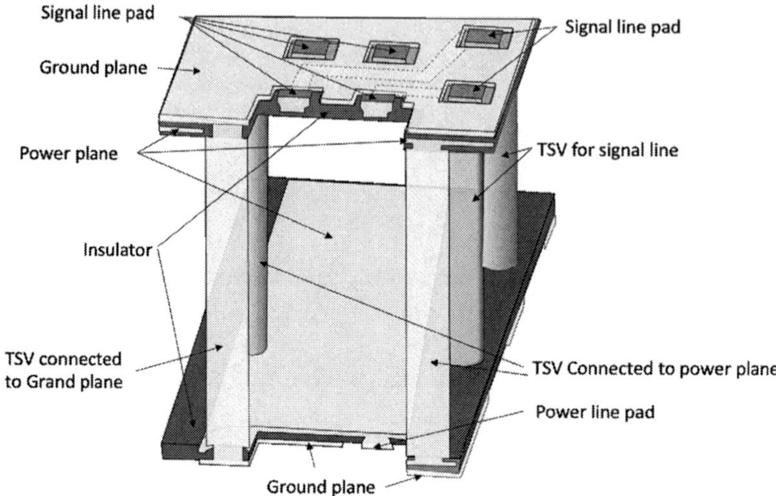

Figure 2. An example of chip or wafer surface for AC3D interconnect.

Figure 4 shows several examples of a fundamental wiring pattern for that purpose.
As a first step, we simulated signal transmission for differential signal lines with periodic electrode arrangements. A simple hybrid bond and the most uncomplicated wiring when there is a ground plane and when there is both a ground plane and a power plane. Since the transmission distance is short, there is almost no effect, but when there is a plane electrode, the influence of impedance disturbance was seen to some extent, as shown in Figure 5.

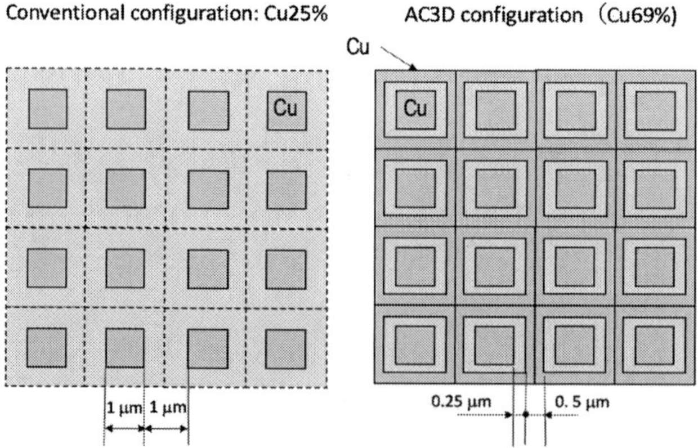

Figure 3. Comparison of an electrode configuration for conventional hybrid bonding and an AC3D interconnect with 1 μm electrodes of 2 μm pitch.

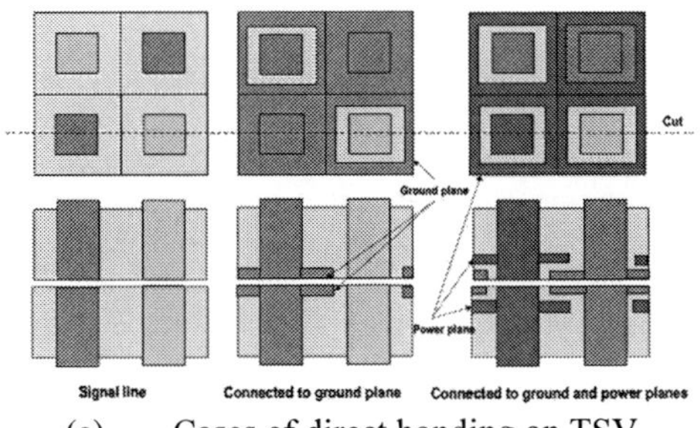

(a)   Cases of direct bonding on TSV.

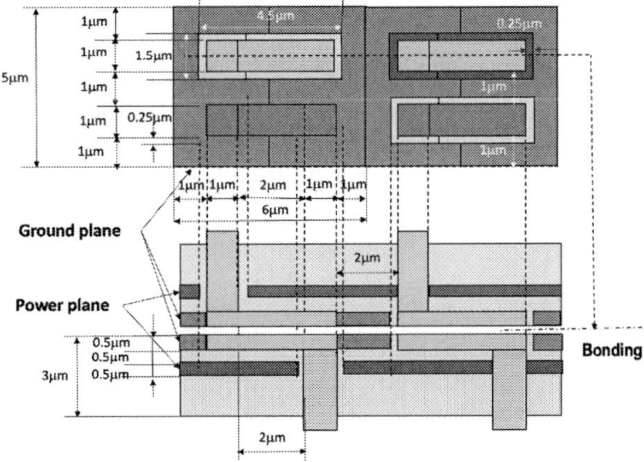

(b) Case of wiring on the bonded interface.

Figure 4. Examples of a fundamental wiring pattern for the AC3D interconnect.

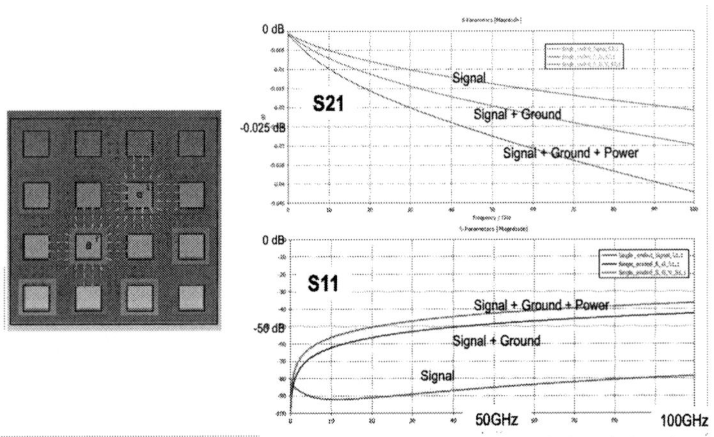

Figure 5. S-parameters for the signal transmission in differential signal for simple signal lines, signal lines with ground plane, and signal lines with ground and power plane.

Conclusion

Two Surface Activated Bonding (SAB) methods were proposed for low-temperature 3D integration. One is a modified SAB combined with a hydrophilic treatment enabling bonding at lower than 200ªC, and the other is an All-Cu 3D (AC3D) interconnect that makes 3D integration only on the Cu surface. The former has already been developed for mass production, and the latter still has many issues, such as Cu-CMP optimization and electrode configuration design. Still, all processes are possible at room temperature. Therefore, it is also considered one of the final forms of 3D integration as a logical and natural consequence.

References

1. T. Suga, Feasibility of surface activated bonding for ultra-fine pitch interconnection - a new concept of bump-less direct bonding for system level packaging, IEEE, Electronic Components & Technology Conf. (ECTC), 50st., Proceedings., Las Vegas, May 21-24. , (2000) 702-705.
2. Shigetou, A., Itoh, T., Matsuo, M., Hayasaka, N., Okumura, K., Suga, T.: Bumpless interconnect through ultrafine Cu electrodes by means of surface-activated bonding (SAB) method, IEEE Transactions on Advanced Packaging, 29, (2006) 218-226.
3. R. He, M. Fujino, A. Yamauchi, Y. Wang, and T. Suga, "Combined Surface Activated Bonding Technique for Low-Temperature Cu/Dielectric Hybrid Bonding," ECS J. Solid State Sci. Technol., vol. 5, no. 7, pp. P419–P424, 2016, DOI: 10.1149/2.0201607jss
4. R. He, M. Fujino, A. Yamauchi, and T. Suga, "Combined surface-activated bonding technique for low-temperature hydrophilic direct wafer bonding," Jpn. J. Appl. Phys., vol. 55, no. 4S, p. 04EC02, Apr. 2016. DOI:10.7567/JJAP.55.04EC02
5. Jun Utsumi, Kensuke Ide, Yuko Ichiyanagi, "Cu/SiO2 hybrid bonding obtained by surface-activated bonding method at room temperature using Si ultrathin films," Micro and Nano Engineering 2 (2019) 1–6
6. M. Uomotoa, A. Muraoka, and T. Shimatsu, "Room Temperature Bonding of Wafers using Si and Ge Films with Extremely Low Electrical Conductivity," ECS Transactions, 86 (5) 199-204 (2018) DOI: 10.1149/08605.0199ecst
7. M. Goto, Y. Honda, M. Nanba, Y. Iguchi, T. Saraya, M. Kobayashi, E. Higurashi, H. Toshiyoshi, T. Hiramoto "Pixel-Parallel Three-Layer Stacked CMOS Image Sensors Using Double-Sided Hybrid Bonding of SOI Wafers," IEEE Transactions on Electron Devices, (Early Access, August 2023) DOI: 10.1109/TED.2023.3298308
8. R. He, M. Fujino, A. Yamauchi, and T. Suga, "Combined surface-activated bonding technique for low-temperature hydrophilic direct wafer bonding," Jpn. J. Appl. Phys., vol. 55, no. 4S, p. 04EC02, Apr. 2016. DOI:10.7567/JJAP.55.04EC02
9. Kai Takeuchi1, F. Mu, A. Yamauchi, T. Suga, "Sequential Plasma Activation for Low Temperature Bonding of Aluminosilicate Glass," ECS Journal of Solid State Science and Technology, Volume 10, Number 5, DOI 10.1149/2162-8777/abfd4b

10. K. Takeuchi, T. Ninomiya, M. Kubota, M. Kawano, T. Takagi, M. Niwa, T. Kuroda, and T. Suga, "Hydrophilic Bonding of SiO2/SiO2 and Cu/Cu using Sequential Plasma Activation" Proc. 244th ECS Meeting (October 8-12, 2023) - Semiconductor Wafer Bonding: Science, Technology, and Applications 17.

ECS Transactions, 112 (3) 111-118 (2023)
10.1149/11203.0111ecst ©The Electrochemical Society

Fabrication and Electrical Characterization of GaAs/GaN Junctions

S. Ishimi[a], M. Hirose[a], Y. Shimizu[b], Y. Ohno[b], Y. Nagai[b], J. Liang[a], and N. Shigekawa[a]

[a] Department of Physics and Electronics, Osaka Metropolitan University, Osaka 5588585, Japan
[b] IMR, Tohoku University, Oarai, Ibaragi 311-1313, Japan

We fabricate p^+-GaAs/n-GaN and n^+-GaAs/n-GaN junctions using surface activate bonding and measure their capacitance-voltage and current-voltage characteristics. We find that the characteristics of the two junctions are close to each other, which suggests that the band profiles of GaN layers in the two types of junctions are almost the same, i.e., the Fermi-level pinning occurs at the GaAs/GaN interfaces. Breakdown occurs at a reverse bias voltage $\approx$ -60 V in both junctions. The observed breakdown voltage corresponds to an electric field of as high as ~ 1.6 MV/cm, which is comparable to a reported breakdown field of GaN. We also excite minority electrons in the p^+-GaAs layer using a 488-nm laser and successfully observe the photocurrent due to the transport of minority electrons across the reverse-biased GaAs/GaN interfaces.

Introduction

GaAs/GaN heterojunctions are an ideal platform for high-frequency/high-output-power electron devices such as heterojunction bipolar transistors (HBTs) because of excellent transport properties of electrons in GaAs and large power capability in GaN (1). The similarity in their coefficients of thermal expansion (2) provides an advantage from the practical viewpoint. We must note, however, that heteroepitaxial growth of GaAs/GaN junctions is quite difficult because of difference in crystal structures (in case of GaAs/hexagonal GaN junctions) and large mismatch in lattice constants (GaAs/cubic GaN junctions) although cubic GaN layers were successfully grown on GaAs substrates (3). AlGaAs/GaAs heterostructures were bonded to GaN layers at temperatures $\geq$ 550 °C in N_2 ambient for 1 hour (wafer-fusion process) to fabricate AlGaAs/GaAs/GaN HBTs (4,5). We note that the bonding temperature was close to or higher than that for epitaxial growth of group-III arsenides.

Low temperature wafer bonding technologies such as surface-activated bonding (SAB) (6) have been successfully applied for fabricating heterojunctions composed of semiconductors with different crystal structures and/or lattice constants (2). The electrical conduction across the SAB-based interfaces have been demonstrated (7). Using SAB, we previously bonded a GaAs epi wafer to a GaN layer epitaxially grown on a Si (111) substrate to investigate characteristics of fabricated GaAs/GaN diodes (8).

In this work, we fabricated GaAs/GaN junctions by bonding GaAs epi wafers to GaN layers grown on freestanding GaN (0001) substrates and investigated their nano-structural and electrical characteristics.

Methods

We prepared a 3-μm n-GaN layer with a concentration of donors N_D of $\sim 1\times10^{17}$ cm^{-3} epitaxially grown on a n$^+$-GaN (0001) freestanding substrate with N_D of $> 1\times10^{18}$ cm^{-3}, a 200-nm p$^+$-GaAs/100-nm InGaP heterostructure epitaxially grown on a semi insulating GaAs (100) substrate, and a 150-nm n$^+$-GaAs/100-nm InGaP heterostructure epitaxially grown on a semi insulating GaAs (100) substrate. Impurity concentrations in the p$^+$-GaAs and n$^+$-GaAs layers were $\sim 5\times10^{18}$ cm^{-3}. Using an atomic force microscopy, roughness average was estimated to be 0.23, 0.26, and 0.28 nm for surfaces of the n-GaN, p$^+$-GaAs and n$^+$-GaAs layers, respectively.

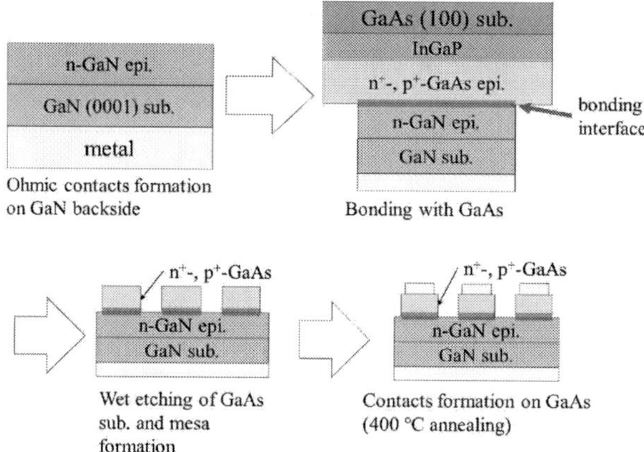

Figure 1. The entire process steps for fabricating GaAs/GaN junctions.

We fabricated p$^+$-GaAs/n-GaN junctions by bonding the p$^+$-GaAs and n-GaN epi layers to each other using SAB, selectively etching off the GaAs substrate used for the epitaxial growth, forming GaAs mesas, and making ohmic contacts on the exposed surface of GaAs layer. Ohmic contacts on the backside of GaN epi wafer were formed before bonding. Surfaces of wafers to be bonded were activated using a fast atom beam (FAB) of Ar. The junctions were annealed at 400 °C for 1 min. in N$_2$ ambient to form ohmic contacts on the GaAs surfaces. Specific structures for relaxing electric field in the vicinity of bonding area were not incorporated. We also fabricated n$^+$-GaAs/n-GaN junctions for comparison. The entire process steps are schematically shown in Fig. 1.

In characterizing fabricated GaAs/GaN junctions, as-bonded and 400-°C/1-min. annealed GaAs/GaN interfaces were observed using cross sectional transmission electron microscope (TEM). The capacitance-voltage (C-V) characteristics of the p$^+$-GaAs/n-GaN and n$^+$-GaAs/n-GaN junctions were measured at room temperature. The frequency for measurements of C-V characteristics was 1 MHz. Relationships between the current density J and V at different ambient temperatures between $\approx$ -175 and $\approx$ +200 °C (J-V-T characteristics) were also measured for both junctions. The flat band voltage and potential barrier of the respective junctions were estimated by analyzing their C-V and J-V-T characteristics. In addition, we performed preliminary measurements of breakdown characteristics, or J-V characteristics for a large reverse bias voltage V_R, of the two junctions in the dark and photocurrent in the reverse-biased p^+-GaAs/n-GaN junction. In the photocurrent measurement, a 488-nm laser beam was focused on the GaAs surface. We subtracted current measured in the dark from current measured under the 488-nm laser irradiance to define the net photocurrent. Power of laser incident on the GaAs surface was varied between 0.5 and 9 mW.

Results

<u>Nano-Structural Properties of GaAs/GaN Interfaces</u>

TEM images of as-bonded and 400-°C annealed GaAs/GaN interfaces are shown in Figs. 2(a) and 2(b), respectively. A ≈ 2-nm thick damaged layer, which was due to the FAB irradiation, is observed in the vicinity of the as-bonded interface. The damaged layer vanished by the 400-°C annealing. Similar change of nano-structural properties at bonding interfaces–recovery of crystallinity due to annealing–was observed for other SAB-based interfaces such as GaAs/Si systems (9). It is also notable that no voids are seen at the 400-°C annealed GaN/GaAs interface.

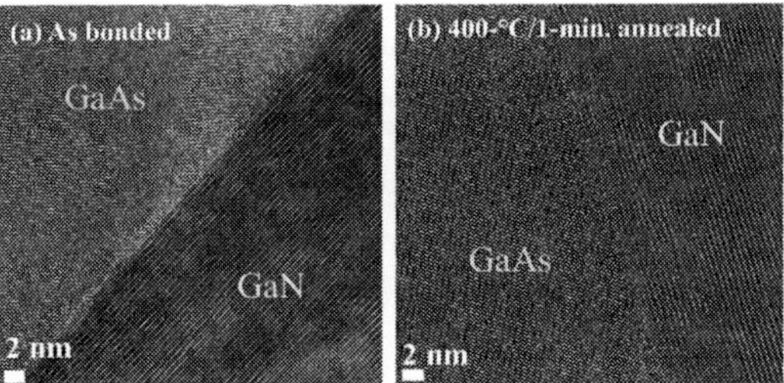

Figure 2.   TEM images of (a) as-bonded and (b) 400-°C/1-min. annealed GaAs/GaN interfaces.

<u>C-V and J-V-T Characteristics</u>

The $1/C^2$-V curves of the p^+-GaAs/n-GaN and n^+-GaAs/n-GaN junctions are shown in Fig. 3. The two $1/C^2$-V curves are close to each other: V_{FB} was found to be 0.77 and 0.68 V for the p^+-GaAs/n-GaN and n^+-GaAs/n-GaN junctions, respectively, by linearly extrapolating the $1/C^2$-V curves to the $1/C^2 \to 0$ limit. The observed small difference in V_{FB} between p^+-GaAs/n-GaN and n^+-GaAs/n-GaN junctions (0.09 V) implies that Fermi level is pinned at the GaAs/GaN interface. Using the slopes of $1/C^2$-V curves, N_D in the n-GaN layer was estimated to be 1.10×10^{17} and 1.09×10^{17} cm^{-3} for the p^+-GaAs/n-GaN and n^+-GaAs/n-GaN junctions, respectively. It is notable that the estimated N_D values are close to the nominal concentration of donors in n-GaN layers.

J-V characteristics measured at different temperatures for the p$^+$-GaAs/n-GaN junction are shown in Fig. 4(a). We defined the saturation current density Js by extrapolating each J-V curve for the forward bias voltage to 0 V. Relationships between Js/T^2 and 1/T are shown in Fig. 4(b). J-V curves for different temperatures and the relationship between Js/T^2 and 1/T for the n$^+$-GaAs/n-GaN junction are shown in Figs. 4(c) and 4(d), respectively.

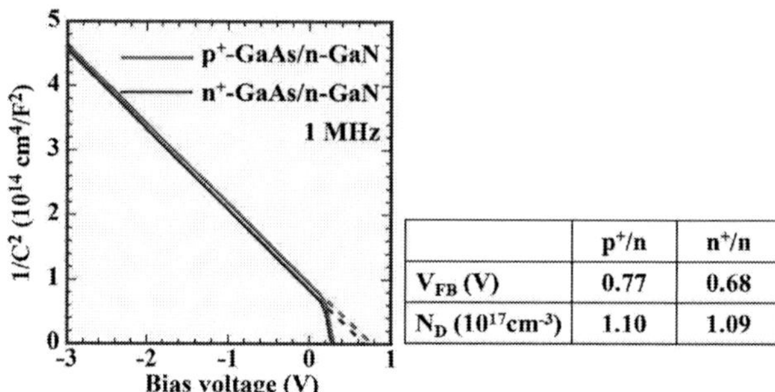

	p$^+$/n	n$^+$/n
V_{FB} (V)	0.77	0.68
N_D (10^{17}cm^{-3})	1.10	1.09

Figure 3. 1/C^2-V characteristics of p$^+$-GaAs/n-GaN and n$^+$-GaAs/n-GaN junctions. V_{FB} and N_D in the n-GaN layer of each junction are also shown.

Using the thermionic emission (TE) model (10), Js is expressed as

$$Js \propto T^2 \exp(-q\phi_B/kT), \tag{1}$$

where k is the Boltzmann constant, q is the elementary charge, and $q\phi_B$ is the barrier height, respectively. We applied this model to the higher-temperature (T > 350 K) part of the relationship between Js/T^2 and 1/T. As is shown in Figs. 4(b) and 4(d), $q\phi_B$ was found to be $\approx$ 0.7 eV in both junctions. Scheme of the Fermi level pinning explains the result that the barrier heights of the two junctions are close to each other.

<u>Reverse-Bias Characteristics and Photocurrent</u>

Room-temperature J-V_R characteristics of the two junctions in the dark are shown in Fig. 5. We observed breakdown at V_R ~60 V in both junctions. Based on the depletion layer approximation, the electric field at GaAs/GaN interface $E_{GaAs/GaN}$, or the maximum electric field in the GaN layer, is given by

$$E_{GaAs/GaN} = [2qN_D(|V_R|+V_{FB})/\varepsilon_{GaN}\varepsilon_0]^{1/2} \approx [2qN_D^*|V_R|/\varepsilon_{GaN}\varepsilon_0]^{1/2}, \tag{2}$$

for $|V_R| \gg V_{FB}$. Here ε_{GaN} and ε_0 are the relative permittivity of GaN (10.4) (11) and the permittivity of vacuum, respectively. We find that $E_{GaAs/GaN}$ is ~1.6 MV/cm for V_R of -60 V. It is notable that the estimated $E_{GaAs/GaN}$ is comparable to a reported breakdown field of in GaN pn diodes (3-4 MV/cm) (12).

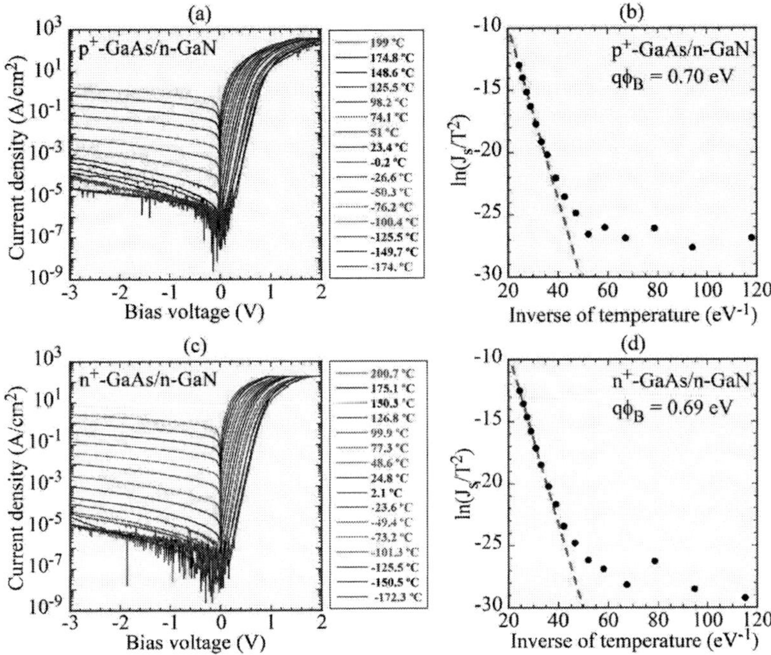

Figure 4. (a) J-V characteristics at different ambient temperatures and (b) Js-T characteristics of a p^+-GaAs/n-GaN junction. (c) J-V characteristics at different ambient temperatures and (d) Js-T characteristics of an n^+-GaAs/n-GaN junctions. Barrier heights based on the thermionic emission model are also shown in (b) and (d).

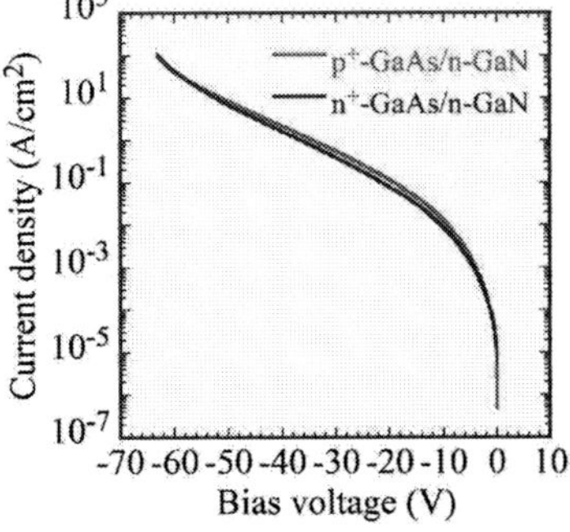

Figure 5. J-V characteristics for reverse-bias of the two junctions. Breakdown occurred at $V_R \approx$ -60 V.

Dependencies of photocurrent in the p^+-GaAs/n-GaN junction on bias voltage are shown in Fig. 6(a). Figure 6(b) gives relationship between photocurrent at 0 V and incident laser power. The photoresponsivity, which should be limited by the conduction-band offset at the GaAs/GaN interface (discussed below), was found to be $\approx 2.8 \times 10^{-4}$ A/W by analyzing the relationship. The internal quantum efficiency of the p^+-GaAs/n-GaN junction was estimated to be $\sim 3 \times 10^{-3}$ by considering the reflectance and absorption coefficient of GaAs at 488 nm (13).

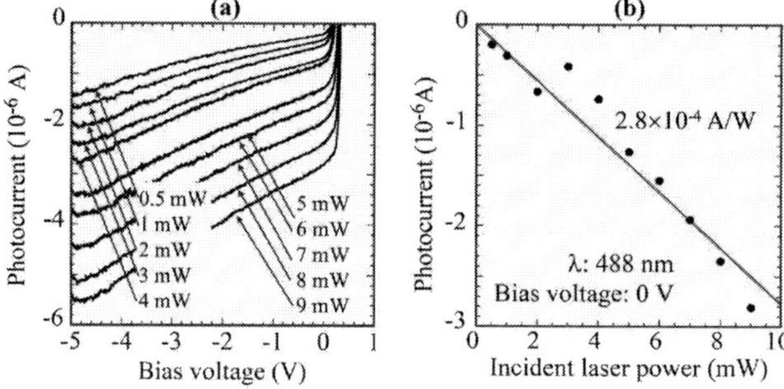

Figure 6. (a) Relationships between photocurrent and reverse-bias voltage in a p^+-GaAs/n-GaN junction for different incident laser powers. (b) Relationship between photocurrent at 0 V and incident laser power. The estimated photoresponsivity is also shown.

Discussion

We applied the charge-neutrality-level model (14) in discussing band lineups in the GaAs/GaN junctions, In this model, the midgap states located at the GaAs/GaN interface, or the interface states, reveal donor-like/acceptor-like features when their energy is higher/lower than the charge neutrality level E_{CNL}. We assumed that the interface states were uniformly distributed in the entire bandgap of interface, i.e., the density of interface states D_{it} was constant. The charge neutrality level was placed at 1 eV above the valence band edge of GaAs (15). We searched D_{it} and the conduction band offset ΔE_C that reproduced the measured C-V characteristics on the condition that the sum of net electrical charges in GaAs and GaN layers and charges in the interface states should be zero.

Using a trial-and-error approach, we found that ΔE_C of ~ 0.4 eV and D_{it} of $\sim 6 \times 10^{13}$ $cm^{-2}eV^{-1}$ reproduced the measured V_{FB} of the two junctions. The band lineups obtained for the p^+-GaAs/n-GaN and n^+-GaAs/n-GaN junctions are shown in Figs. 7(a) and 7(b), respectively. It is notable that the estimated ΔE_C is close to theoretical prediction (0.3 eV) (16). The estimated D_{it}, which is >10 times higher than that for Ni/GaN Schottky barrier diodes (17), is assumed to be due to the FAB irradiation before bonding. Such a large D_{it} is likely to be the origin of the strong Fermi level pinning at GaAs/GaN interfaces.

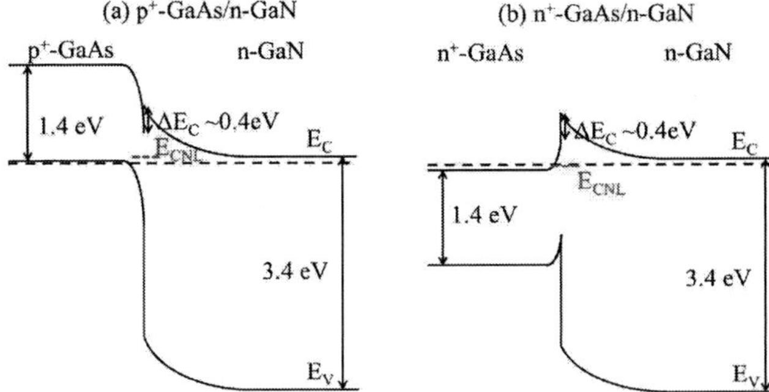

Figure 7. Estimated band lineups in (a) p$^+$-GaAs/n-GaN and (b) n$^+$-GaAs/n-GaN junctions.

We assume that the band lineups in p$^+$- and n$^+$-GaAs layers in the GaAs/GaN junctions are not sensitive to bias voltage. On this assumption qϕ_B is given by the sum of qV$_{FB}$ and the separation of the Fermi level from the conduction band edge in n-GaN ΔE_F (qϕ_B = qV$_{FB}$+ΔE_F). Given that ΔE_F should be $\approx$ 0.07 eV at room temperature, qϕ_B is assumed to be $\approx$ 0.8 eV. The slightly lower qϕ_B values extracted from the Js-T characteristics ($\approx$ 0.7 eV) might be due to the standpoint of the TE model that tunneling of carriers across the depletion layer of n-GaN (18) is ignored. Barrier heights closer to prediction based on the C-V characteristics are assumed to be obtained by applying the thermionic field emission model (19, 20) in analyses of the Js-T characteristics.

Results of measurements of reverse-bias characteristics that the breakdown field was ~ 1.6 MV/cm indicate that SAB-based GaAs/GaN junctions are potentially applicable as highly revers-biased parts of electron devices such as base/collector junctions in HBTs. Impacts of Fermi level pinning at GaAs/GaN interfaces and limited transport properties of minority electrons are assumed to be mitigated by optimizing the band structures in the vicinity of bonding interfaces.

Conclusion

We fabricated p$^+$-GaAs/n-GaN and n$^+$-GaAs/n-GaN junctions by bonding GaAs and GaN epi wafers to each other using SAB and subsequently applying device process steps. TEM observation implied that a thin ($\approx$2 nm thick) damaged layer was formed at the as-bonded interface and the damaged layer disappeared after annealing the junction at 400 °C. Their C-V and J-V-T characteristics suggested that the Fermi level was pinned at the bonding interfaces. The interface states, whose density was estimated using the charge-neutrality-level model, are likely to be the origin of Fermi level pinning. The breakdown field of the two junctions was found to be ~ 1.6 MV/cm. GaAs/GaN junctions are, consequently, assumed to play an important role as reverse-biased vital part of advanced electron devices by designing layer structures to mitigate impacts of interface states and improve the transport properties of minority electrons.

Acknowledgments

TEM samples were fabricated under the Inter-University Cooperative Research in IMR of Tohoku University. GaAs and GaN epi wafers used in the work were provided from Sciocs (present Sumitomo Chemical) Co., Ltd.

References

1. T. P. Chow, I. Omura, M. Higashiwaki, H. Kawarada, and V. Pala, *IEEE Trans. Electron Devices*, **64**, 856 (2017).
2. O. Moutanabbir and U. Gösele, *Annu. Rev. Mater. Res.*, **40**, 469 (2010).
3. J. Möreke, M. J. Uren, S. V. Novikov, C. Foxon, S. H. Vajargah, D. J. Wallis, C. J. Humphreys, S. J. Haigh, A. Al-Khalidi, E. Wasige, I. Thayne, and M. Kuball, *J. Appl. Phys.*, **116**, 014502 (2014).
4. C. Lian, H. G. Xing, C. S. Wang, D. Brown, and L. McCarthy, *Appl. Phys. Lett.*, **91**, 063502 (2007).
5. C. Lian, H. G. Xing, C. S. Wang, L. McCarthy, and D. Brown, *IEEE Electron Device Lett.*, **28**, 8 (2007).
6. H. Takagi, K. Kikuchi, R. Maeda, T. R. Chung, and T. Suga, *Appl. Phys. Lett.*, **68**, 2222 (1996).
7. N. Shigekawa, J. Liang, and Y. Ohno, *Jpn. J. Appl. Phys.*, **61**, 120101 (2022).
8. S. Yamajo, J. Liang, and N. Shigekawa, *Jpn. J. Appl. Phys.*, **57**, 02BE02 (2018).
9. Y. Ohno, J. Liang, N. Shigekawa, H. Yoshida, S. Takeda, R. Miyagawa, Y. Shimizu, and Y. Nagai, *Appl. Surf. Sci.*, **525**, 146610 (2020).
10. S. M. Sze and K. K. Ng, *Physics of Semiconductor Devices (Third Edition)*, p. 154, Wiley Interscience, New Jersey (2007).
11. A. S. Barker, Jr. and M. Ilegems, *Phys. Rev. B*, 7, 743 (1973).
12. T. Maeda, T. Narita, S. Yamada, T. Kachi, T. Kimoto, M. Horita, and J. Suda, *IEEE Electron Device Lett.*, **43**, 96 (2022).
13. J. S. Blakemore, *J. Appl. Phys.*, **53**, R123 (1982).
14. S. Bengtsson, G. I. Andersson, M. O. Andersson, O. Engström, *Journal of Applied Physics*, **72**, 124 (1992).
15. L. Chai, J. Liang, and N. Shigekawa, *Jpn. J. Appl. Phys.*, **55**, 068002 (2016).
16. J. Robertson and B. Falabretti, *J. Appl. Phys.*, **100**, 014111 (2006).
17. C.-T. Lee, C.-C. Lin, H.-Y. Lee, and P.-S. Chen, *J. Appl. Phys.*, **103**, 094504 (2008).
18. T. Maeda, M. Okada, M. Ueno, Y. Yamamoto, T. Kimoto, M. Horita, and J. Suda, *Appl. Phys. Express*, **10**, 051002 (2017).
19. S. Oyama, T. Hashizume, and H. Hasegawa, *Appl. Surf. Sci.*, **190**, 322 (2002).
20. M. Hara, S. Asada, T. Maeda, and T. Kimoto, *Appl. Phys. Express*, 13, 041001 (2020).

ECS Transactions, 112 (3) 119-124 (2023)
10.1149/11203.0119ecst ©The Electrochemical Society

Surface Activated Si-Si Wafer Bonding Using Different Ion Species

M. Danner[a,b], B. Rebhan[a], P. Kerepesi[a] and W. Werner[b]

[a] EV Group, DI E. Thallner Straße 1, St. Florian/Inn 4782, Austria
[b] Institut für Angewandte Physik, Vienna University of Technology, Wiedner Hauptstrasse 8-10,
1040 Vienna, Austria

Surface activated bonding on wafer level is enabled by an advanced direct wafer bonding system for irradiation with different ion species. In this process, the native oxide of 200 mm Si wafers is sputter-removed and an amorphous layer is generated. After ion treatment, the wafers are bonded in ultra-high vacuum at room temperature. The impact of Ar, Kr and Xe ion irradiation on the amorphous layer thickness was investigated with the goal of optimizing the bonding process for establishing interfaces with electronic functionality. This was i.a. motivated by the fact, that the presence of an amorphous layer reduces the electrical conductivity across the wafer interface.

Introduction

Wafer bonding has become a key technology for the fabrication of 3D integrated circuits (IC), photonics devices and power devices. With the development of sophisticated bonding methods, surface activated bonding (SAB) emerged as a powerful wafer bonding technique which enables direct wafer bonding in ultra-high vacuum (UHV) at room temperature. This provides certain advantages such as hermetic UHV encapsulation of devices, bonding materials with different coefficients of thermal expansion (CTE) and establishing oxide-free conductive bonding interfaces.

The method of SAB involves the activation of wafer surfaces through ion beam irradiation. In this process, the native oxide is sputter-removed. This leads to the formation of dangling bonds on the wafer surface. As the ions are transported through the wafer, energy and momentum is transferred to the target atoms resulting in atomic displacements. The accumulation of ion beam damage as a result of ion-solid interactions constitutes an amorphous layer. The presence of such layer reduces the conductivity across the bonding interface [1]. As this is an undesired effect for most electronic applications, it is essential to minimize the amorphous layer thickness (ALT). This can be achieved by changing the activation conditions as well as by post bond annealing.

In this work, the effect of angle of incidence (AoI), ion energy, ion species and post-bond annealing on the ALT of 200 mm Si wafers is investigated. Surface measurements are performed by spectroscopic ellipsometry (SE) for measuring the ALT, while the amorphous interface of bonded wafers is measured by transmission electron microscopy (TEM). Moreover, the bonding energy is obtained by applying the Maszara method [2].

Experimental Setup

For the conducted experiments, 200 mm prime grade Si wafers are used that fulfill the requirements for direct bonding. The entire bonding procedure is performed on the EVG®580 ComBond®, which is a fully automated wafer bonding system. It is equipped with a robot arm in the center for handling wafers to the respective modules. To avoid reoxidation after activation, the ComBond® is operated in UHV at pressures below $5 \cdot 10^{-8}$ mbar. After both wafers are activated, one of them is flipped. Subsequently, both wafers are transferred to the bonding module where they are bonded.

Single wafers were measured after activation by spectroscopic ellipsometry (SE), which is a non-destructive method for surface analysis where the change in light polarization upon reflection on the sample is measured. Layer thicknesses can be indirectly measured by decomposition of the detected convoluted signal based on an optical model. The chosen optical model consists of a three-layered structure as sketched in Figure 1.

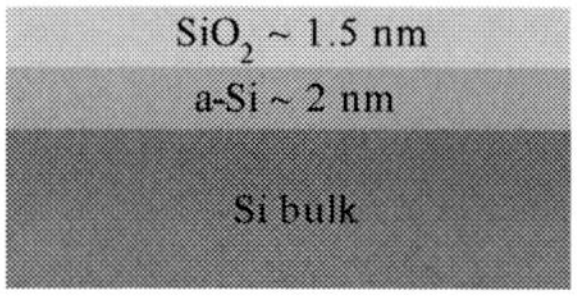

Figure 1: Layer configuration for SE model. The configurations for SiO_2 and Si are based on data from Herzinger et al. [3]. Parameters for the a-Si layer are adjusted to the TEM results.

For every measurement in this work the same ellipsometry model is applied. This simplification is justified as the refractive index converges above a certain ion dose depending on the ion type according to the publication of Pelaz et al. [4]. The layer thicknesses are determined by averaging over 29 cartesian arranged data points where each point is measured from three different angles (60°, 65°, 70°).

Transmission electron microscopy (TEM) measurements are performed to underline the SE measurements. The bonding energy is measured by applying the Maszara method. Therefore, a blade is inserted into the bonding interface and the bonding energy is determined by measuring the propagated crack length.

Results and Discussion

Single wafers:
Surface analysis was performed by SE on wafers after activation with the goal of determining the influence of ion energy, ion species and AoI on the ALT. Figure 2 shows the ALT as function of the ion energy for different ion types. It is evident that heavy ions generate a thinner amorphous layer than light ions in the measured energy range. This can be attributed to the different scattering cross-sections for the ion-target configurations. Although the energy transfer from Ar to Si is higher than for Kr or Xe on Si, heavy ions have a larger scattering cross-section, which results in a reduction of the implantation depth.
Ultimately, the nuclear stopping cross-section, which describes the ion stopping in materials, is determined by the combined contributions of the energy transfer and the scattering cross-section.

For all configurations presented in this work, electronic stopping can be neglected in good approximation. A striking feature is that there is a minimum at an energy of $1.25 \cdot E_0$ for each ion species. This minimum most likely originates from physical sputter-implantation dynamics. While ions are implanted into the material, sputtering occurs and as the surface is removed, the implantation profile gets shifted towards the surface. This process eventually leads to a stationary implantation profile which depends on the implantation mechanics and the sputtering rates of the setup. Measurements were performed on the same system which showed that the sputtering rates for Ar on a-Si are decreasing rapidly for energies below $1.25 \cdot E_0$ [5]. Therefore, the effective stationary implantation profile of low sputtering rates predicts a higher ALT.

The ALT was also measured for different AoI using Ar, Kr and Xe as shown in Figure 2. Here it is also observed that heavy ions generate a thinner amorphous layer than light ions. The plot also shows that the ALT decreases with increasing AoI. This directly results from the fact, that the ions are projected into the wafer and therefore have a lower penetration depth with regards to the surface normal. In addition, the sputtering yield is increasing with the AoI in a certain range. This changes the stationary implantation profile for the same reason as mentioned above and therefore the final ALT is lower for such configurations.

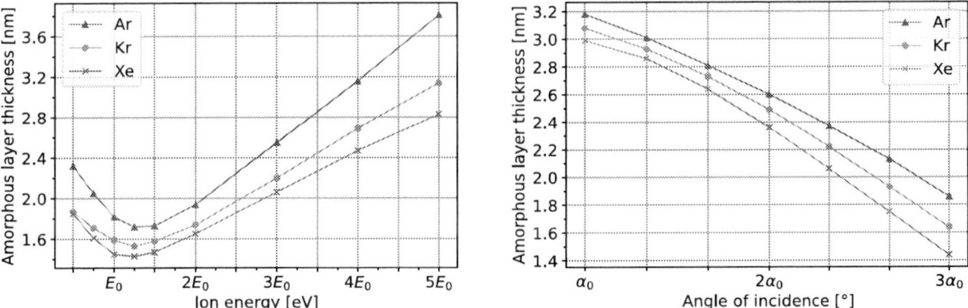

Figure 2: SE measurements of Si wafers after activation where the ALT is plotted over the ion energy (left) and over the AoI (right).

Bonded wafers:
Si wafers were bonded by using Ar, Kr and Xe activation with an energy of $E = E_0$ and then prepared mechanically for TEM. Additionally, some samples were cut out of the wafers for thermal annealing at 450°C for 5 h with a linear temperature gradient of 5°C/min. The TEM results are presented in Figure 3 and confirm the trend of heavy ions generating a thinner amorphous layer than light ions as it was also measured by SE. This underlines the suitability of the SE model for measuring the ALT of activated wafers. Furthermore, the result from the annealed samples show that annealing reduces the amorphous layer thickness. This is most likely a result of recrystallization at the amorphous interface and was also found in the publication of J. S. Williams [6].

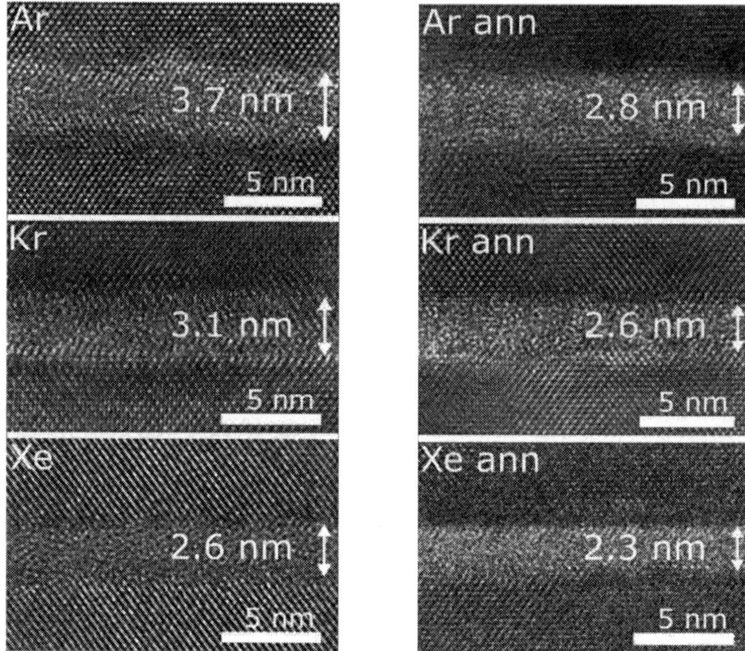

Figure 3: TEM measurements of bonded wafers using different ion species (left) and annealed samples from the same wafers (right). Ion energies of $E = E_0$ were used for activation.

Bonding energy measurements were conducted using the Maszara method, wherein several activation parameters were varied. The blade was inserted at three different positions along the <110> directions. The value for the bonding energy was determined by taking the average of these positions. At least two wafer pairs were bonded for each parameter configuration. Here, again the average is taken. The results are summarized in Table 1. Bonded wafers which were activated by using low ion energies, low activation times and low beam currents yield low bonding energy. This correlation can be attributed to the fact that the sputtering rate depends on all these parameters. In case of low bonding energy, the sputtering rate may not be sufficient to remove the native oxide completely. The bonding energy for bonded wafers using Xe activation is high for all tested parameter configurations. This is most likely due to the fact, that the sputtering rate for heavy ions is higher than the sputtering rate for light ions in case of the employed experimental setup.

Table 1: Bonding energy measurements were performed using the Maszara method. For the sake of comparison, results for Ar from Flötgen [7] are also shown.

Ion type	Time	Ion energy	Bonding energy [J/m^2]
Ar	t_0	E_0	1.4
	$2 \cdot t_0$	E_0	2.1
	$4 \cdot t_0$	$0.5 \cdot E_0$	2.3
	$4 \cdot t_0$	E_0	2.5
Kr	$2 \cdot t_0$	$0.5 \cdot E_0$	1.0
	t_0	E_0	1.4
	$2 \cdot t_0$	E_0	2.0
	$4 \cdot t_0$	E_0	2.5
Xe	t_0	E_0	2.0
	$2 \cdot t_0$	$0.5 \cdot E_0$	2.1
	$4 \cdot t_0$	E_0	2.2
	$4 \cdot t_0$	$3 \cdot E_0$	2.4

Conclusion

Surface activated wafer bonding was employed using low energy Ar, Kr and Xe ion irradiation onto 200 mm Si wafers. The influence of ion type, ion energy and angle of incidence (AoI) on the amorphous layer thickness (ALT) was investigated by spectroscopic ellipsometry (SE) and transmission electron microscopy (TEM). These measurements show that heavy ions generate a lower ALT than light ions. The ALT exhibits a minimum in the function of the ion energy which is most likely due to sputter-implantation dynamics. Furthermore, it was discovered that the ALT decreases with increasing AoI for each ion type. Additional TEM measurements were performed on post-bond annealed wafer pairs. The obtained results indicate that the ALT decreases with annealing due to recrystallization in the bonding interface. TEM measurements are in good agreement with the SE measurements and underline the feasibility of the applied SE model. Further research on surface activated bonding using different ion types will focus on the investigation of different wafer materials.

Acknowledgements

The authors want to thank Jacek Gasiorowski, Michael Dornetshumer, Christoph Flötgen and Viorel Dragoi for their valuable scientific input as well as Peter Oberhummer and Katrin Stadlmann for performing the TEM sample preparation and measurements.

References

1. M. E. Liao, K. Huynh, T. Bai, C. Flötgen, and M. S. Goorsky, ESC Trans., **98**(4), 81-85 (2020)
2. W.P. Maszara, G. Goetz, A. Caviglia, J.B. McKitterick, J. Appl. Phys., **64**, 4943 (1988)
3. C. M. Hertzinger, B. Johs, W. A. McGahan, J. A. Woollam, and W. Paulson, J. Appl. Phys., **83**(6), 3323-3336 (1998)
4. L. Pelaz, L. A. Marqués, and J. Barbolla, J. Appl. Phys., **96**(11), 5947-5976 (2004)
5. M. Danner, "In-Situ Sputtering for Advanced Semiconductor Wafer Bonding with Different Ions Species", TU Wien (2023)
6. J. S. Williams, Materials Science and Engineering A 253.1-2 (1998)
7. C. Flötgen, "Wafer-scale functional interfaces fabrication at low temperatures: technology development and interface characterization", JKU Linz (2017)

ECS Transactions, 112 (3) 125-137 (2023)
10.1149/11203.0125ecst ©The Electrochemical Society

Vacuum Quality Impact on Covalent Bonding

K. Abadie[a](*), Q. Lomonaco[a], L. Michaud[b], F. Fournel[a], and C. Morales[a]

[a] Univ. Grenoble Alpes, CEA, LETI, 38000 Grenoble, France
[b] EV Group, DI E. Thallner Straße 1, St. Florian/Inn 4782, Austria

(*) corresponding author: karine.abadie2@cea.fr

Covalent bonding is based on a direct bonding process. The first step of this process consists in creating dangling bonds at the wafers surface. When the two activated surfaces are brought in contact, covalent bonds result between them. Dangling bonds are highly reactive. Any queue time between activation and bonding is crucial, as dangling bonds must be preserved. It can be even more difficult to preserve the dangling bonds in the case of bonding process in temperature. One way, commonly used, is to always stay under Ultra High Vacuum (UHV). However, the UHV environment may affect the bonding process. This paper aims at studying the impact of the UHV quality on the dangling bonds stability and bonding quality.

Introduction

Nowadays, wafer bonding is widely used in the microelectronics industry, as a manufacturing step for MEMS, NEMS or three dimensional devices, and for various layer transfer. For example, hybrid direct bonding is commonly used for the manufacturing of CMOS image sensors [1], whereas hydrophilic direct bonding is key for the manufacturing of SOI substrates [2]. More recently, covalent bonding has been used for the manufacturing of SiC advances substrates [3], and for various photonics applications such as the transfer of a GaN layer onto a Si substrate [4].

Wafer bonding encompasses different kinds of processes, some of them using polymers as interlayers for bonding, others with van der Walls forces between materials or anodic/electrical interactions. Direct bonding is spontaneous and does not call upon any interlayer for bonding, the two wafers surfaces are simply brought into contact. Covalent bonding is one way to perform a direct bonding of semiconductor [5,6,7,8] or metallic surfaces [9]. It can also be used to fabricate heterostructures [10].

The first step of this process consists in removing native oxide and surface contaminants, but also in creating dangling bonds at the wafer surface using an Ar^+ ion bombardment. Then, the two activated surfaces are brought into contact, resulting in covalent bonds between them. With silicon surfaces, no further annealing is required to enhance the bonding strength. This is at variance with direct hydrophilic bonding where an annealing step at 1000°C or above is required to completely stabilize a room temperature Si/Si bonding. The adherence energy ($G_c = 2\gamma_c$) [11] of covalent Si/Si bond pairs reaches the silicon fracture energy (5 J/m²) [12]. Indeed, all bonded samples break during double cantilever beam (DCB) measurements of it, performed in anhydrous atmosphere [13].

Dangling bonds are highly reactive. Queue time between activation and bonding is crucial, as dangling bonds must be preserved. One way, commonly used, is to process activated materials while being under Ultra High Vacuum (UHV). Indeed, reactive dangling bonds should not get in contact with others reactive molecules, like H_2O, O_2 or N_2, for instance. However, some molecules always remain whatever the vacuum pressure of the studied environment. Depending on their nature, the UHV "quality" for bonding purpose might be impacted. This paper aims at studying the impact of the UHV quality on the dangling bonds stability and bonding quality. In the first part, the UHV environment of an EVG®ComBond® System is characterized using a mass spectrometer, highlighting the presence of reactive molecules despite the very low pressure level of such tool. The second part focuses on the covalent bonding process and how reactive molecules can impact it. Some pre conditioning procedures for the equipment are discussed. In the third part, impact of reactive molecules and pre conditioning sequences on covalent bonding processes performed in temperature (>100°C) are studied.

UHV environment in an EVG®ComBond® system

Current experiments were performed in an EVG®ComBond® system. This platform includes a central UHV cluster with loadports, robot, prealigner, flipper, and two process chambers: one for the activation of the substrates named CAM® for ComBond® Activation module and a second module, which is used to bring in contact the two substrates named bonder (**Figure 1**). Both process chambers are equipped with a turbo pump. The central cluster is equipped with a turbo pump and a cryopump system in order to reach a very low pressure in the entire tool (in the range of 10^{-8}mbars).

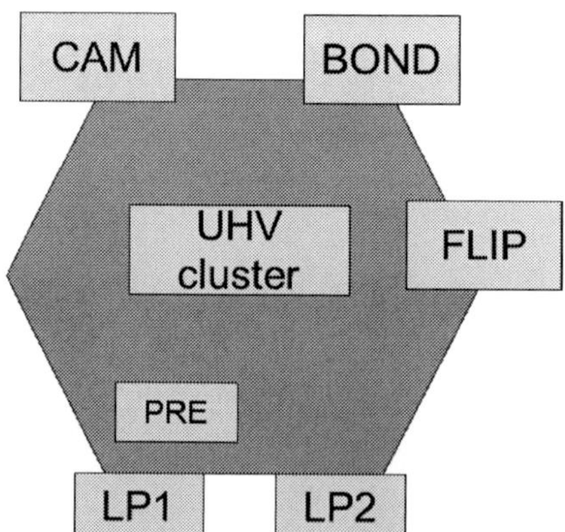

Figure 1. Schematic of an EVG®Combond® system

During a covalent bonding process, the CAM® operates in a vacuum in the range of 10^{-4} mbars due to the Ar beam. The bonder always stays at a very low vacuum level of 10^{-8} mbars, as well as the cluster which is used as transfer module. As our tool is not equipped with two CAM® process chambers, the two substrates are not activated simultaneously, but successively. Once the first wafer is activated, it is brought into the bond chamber, while the second is loaded in the CAM® chamber for activation. We assume that the most critical moment of the covalent bonding process is when both wafers are transferred and wait to be bonded after activation. It happens when they are on hold in the bonder. That is why our studies about the vacuum quality focused on this part of the system.

In order to study the UHV quality, a mass spectrometer was installed inside the bond chamber in order to perform residual gas analysis (RGA). First, a measurement of the atmosphere inside this chamber was performed. The goal was to underline which elements were present. Thanks to a partial pressure analysis of molar masses, it was observed than the most predominant element was H_2O (molar mass of 18). This measurement is shown in **Figure 2**. The others species detected were H, H_2, O, OH, N_2, O_2, CO_2, with molar masses of 1, 2, 16, 17, 28, 32, and 44, respectively. Partial pressure presented in this figure are not absolute values, but relative ones, instead. The global chamber pressure during the measurement was about 3.10^{-8} mbars

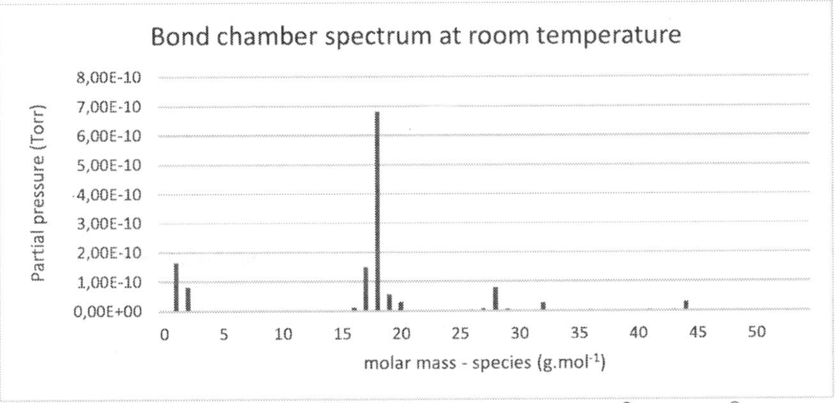

Figure 2. RGA measurement in the bond chamber of an EVG®Combond® system

In the case of silicon to silicon bond pairs, H is highly reactive with Si activated surfaces. Naturally, the wafer surface, full of Si dangling bonds right after activation, will look for passivation using existing H inside the chambers. For those two reasons, we have focused our attention on the partial pressure of water.

A spectrometer measurement was performed overnight, in order to assess the stability of the water partial pressure. After 12h recording, the relatively flat curve in **Figure 3** demonstrates that it is indeed stable.

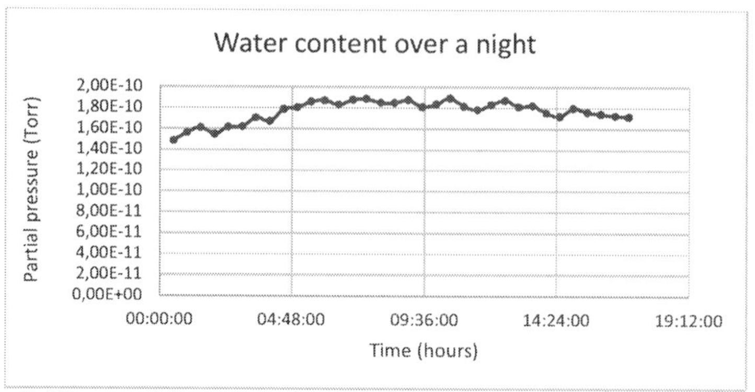

Figure 3. Water partial pressure of the bond chamber of an EVG®Combond® system, over a night

Vacuum system bakeout is a well-known technique to remove adsorbed water molecules from metallic surfaces [14]. Although background water concentration in UHV is hardly detectable at room temperature, tracking its partial pressure during bakeout cycles enables to define a water partial pressure threshold. Indeed, during a bakeout cycle, a water concentration peak is clearly seen by the mass spectrometer, as shown in **Figure 4**. The impact of up to four bakeouts of the entire EVG®ComBond® system at 100°C was evaluated. After each bakeout, a Si/Si bonding adherence energy was measured. After the first bakeout, the adherence energy was only around 2.5 J/m². However, after the second bakeout, it reached the silicon fracture energy of 5 J/m². In **Figure 4**, it can also be seen that the water partial pressure curve is the same during the 2nd, the 3rd and the 4th bakeout. This implies that no significant amount of water is released during these bakeouts.

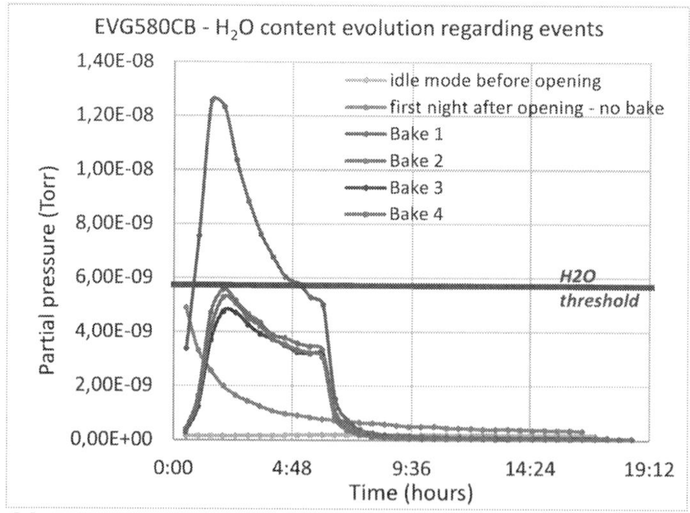

Figure 4. Mass spectrometer measurements of the water pressure in the bond chamber of an EVG®Combond® system during different events.

Thanks to this study about the vacuum quality required for covalent bonding, a pre conditioning sequence of the EVG®ComBond® system was put in place. It included not only one, but two bakeout sequences of the entire tool, performed at 100°C.

The second part of this paper will now focus on the impact of the vacuum quality on the covalent bonding process.

Impact of vacuum quality on covalent bonding

<u>Waiting time in bonder</u>

The impact of queue times between wafer surface activation and bonding was also studied. For a standard process, this waiting time is the time needed to activate both substrates (in a system having only one activation chamber), and to move them from the activation chamber to the bond chamber. The impact of queue time in the bond chamber is studied through two different characterization techniques. **Figure 5** shows C-SAM (C-mode Scanning Acoustic Microscopy) images after bonding for all bonded pairs. **Figure 6** graph gives the adherence energy for Si/Si covalent bonding as a function of the waiting time inside the bond chamber and after activation of both substrates. This energy was determined using the DCB technique in anhydrous atmosphere on 2cm wide beams. A waiting time of 0 min means that the best known method (BKM) recipe was used for Si/Si covalent bonding. A 150mA/200V surface activation was performed on each Si wafer for 1 min in the CAM® chamber. Meanwhile, a 10 kN force was used to put in contact both substrates in the bond chamber.

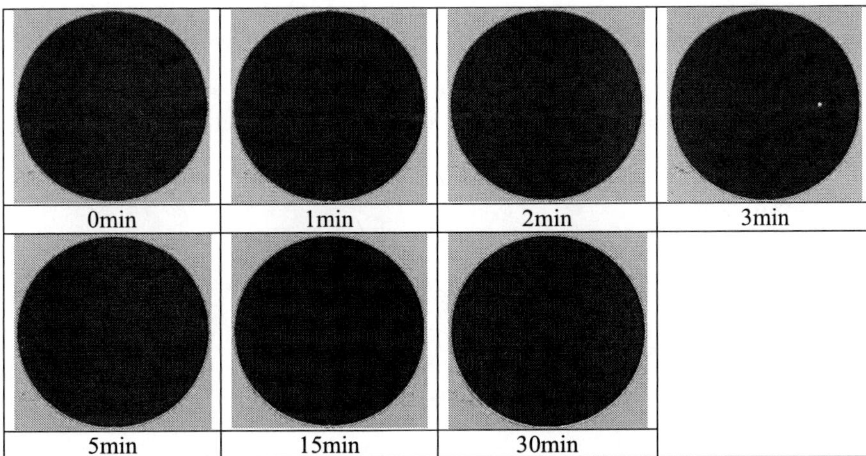

Figure 5. C-SAM inspection of bond pairs processed with different queue time between activation and bonding.

Figure 5 shows that the added queue time has no impact on the bonding defectivity, as no major voids can be detected. In **Figure 6**, it is shown that the adherence energy is impacted by the UHV quality. With our best tool conditioning, i.e. two baking sequences, an adherence energy higher than 3.4 J/m² can be maintained with up to 5 min added to the minimum queue time. The adherence energy is drastically lower for longer queue times, meaning that more and more dangling bonds are affected by the remaining water.

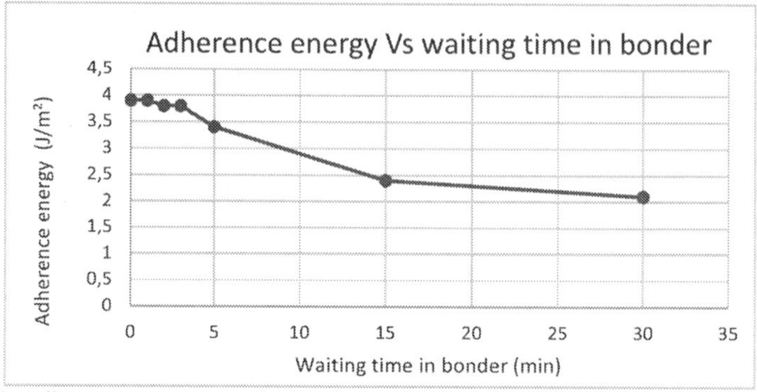

Figure 6. Adherence energy evolution depending on the queue time between activation and bonding for a Si-Si covalent bonding.

Waiting time in CAM®

The impact of the queue time between activation and bonding is now studied by applying a queue time inside the CAM® chamber, instead of the bond chamber. The first Si wafer was activated in the CAM® then stayed under Ar inside this chamber. After a certain queue time, varying from 0 min up to 30 min, the first wafer was brought inside the bond chamber and the second Si wafer activated, in the same way than during a BKM process. Both Si/Si wafers were subsequently put in contact in the bond chamber with the same 10 kN force than before.

Seven Si/Si bond pairs were processed. They were then cut into 2cm wide beams and their adherence energy was measured using the DCB technique under anhydrous atmosphere. **Figure 7** shows the adherence energy measured depending on the queue time in the CAM® chamber.

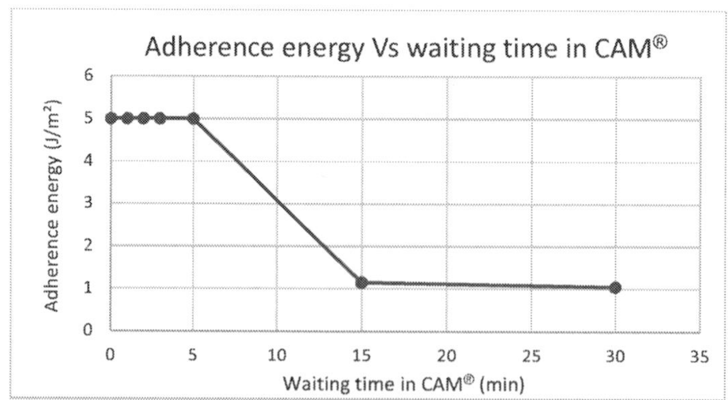

Figure 7. Adherence energy evolution depending on the queue time in an Ar flow between activation and bonding for a Si-Si covalent bonding.

Figure 7 shows that, under an Ar flow, dangling bonds can be fully maintained for a queue time inside the CAM® chamber of up to 5 min. Indeed, the adherence energy measured on bonded pairs is maximum, as samples broke during blade insertion. It means that not only the vacuum level is important to preserve dangling bonds, but also its quality. With an atmosphere filled with chemically inert Ar molecules (pressure level of 10^{-4} mbar), Si dangling bonds stay reactive. However, we can see that the adherence drops drastically after a queue time of 15 and 30min. We assume that this is due to the quality of the Ar gas used, which is not pure enough. Residual contaminants such as O_2 or H_2O might have affected the dangling bonds for queue times longer than 5 min.

Impact of vacuum quality on covalent bonding process in temperature (>100°C)

Thanks to our EVG®Combond® system, covalent bonding in temperature can be performed in temperature using heated electrostatic chucks (ESC) [10]. However, even after two or more system bakeouts, high temperature covalent bondings did not exhibit high adherence energies (in other words, it was not possible to reach the silicon fracture energy). **Figure 8** presents adherence measurements performed on bond pairs processed at different temperatures. The room temperature bond pair, used as a reference, exhibit a very high adherence of 4.1 J/m². It is actually the bond pair used for tool qualification after two bakeouts of 12h each at 100°C. However, for a new bond pair processed with the same conditions, but with ESC pre heated at 150°C, the adherence energy is about 1J/m², e.g. a value nearly 4 times lower. This drop down continues to only few of hundreds of mJ/m² for ESC pre heated at even higher temperatures (200°C & 250°C).

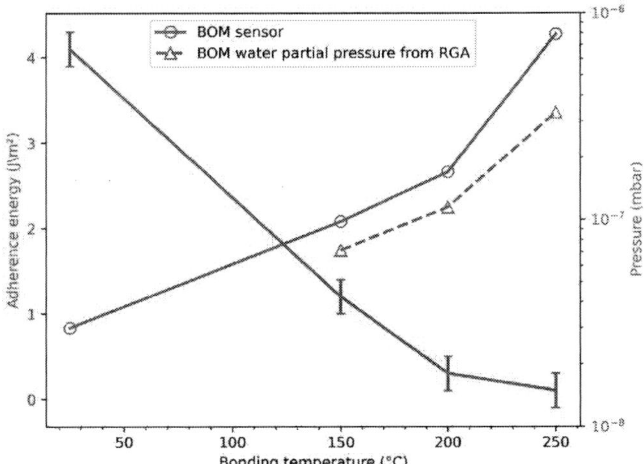

Figure 8. Si-Si adherence energy evolution and bond chamber pressure depending on the bonding temperature

At the same time, the pressure level of the bond chamber was registered during the bonding of these Si/Si bond pairs. It was noticed than when the temperature of the ESC increased, the temperature of the chamber also globally increased and so the pressure level (pressure level of 10^{-8} mbar at room temperature ⇔ up to 10^{-6} mbar at 250°C). It could be due to the increase of collisions between remaining molecules, a normal phenomenon when the temperature increases. It could also be due to a release of molecules that were not removed during the bakeout sequences performed at only 100°C. In the current study, temperatures up to 250°C were used and some water could still be adsorbed on metallic parts.

Using the mass spectrometer to track the partial pressure of water inside the bonding chamber during a high temperature bakeout of the ESC at 250°C showed that water still desorbed during this process, as illustrated in **Figure 9** and in **Figure 10**. **Figure 9** shows that water and hydrogen are still the most present molecules in the bond chamber at 250°C. The partial pressure of water increases more than 10 times during a ESC heating at 250°C (Figure 10).

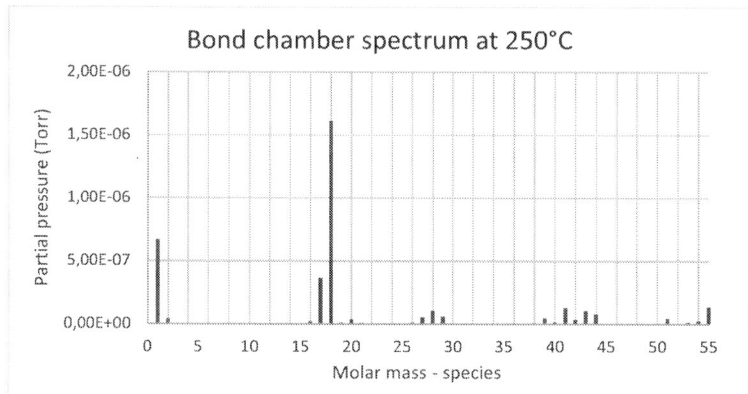

Figure 9. RGA measurements in the bond chamber of an EVG®Combond® system, with ESC heated at 250°C

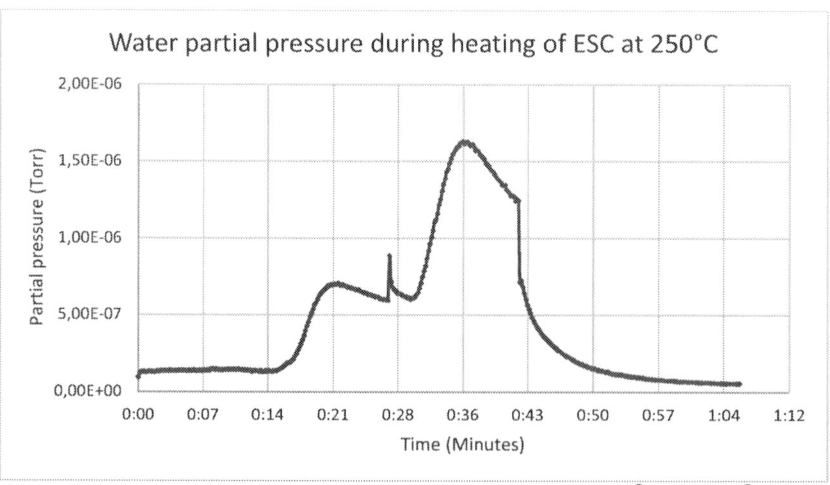

Figure 10. Water partial pressure in the bond chamber of an EVG®Combond® system, with ESC heated at 250°C

To conduct this measurement, ESCs were pressed together with a force of 10 kN till the 27th minute (**Figure 10**). Then, ESC are opened, and the heat continues to increase inside the chamber. A water peak is reached at 36 min. Then water partial pressure starts to decrease. To stop the experiment, the cooling of the ESC is turned on at 43min and they are pressed together in order to enhance heat exchanges under UHV and speed up the process.

Optimized tool pre conditioning must thus be implemented for such specific hot bonding, with a need for global baking (even of internal chamber pieces). The partial pressure of water was again registered during ESC pre conditionings at 150°C, 200°C and 250°C. Data are provided in **Figure 11**. During the first ESC pre conditioning, the partial pressure of water directly increases when ESC starts to heat. The water partial pressure peak increases with the ESC temperature. There is clearly a water release from some heated parts of the bond chamber.

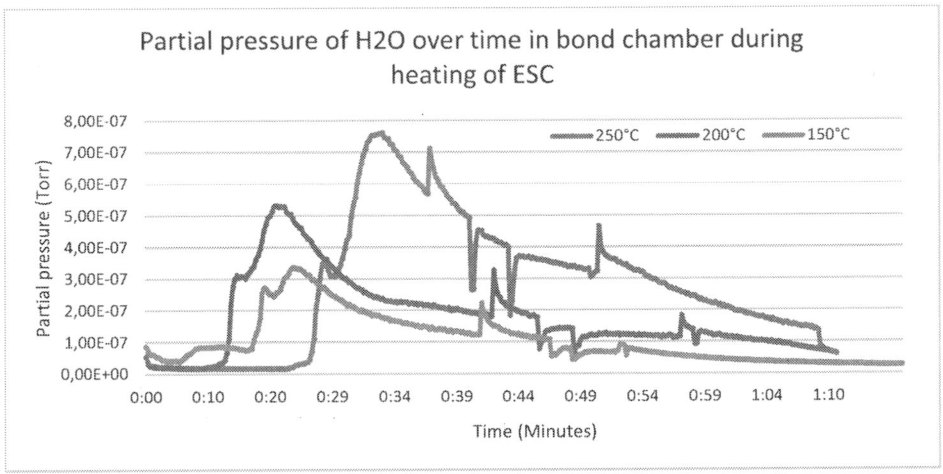

Figure 11. Water partial pressure in the bond chamber of an EVG®Combond® system, with ESC heated at 150°C, 200°C and 250°C

It means that the ESC must be pre conditioned at the highest temperature possible. The EVG®Combond® system allows to heat ESC chucks up to 400°C. However, this temperature is too high to perform RGA measurement, as it could damage de mass spectrometer. We chose to perform 400°C ESC preheat conditioning sequences twice without measuring the chamber pressure. An adherence energy measurement was performed on a new Si/Si bond pair processed at 250°C right after such two 400°C ESC bakeout sequence. The same high bond strength of about 4 J/m² than at room temperature was then recovered (see **Figure 12**).

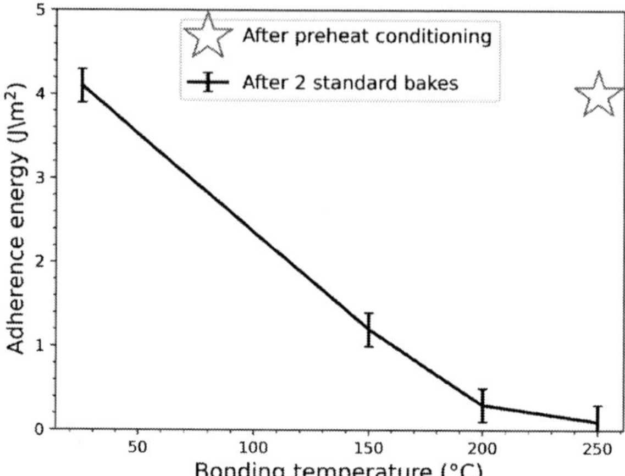

Figure 12. Si-Si adherence energy as a function of the bonding temperature, this after two standard bakes at 100°C and after a preheat conditioning of the ESC

After both pre conditionings of the EVG®ComBond® system and the ESC, another study of the queue time between the activation and the bond was conducted for covalent bondings performed in temperature (180°C).

First, it must be noted that to realize a covalent bonding in temperature, both wafers must be thermalized at the desired temperature after activation and prior to contacting. ESCs are used for such a thermalization. As it happens under UHV, thermalization takes much more time compared to atmospheric pressure process, since heat exchanges relies only on radiation and contact. For bonding to be performed at 180°C, it for example takes at least 5.5 min to thermalize both wafers. It was demonstrated using a HighTemp-400 device from KLA-Tencor. Moreover, this measurement demonstrates that the temperature is quite homogenous over the wafer surface (see **Figure 13**), with less than 5°C of difference between the center and the edge of a wafer.

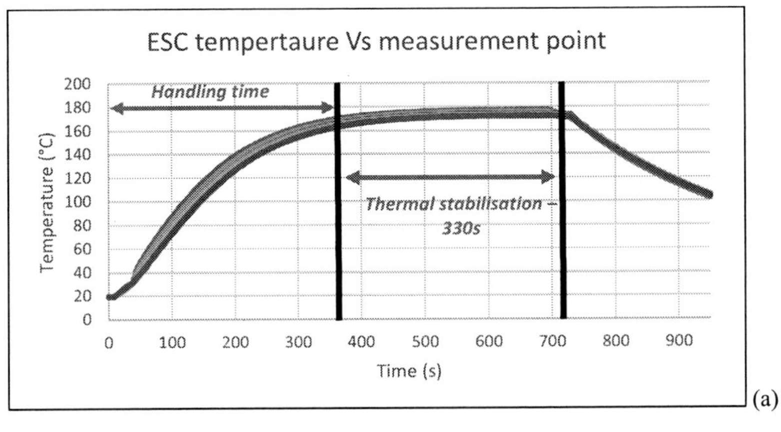

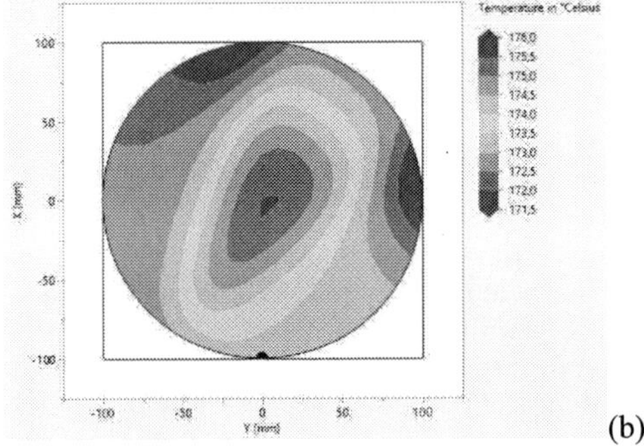

Figure 13. HighTemp-400 system measurements: (a) Temperatures on the 18 measurements points over the ESC as function of time. There is 360s of handling just to load the system into the bond chamber. (b) Temperature homogeneity over the ESC after 700s of thermalization

Three bond pairs were fabricated at 180°C, using 5.5, 15.5 and 30.5 minutes of thermalization as queue times. The three bond pairs were cut in 2cm wide beams and the adherence energy measured in anhydrous atmosphere using the DCB technique. Results are presented in **Figure 14** (red curve). Despite the pre conditioning of both the entire tool and the ESC chucks, the adherence of bond pairs processed in temperature is slightly lower than the one performed at room temperature. It otherwise decreases as the queue time increases. It means that, if the pre-conditioning of the tool is adapted, dangling bond will be impacted the same way by waiting time for RT and in temperature processes.

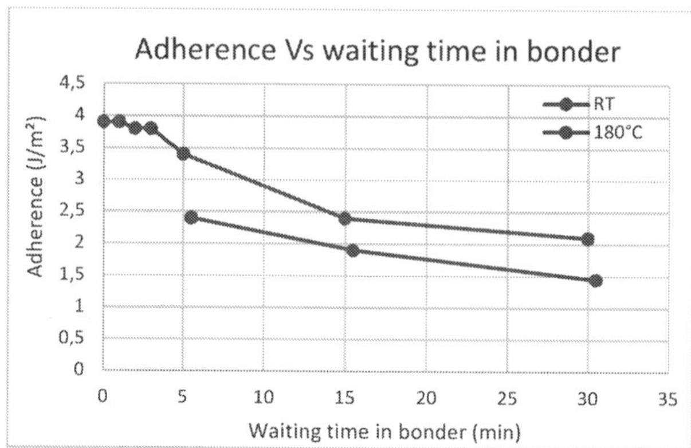

Figure 14. Adherence energy evolution depending on the queue time between activation and bonding for Si-Si covalent bonding at room temperature and at 180°C

Conclusion

In conclusion, the impact of the UHV quality on the dangling bond stability and adherence has been evaluated. The UHV environment of an EVG®ComBond® System was characterized using a mass spectrometer, highlighting the presence of reactive molecules like water and hydrogen despite the very low background pressure of the cluster tool. It enabled us to set up a preconditioning of the entire EVG®ComBond® System, which is based on two bakeouts performed at 100°C during 12h in order to reach the silicon fracture energy with control bonding at RT.

The impact of the queue time between wafer surfaces activation and bonding on the dangling bonds was studied for room temperature Si-Si covalent bonding. It was shown that below 5min queue times, the Si-Si adherence energy stayed very high for Si/Si. If such a waiting occurred under an Ar flow, the impact on dangling bonds was suppressed.

Then the bonding chamber environment was again studied, but in temperature (>100°C). It was shown than even after the two 12h bakeout sequences at 100°C, some water was still be trapped on metallic parts, especially in the bond chamber. A specific preconditioning of the ESC chucks of the bond chamber was then then set up, in order to assure a high adherence of Si/Si bond pairs processed at temperatures higher than 100°C.

Acknowledgments

The team would like to thanks KLA-Tencor for their support and help during the measurements of the ESC temperature with the HighTemp-400 device.

References

1. S. Lhostis, A. Farcy, E. Deloffre, F. Lorut, S. Mermoz, Y. Henrion, L. Berthier, F. Bailly, D. Scevola, F. Guyader, F. Gigon, C. Besset, S. Pellissier, L. Gay, N.

Hotellier, A.-L. Le Berrigo, S. Moreau, V. Balan, F. Fournel, A. Jouve, and S. Chéramy, Reliable 300mm Wafer Level Hybrid bonding for 3D Stacked CMOS Image Sensor, in 2016 IEEE 66th Electronic Components and Technology Conference, 2016. p.869-876 (2016)

2. M. Bruel, Application of hydrogen ion beams to Silicon On Insulator material technology, in Nuclear Instruments and Methods in Physics Research Section B: Beam Interactions with Materials and Atoms, Volume 108, Issue 3, 1 February 1996, p. 313-319

3. Ko Imaoka, Motoki Kobayashi, Hidetsugu Uchida, Kuniaki Yagi, Takamitsu Kawahara, Naoki Hatta, Akiyuki Minami, Toyokazu Sakata, Tomoatsu Makino, Mitsuharu Kato, Patent No . : US 9, 773, 678 B2.

4. Shi Zhou, Shun Wan 3, Bo Zou, Yanping Yang, Huarui Sun, Yan Zhou, and Jianbo Liang, Interlayer Investigations of GaN Heterostructures Integrated into Silicon Substrates by Surface Activated Bonding, in Crystals 2023, 13, 217

5. T. Suga, Y. Takahashi, H. Takagi, B. Gibbesch, and G. Elssner, Structure of Al-Al and Al-Si$_3$N$_4$ interfaces bonded at room temperature by means of the surface activated method, in Acta Metallurgica et Materialia, Volume 40, Supplement, 1992, p.133-137

6. H. Takagi, K. Kikuchi, R. Maeda, TR. Chung, and T. Suga, Surface activated bonding of silicon wafers at room temperature, in Appl Phys Lett. 15 avr 1996;68(16):2222-4.

7. S. Taniyama, YH. Wang, M. Fujino, and T. Suga, Room temperature wafer bonding using surface activated bonding method, in 2008 IEEE 9th VLSI Packaging Workshop of Japan. 2008. p. 141-4.

8. C. Flötgen, N. Razek, V. Dragoi, and M. Wimplinger, Novel Surface Preparation Methods for Covalent and Conductive Bonded Interfaces Fabrication, in ECS Trans. 14 août 2014;64(5):103.

9. T.H. Kim, M.M.R. Howlader, T. Itoh, and T. Suga, Low Temperature Direct Cu-Cu Bonding with Low Energy Ion Activation Method, in IEEE Advances in Electronic Materials and Packaging 2001 Conference, p. 193-195

10. Q. Lomonaco, K. Abadie, C. Morales, LG. Michaud, J. Richy, S. Moreau, and F. Fournel, Stress Engineering in Germanium-Silicon Heterostructure Using Surface Activated Hot Bonding, in ECS Trans. 30 sept 2022;109(4):277-87.

11. Vallin, Örjan, Kerstin Jonsson, and Ulf Lindberg. « Adhesion Quantification Methods for Wafer Bonding ». *Materials Science and Engineering: R: Reports* 50, n° 4-5 (décembre 2005): 109-65. https://doi.org/10.1016/j.mser.2005.07.002.

12. Ebrahimi, Fereshteh, and Lakshman Kalwani. « Fracture Anisotropy in Silicon Single Crystal ». *Materials Science and Engineering: A* 268, n° 1 (15 août 1999): 116-26. https://doi.org/10.1016/S0921-5093(99)00077-5.

13. F. Fournel, L. Continni, C. Morales, J. Da Fonseca, H. Moriceau, F. Rieutord, A. Barthelemy, and I. Radu, Journal of Applied Physics **111**, 104907 (2012).

14. A. Berman, Water vapor in vacuum systems, in Vacuum. avr 1996;47(4):327-32.

ECS Transactions, 112 (3) 139-145 (2023)
10.1149/11203.0139ecst ©The Electrochemical Society

Soft Surface Activated Bonding of Hydrophobic Silicon Substrates

Q. Lomonaco[a](*), K. Abadie[a], J.-M. Hartmann[a], C. Morales[a], P. Noël[a], T. Marion[a],
C. Lecouvey[a], A.-M. Papon[a], and F. Fournel[a]

[a] Univ. Grenoble Alpes, CEA, LETI, 38000 Grenoble, France

(*) corresponding author: quentin.lomonaco@cea.fr

Surface Activated Bonding (SAB) is interesting for strong silicon to silicon bonding at room temperature without any annealing needed, afterwards (1). This technique has been recognized by the scientific community for more than two decades now and was used for numerous reviewed applications (2). Although it is a well-known technique, the activation step, in particular, is scarcely documented. This paper offers insights about the impact of soft activation parameters on the amorphous region at the bonding interface. In addition, the adherence energy of hydrophobic silicon after SAB bonding is quantified, to better understand bonding mechanisms. Soft activation parameters on hydrophobic silicon substrates yield exceptionally thin bonding interfaces with acceptable bonding energy at room temperature. According to cross-sectional Transmission Electron Microscopy imaging, a 0.53 nm thick amorphous silicon interface was achieved with an adherence energy of 1337 ± 137 J/m² measured by the Double Cantilever Beam method.

Introduction

Surface Activated Bonding (SAB) is based on two steps. The first step cleans, remove the native oxide, and activates surfaces thanks to Ar^+ beam bombardment. Meanwhile, the second step is the spontaneous covalent bonding under ultra-high vacuum (UHV) without any heat treatment. Conventional SAB activation parameters are relatively powerful (3–5), with 0.7 up to 2kV acceleration voltages and 10 to 150 mA currents (governing the dose). It eventually leads to amorphization of irradiated surfaces. Transmission Electron Microscopy (TEM) imaging prior to annealing showed amorphous bonding interfaces up to 15 nm thick for binary alloys such as SiC.

Meanwhile, this paper focus on much softer activation parameters, the aim being to obtain interfaces with the least possible crystalline disturbance. We used particular substrates to investigate the generation of this amorphous region and ultimately its impact on SAB mechanisms. In the first part of this paper, the specific hydrophobic substrates used in this study are described, together with the time resolved exposition to a specific set of activation parameters. The second part presents several characterizations results obtained on samples before and after bonding. Finally, some hypothesis based on these preliminary results are provided.

Materials and method

Softer activation parameters should reduce the amorphous silicon region generated by Ar^+ ion bombardment (6). However, with very low dose and acceleration activation parameters during SAB, surface preparation prior to bonding becomes of paramount importance. Indeed, the silicon native oxide that must be removed during conventional activation steps in order to generate dangling bonds has to be minimized by other means.

In order to work around this potential roadblock, we used hydrophobic surface preparations to remove native oxide, before entering into the activation step. Two types of preparation were evaluated in this study. First, a standard "HF-Last" chemical wet cleaning was used on standard silicon wafers. This treatment consumed the silicon native oxide and passivated up to 85% the surface with Si-H, and to a lesser extent, Si-F bonds(7,8). The surface preparation of this set of samples is common in the industry; it will therefore serve as a control group in our study, notably for surface roughness assessments.

We otherwise used epitaxy-reconstructed silicon wafers with fully hydrophobic surfaces (7). Silicon native oxide was removed thanks to an ultra-pure H_2 bake at 1100°C, 20 Torr for 2 minutes in an epitaxy chamber. Then, several tens of nanometer of silicon were deposited at 950°C to obtain, after another H_2 bake (at 950°C, 20 Torr and for 5 minutes), a silicon surface fully passivated by hydrogen atoms (9) with atomically smooth terraces and mono-atomic step edges.

Then, we loaded wafers with such surfaces in our EVG®ComBond® bonding tool equipped with an accelerated argon ion beam. The softest functional settings in our set up, 50V (acceleration) and 26 mA (dose) were used for the activation step. After beam initialization, the two substrates passed through the activation chamber and were transferred to the bonding chamber within 5 minutes of handling under UHV.

We performed a screening of the exposure time in the activation chamber. The goal was to remove adsorbed hydrogen atoms on the silicon surface and obtain dangling bonds without any amorphous silicon generation.

We investigated the surface state of samples after different exposure times using atomic force microscopy (AFM). We also studied the bonding interface via Fourier-transform infrared spectroscopy (FTIR). Finally, we took a closer look at the atomic structure of the interface thanks to transmission electronic microscopy (TEM).

Results

<u>Adherence energy measurements by the Double Cantilever Beam method</u>

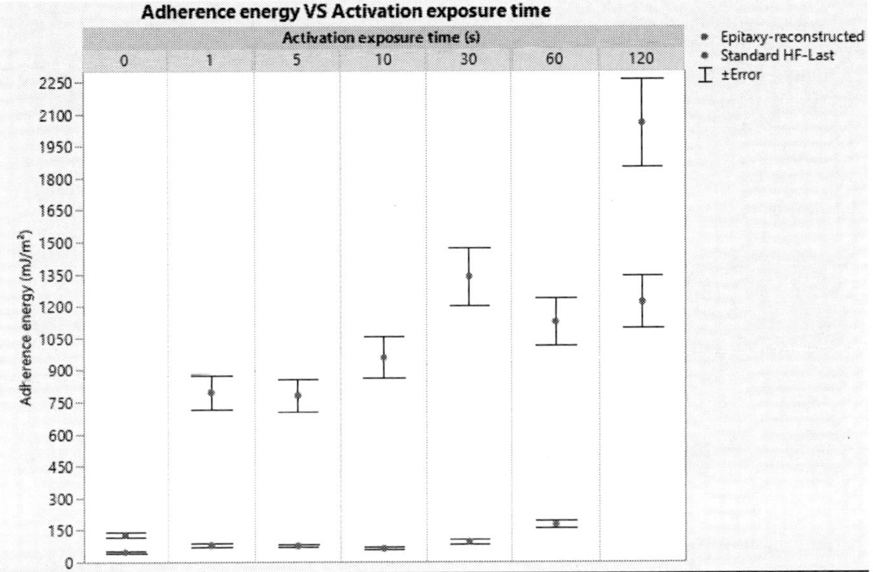

Figure 1. Adherence energy versus Activation exposure time (activation parameters: 50V 26 mA).

The adherence energy ($G_c = 2\gamma_c$) in mJ/m² as a function of exposure time to Ar^+ with soft activation parameters for both types of wafers (e.g. with "HF-Last" or H_2 bake surface preparation) is shown in **Figure 1,** The 0 second reference bondings were conducted without passing through the activation module. We then had very low adherence energies, around 50 mJ/m², as expected for standard hydrophobic silicon wafer bondings under UHV (10). Upon Ar^+ exposure, behaviors were very different depending on the initial surface preparation. The adherence energy barely increased with the Ar^+ exposure time for "HF-Last" surfaces. Meanwhile, even 1s of exposure to Ar^+ had a significant impact on the adherence energy of epi-reconstructed, atomically smooth silicon surfaces, which was definitely higher. The highest energy difference between the two wafer preparations happened for 30 up to 60 seconds exposure times. Above 60s, there was a bonding mechanism transition as the comparatively high roughness of the "HF-Last" silicon wafer started to be counter-balanced by argon beam activation. For 120 seconds samples, the adherence energy of the "HF-Last" control group rose above 200 mJ/m², closing the gap with epi-reconstructed samples. We can infer that a threshold was crossed during Ar^+ treatment above which bonding was favored.

Atomic Force Microscopy

First, we looked at the surface morphology prior to bonding. We manufactured blanket wafers using the epitaxy reconstruction process mentioned in the previous section, a reference (zero second) and three samples with different Ar^+ exposure times: 1s, 30s and 60s. We then performed 1 μm x 1 μm scans at the center of the wafers. On **Figure 2**, the reference (a.) and the 60s sample (b.) exhibit a nearly identical morphology, we can infer that the soft activation process does not modify the surface greatly. In addition, graph (c.) shows surface Root Mean Square (RMS) roughness and Peak-to-Valley (PV) results performed on the four samples. No significative changes in the RMS roughness, nor in the PV as function of the activation time exposure can be pointed out, confirming the assumption made from the morphological observations.

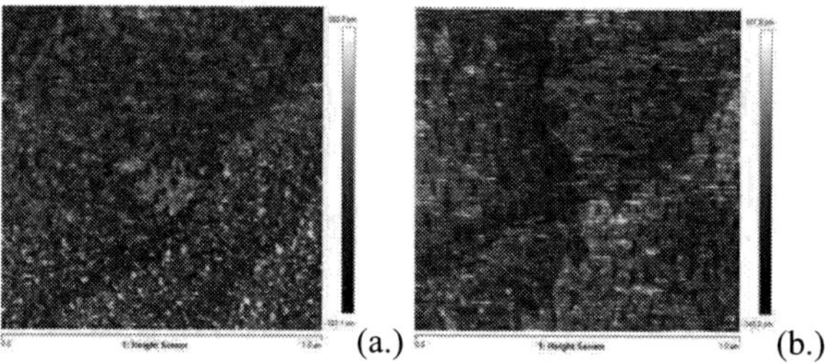

(a.) (b.)

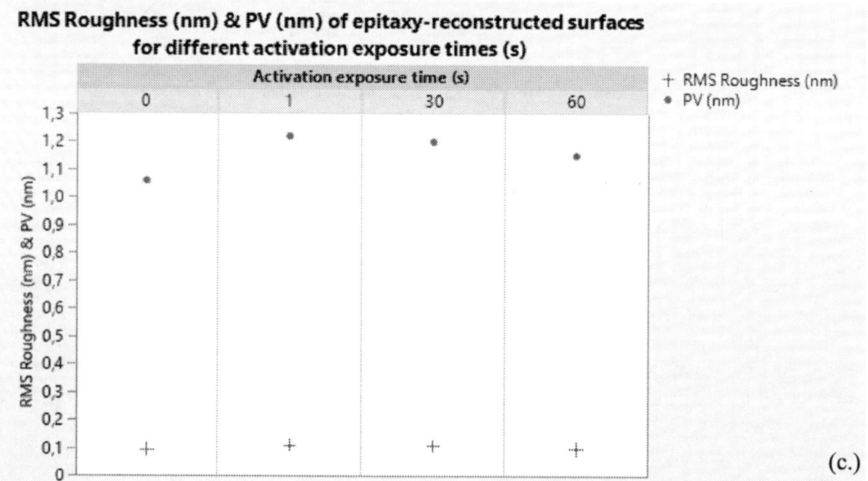

(c.)

Figure 2. Atomic Force Microscopy images of samples after activation, for different exposure times: 0s (a.) 60s (b.) and the four samples topological data (c.).

Based on RMS roughness, peak to valley and morphology data in **Figure 2**, soft activation parameters do not have any significant impact on the sample surface for the various exposure times explored.

<u>Fourier-transform infrared spectroscopy</u>

One aim of this study was to quantify the "effectiveness" of a fast atom beam treatment (FAB). In other words, one goal was to assess the capability of the activation step to produce dangling bonds. In practice, we were looking for Si-H bonds remaining after soft activation. To that end, we performed multiple internal reflections Fourier-transform infrared spectroscopy (MIR-FTIR) measurements at the bonding interface. Samples were manufactured under UHV, by assembling two substrates exposed to the same activation steps. The backsides of bonded wafers were treated with an ozone plasma in order to deplete the external surfaces of Si-H bonds. Hence, we can fairly assume that the IR absorption band relative to Si-H bonds is proportional only to Si-H remaining at the bonding interface.

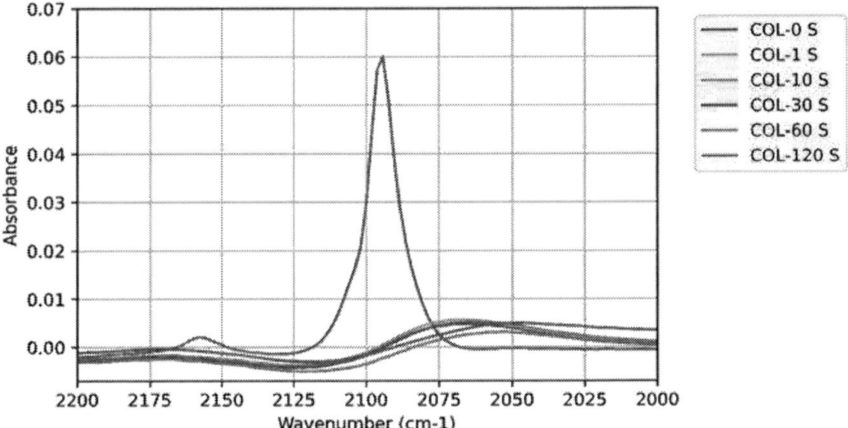

Figure 3. FTIR-MIR absorption spectrum of bonded samples after activation, for different Ar^+ exposure times: 0s, 1s, 10s, 30s, 60s, 120s.

As seen in **Figure 3**, the intensity of the IR absorption band due to $Si-H_x$ bonds drops by a factor of 12 after 1s of soft activation. This indicates a drastic decrease in the $Si-H_x$ bonds population at the bonding interface. Also, the peak associated to $Si-H_x$ bonds shifts from 2095 cm^{-1} to 2065 cm^{-1}. Such a change can be explained by $Si-H_x$ bonds' vibration mode changes. The peak at 2095 cm^{-1} would be due to surface $Si-H_x$ bonds vibrating "relatively" freely whereas the 2065 cm^{-1} peak would be associated to a more "confined" vibration mode (11). Such a hypothesis about this modification in the vibration regime is coherent with the net increase in adherence energy.

<u>Transmission electronic microscopy</u>

TEM is the method of choice to detect the presence of an amorphous phase at the bonding interface, as we can image the area with atomic resolution.

Cross-sectional TEM imaging of the bonding interface were thus performed on two samples with (a) 1 sec et (b) 30 sec of Ar^+ exposure prior to bonding, without annealing. ~ 100nm thick TEM lamella were imaged with the same magnification factor of 450K.

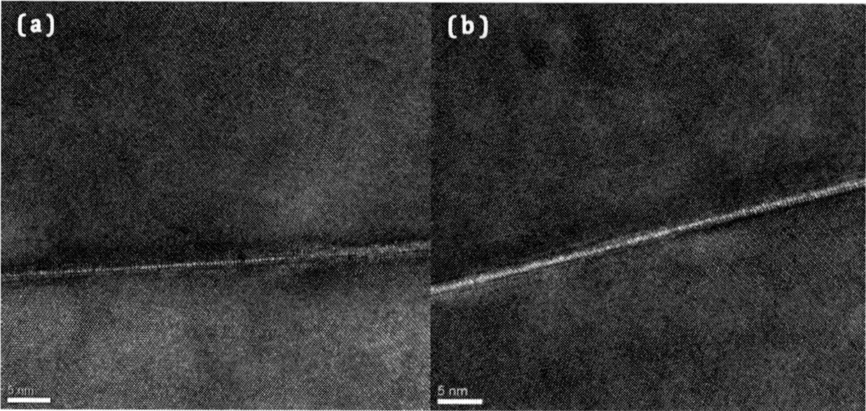

Figure 4. TEM imaging of the bonding interface of the 1s (a) et 30s (b) samples

On **Figure 4,** there is a very thin amorphous area, whiter than the monocrystalline regions on each side, at the bonding interface, for both samples. Image (b) interface is thicker, about 0.53nm, corresponding to four atomic planes.
From these images, we can conclude that soft activation parameters yield particularly thin amorphous regions at the bonding interface, with a thickness that increases with the Ar^+ beam exposure time.

Conclusions

We performed SAB with soft Ar^+ activation parameters on two sets of silicon hydrophobic surfaces. We then characterized the surfaces and the interfaces of such samples with several techniques. It would seem that the very thin amorphous region formed on H_2 baked Si surfaces yields relatively "high" bonding energies when such surfaces are brought into contact. Soft activation parameters efficiently removed hydrogen passivation on such atomically smooth surfaces even for 1 second of soft Ar^+ activation. Nevertheless, other AFM and TEM measurements are needed to draw definite conclusions concerning the impact of the amorphous region on the adherence energy. However, DCB measurements indicated a bonding mechanism regime change after 30 seconds of exposure. The adherence energy of 120 seconds samples from the "HF-Last" group was high and close to that of H_2 baked samples. The amorphous domain at the bonding interface seems to yield here high adherence energies.

Bibliography

1. Suga T, Takahashi Y. Takagi H., Gibbesch B., Elssner G. Structure of AlAl and AlSi3N4 interfaces bonded at room temperature by means of the surface activation method. Acta Metallurgica et Materialia, Volume 40, 1992.

2. Suga T, Mu F. Surface Activated Bonding Method for Low Temperature Bonding. In: 2018 7th Electronic System-Integration Technology Conference (ESTC). 2018.

3. Higurashi E, Sasaki Y, Kurayama R, Suga T, Doi Y, Sawayama Y, et al. Room-temperature direct bonding of germanium wafers by surface-activated bonding method. Jpn J Appl Phys. 1 mars 2015.

4. Mu F, Iguchi K, Nakazawa H, Takahashi Y, Fujino M, Suga T. Room-temperature wafer bonding of SiC–Si by modified surface activated bonding with sputtered Si nanolayer. Jpn J Appl Phys. 18 mars 2016.

5. Morisaki R, Hirai Y, Oka C, Mizoshiri M, Yamazaki T, Sakurai J, et al. Development of a fast atom beam gun for surface-activated bonding. Precis Eng. 1 mars 2020.

6. Takagi H, Kikuchi K, Maeda R, Chung TR, Suga T. Surface activated bonding of silicon wafers at room temperature. Appl Phys Lett. 15 avr 1996.

7. Sordes D, Thuaire A, Reynaud P, Rauer C, Hartmann JM, Moriceau H, et al. Nanopackaging of Si(100)H Wafer for Atomic-Scale Investigations. In: Kolmer M, Joachim C, éditeurs. On-Surface Atomic Wires and Logic Gates. Cham: Springer International Publishing; 2017.

8. Abbadie A, Hartmann JM, Holliger P, Séméria MN, Besson P, Gentile P. Low thermal budget surface preparation of Si and SiGe. Appl Surf Sci. 30 mars 2004.

9. Hersam MC, Guisinger NP, Lyding JW, Thompson DS, Moore JS. Atomic-level study of the robustness of the Si(100)-2×1:H surface following exposure to ambient conditions. Appl Phys Lett. 12 févr 2001.

10. Tong QY, Lee TH, Gösele U, Reiche M, Ramm J, Beck E. The Role of Surface Chemistry in Bonding of Standard Silicon Wafers. J Electrochem Soc. 1 janv 1997.

11. Ling L, Kuwabara S, Abe T, Shimura F. Multiple internal reflection infrared spectroscopy of silicon surface structure and oxidation process at room temperature. J Appl Phys. 15 mars 1993.

ECS Transactions, 112 (3) 147-158 (2023)
10.1149/11203.0147ecst ©The Electrochemical Society

Preferred Grain Orientation to Enhance Interdiffusion at Room Temperature in Atomic Diffusion Bonding:
A Fundamental Study using Ni and Cu Films

M. Uomoto[a], S. Kikuchi[a,b], F. Goto[a,b], and T. Shimatsu[a, c]

[a] Frontier Research Institute for Interdisciplinary Sciences (FRIS),
Tohoku University, Sendai, 980-8578, Japan
[b] Department of Electronic Engineering, Graduate School of Engineering,
Tohoku University, Sendai 980-8579, Japan
[c] Research Institute of Electrical Communication (RIEC),
Tohoku University, Sendai, 980-8577, Japan

The interdiffusion and interface structure at the bonded interface of Cu and Ni films obtained using atomic diffusion bonding (ADB) processing was assessed in relation to films structures used for bonding. Improvement of the (111) preferred grain orientation in Ni and Cu films used for bonding enhanced the crystal lattice rearrangement at the bonded interface of Ni–Cu bonded films, leading to large interdiffusion. The representative interdiffusion length evaluated using magnetic characterization was 5.4 nm for a Ni(20 nm)–Cu(10 nm) bonded interface with Ti underlayers. Grain boundary diffusion partially contributed to the interdiffusion length independently of the (111) preferred grain orientation of films. These results indicate that ADB bonding performance enhancement can be achieved with a high degree of (111) preferred grain orientation and low surface roughness in ADB processing using metal films having an fcc crystal structure such as Al, Au, Ag, Cu, Ni, and Pt.

Introduction

Atomic diffusion bonding (ADB) of wafers using thin metal films is a promising process to achieve room-temperature wafer bonding (1–3), as is surface-activated bonding (SAB) (4–7). For ADB processing using metal films, the metal films are fabricated on two flat wafer surfaces using sputter deposition, with subsequent bonding of the two films on the wafers in vacuum, as shown in Figure 1. This bonding technique is applicable to any mirror-polished wafer, with bonding using almost any metal film.

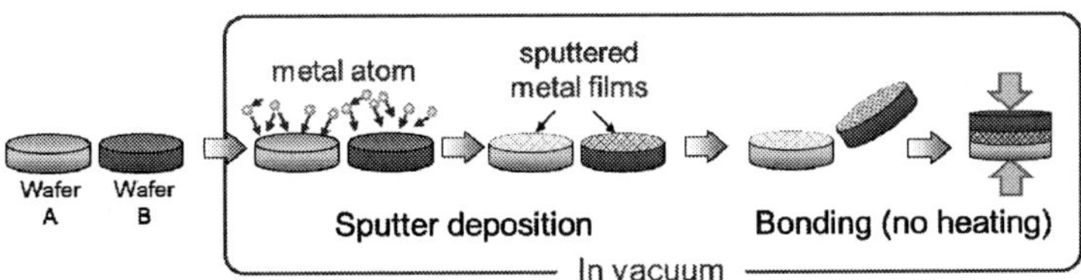

Figure 1. Schematic illustration of the bonding process in vacuum.

During ADB processing, dynamic crystallographic change occurs at the bonded interface. Grain boundary diffusion plays an important role in bonding in addition to crystal lattice rearrangement. However, it remains unclear how much interdiffusion of the two films occurs at the bonded interface. As a representative bonded interface structure, Figure 2 portrays cross-section images of a bonded interface observed using transmission electron microscopy TEM using (A) 20-nm-thick Au film on each side, (B) 20-nm-thick Cu film on each side, and (C) 20-nm-thick W film on each side (1,2). These are structures bonded in vacuum without post-bonding annealing. In panels (A) and (B), the original bonded interface disappeared. Some crystal grains formed over the entire thickness because, during ADB processing, crystal lattice rearrangement occurs when two film surfaces mutually contact at room temperature, as illustrated schematically in Figure 3.

Crystal lattice rearrangement is observed to a remarkable degree in ADB processing, particularly when using metal films having large self-diffusion coefficients D at room temperature such as Al, Au, Ag, Ti, and Cu (1,2). An interface corresponding to the original film surface was visible for bonded W–W films in (C). However, no vacancy was observed. It is noteworthy that the value of D of W is the smallest among normally used metals. In area (a) enclosed in the dotted circle, some diffusion of W was observed clearly around the grain boundaries. Results show that grain boundary diffusion plays an important role in ADB using W films, although no remarkable crystal lattice rearrangement occurs at the bonded interface. These results suggest that grain boundary diffusion occurs also in Au–Au and Cu–Cu interfaces shown in (A) and (B), although the crystal lattice rearrangement plays a considerably important role in determining the structure of bonded films. Moreover, it is reasonable to infer that the degree of the interdiffusion of the two films at the bonded interface, including crystal lattice rearrangement, depends on the crystallographic grain orientation of the films used for bonding, in addition to the surface roughness. However, it is limited to evaluate the details of interdiffusion at the bonded interface consisting of the same material two films.

For this study, Cu film and Ni film were bonded using ADB in vacuum. Interdiffusion at the bonded Cu–Ni film interface was examined using the values of saturation magnetization per unit volume M_s of the bonded films, in addition to structural analysis. Physical properties of Cu and Ni are presented in Table 1. The values of D and interdiffusion coefficient D_{inter} at 300 K, as calculated using the Arrhenius equation with the frequency factor and the activation energy (8), are also presented in the table. Actually, Cu and Ni have an fcc crystal structure and show a solid solution in the whole Cu–Ni composition range. For Cu–Ni alloys, the value of M_s shows a high value at 100 at%Ni and decreases as Cu content increases. Therefore, the value of M_s of the bonded films is expected to decrease as the interdiffusion length at the Cu–Ni bonded interface increases. The values of lattice constants of Cu and Ni are nearly equal. Therefore, the lattice mismatch between Cu and Ni is small, though not negligible, at 3%. The small lattice mismatch is important to suppress the increase of lattice strain energy when the substitution of Cu and Ni atom occurs in the fcc crystal lattice by crystal lattice rearrangement. Moreover, Cu shows a large value of D. Therefore, the bonded interface in Cu(20 nm)–Cu(20 nm) bonded films disappeared as described above. Although the value of D for Ni is smaller than that of Cu, we confirmed that the bonded interface disappears in bonded Ni–Ni films (9). The values of D_{inter} of Cu to Ni, and that of Ni to

Cu are intermediate between the D values of Cu and Ni. We assessed the effects of film structure on the interdiffusion thickness at the bonded interface through crystal lattice rearrangement and grain boundary diffusion.

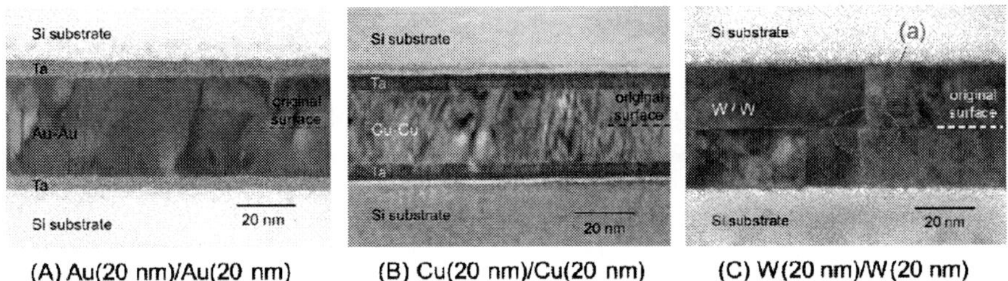

(A) Au(20 nm)/Au(20 nm)   (B) Cu(20 nm)/Cu(20 nm)   (C) W(20 nm)/W(20 nm)

Figure 2. TEM cross-section images of Si wafers bonded in vacuum using (A) Au(20 nm) film on each side, (B) Cu(20 nm) film on each side, and (C) W(20 nm) film on each side.

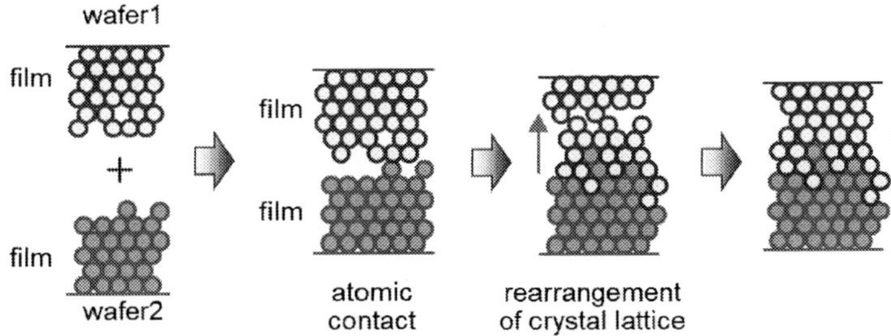

Figure 3. Schematic illustration of crystal lattice rearrangement occurring at the bonded interface of two films.

Table 1. Physical properties of Cu and Ni. Values of D and D_{inter} calculated for 300 K are also shown.

Metals	Cu	Ni
Crystal structure	fcc	
Lattice constant (nm)	0.36147	0.35238
Self-diffusion coefficient D (m^2/s, 300 K)	1.4×10^{-41}	1.5×10^{-53}
Interdiffusion coefficient D_{inter}(Cu to Ni) (m^2/s, 300 K)	6.8×10^{-50}	
Interdiffusion coefficient D_{inter}(Ni to Cu) (m^2/s, 300 K)	2.2×10^{-45}	

Experiment Procedures

<u>Sample Preparation and Characterization</u>

Two-inch (ca. 5.1 cm) diameter Si(001) wafers were used. The surface roughness S_a of the Si wafers was evaluated as 0.12 nm using atomic force microscopy (AFM). DC-magnetron sputtering was used for film deposition. Figure 4 presents the layer structure of bonded films. The Cu and Ni films were deposited respectively on Si wafers. The Ni film thickness was fixed at 20 nm, but the Cu film thickness was varied from 5 nm to 300 nm. For both films, 2-nm-thick Ta or Ti underlayer films were deposited underneath. After film deposition, subsequent bonding was accomplished in the same vacuum. No substrate heating was conducted during deposition or during bonding processes. The value of M_s was evaluated using a vibrating sample magnetometer (VSM). The surface roughness and preferred grain orientation of films used for bonding was analyzed using AFM and X-ray diffraction (XRD). Figure 5 presents a schematic illustration for the evaluation of interdiffusion between Ni and Cu films. Panels (A-1) and (A-2) respectively present the depth profile of Ni composition and magnetic moment m, assuming no interdiffusion at the bonded interface between Ni and Cu films. The magnetic moment in panel (A-2) is normalized by that of pure Ni, m(Ni). Panels (B-1) and (B-2) present them assuming the interdiffusion at the bonded interface with the interdiffusion length X, as the figure shows. Here we assumed that a linear interdiffusion of composition occurs between Ni and Cu films, with equal interdiffusion length from the original interface to Ni and Cu. The value of M_s in Ni–Cu binary alloys decreases almost linearly with decreasing Ni content from 100 at% to 69 at%. (i.e. with increasing Cu content from 0 to 31 at%), and becomes zero at 69 at%Ni composition (10). Therefore, the variation of m/m(Ni) is described linearly as that in (B-2). The value of M_s of the bonded films was obtained by integrating m/m(Ni) against the depth. M_s of the bonded films decreases as X increases. A simple calculation revealed X, described as the following, using M_s of pure Ni, M_s(Ni).

$$X = [1 - M_s/M_s(\text{Ni})] / 0.345 \qquad [1]$$

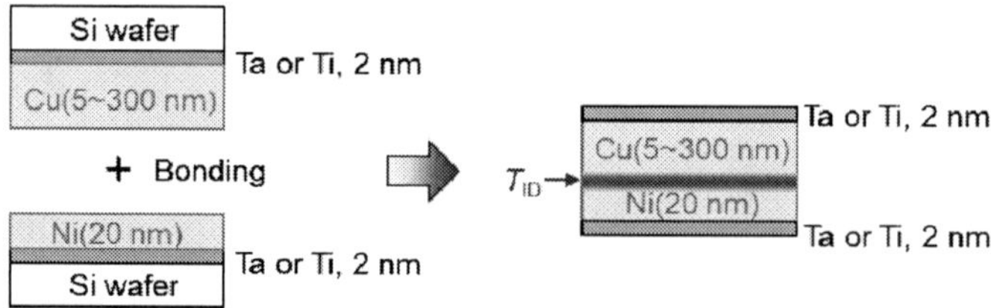

Figure 4. Layer structure of bonded films.

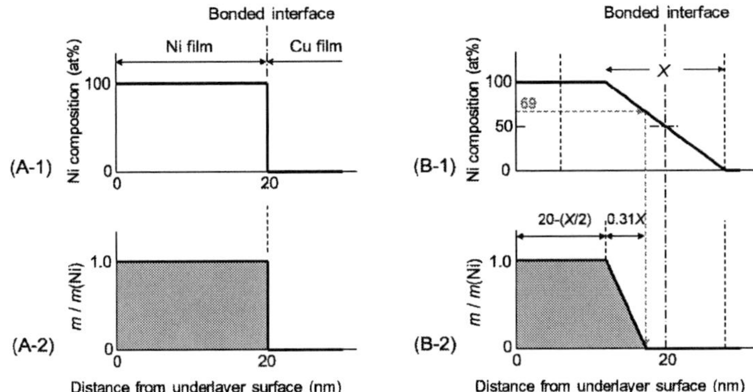

Figure 5. Schematic illustration for the evaluation of interdiffusion between Ni and Cu films. (A-1) and (A-2) show depth profiles of the Ni composition and magnetic moment m assuming no interdiffusion at the bonded interface. (B-1) and (B-2) show those values assuming interdiffusion at the bonded interface with interdiffusion length X.

Results and Discussion

<u>Bonding Performance as a Function of Cu Film Thickness</u>

We examined the interdiffusion length as a function of the Cu film thickness. For this study, 2-nm-thick Ta underlayers were used for both Ni and Cu films. It is reasonable to infer that the surface roughness is an important factor affecting interdiffusion. First, we estimated the surface roughness of Ni and Cu films used for bonding. Figure 6(A-1) and (A-2) portray AFM images of Ni(20 nm) film and Cu(20 nm) film. Figure 6(B) presents values of S_a for Cu films as a function of Cu film thickness. The 2-nm-thick a-Si films were deposited on the top of Cu films as capping layers to suppress change of surface morphology of Cu films by exposure to air. The values of S_a were 0.25 nm for Ni (20 nm) film and 0.32 nm for Cu (20 nm) film. The values of S_a for Cu films increased from 0.21 nm to 0.85 nm as the Cu film thickness increased from 5 nm to 300 nm. From the viewpoint of S_a, thinner Cu films are expected to be better for bonding performance enhancement.

Figure 7(A) presents values of M_s normalized by M_s(Ni) for Ni(20 nm)–Cu bonded films as a function of Cu film thickness. Figure 7(B) shows the values of the interdiffusion thickness T_{ID} for these films estimated from M_s/M_s(Ni) values. It is noteworthy that the bonding strength of these films was great: the blade could not be inserted between the wafers during blade testing. However, the bonding strength for Ni(20 nm)–Cu(300 nm) bonded film was weak because of the large surface roughness. Therefore, this sample was excluded from analyses. The value of M_s/M_s(Ni) shows the minimum for a 50-nm-thick Cu film, showing a maximum T_{ID} of 6.5 nm. S_a decreased as the Cu thickness decreased from 50 nm as described above. Surprisingly T_{ID} decreased remarkably. However, T_{ID} decreased gradually as the Cu thickness increased from 50 nm, probably because of an increase of S_a. It is noteworthy that these variations of T_{ID} are not related directly to the bonding strength at the Ni–Cu interface, as described above.

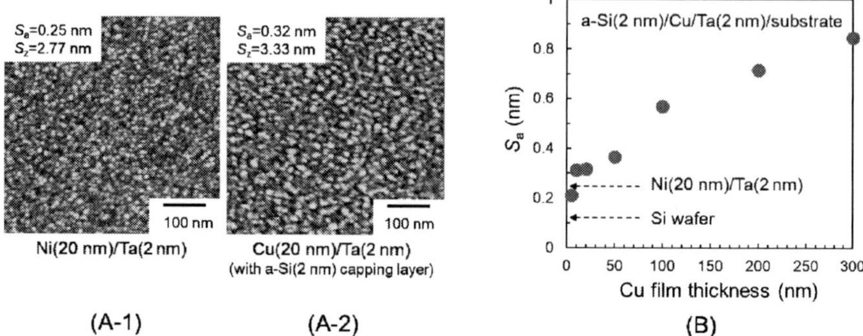

Figure 6. AFM images of (A-1) Ni(20 nm) film and (A-2) Cu(20 nm) film. (B) Values of S_a for Cu films as a function of Cu film thickness. 2-nm-thick a-Si films were deposited on the top of Cu films as capping layers.

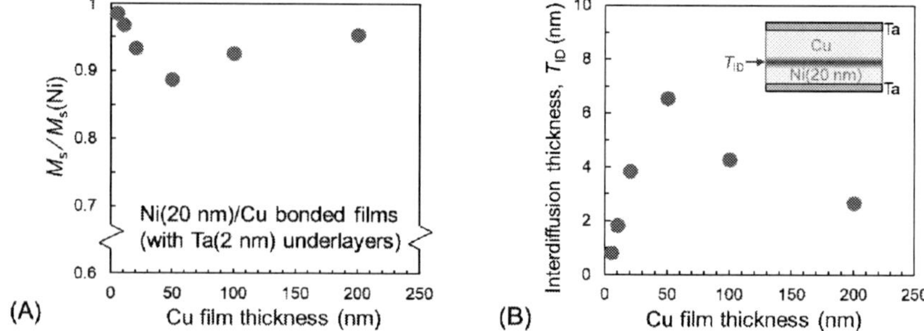

Figure 7. (A) Values of M_s/M_s(Ni) for Ni(20 nm)–Cu bonded films as a function of Cu film thickness. (B) Values of T_{ID} for these bonded films were estimated from the M_s/M_s(Ni) values.

To clarify the mechanism reducing T_{ID} in the thickness region below 50 nm, we characterized the preferred grain orientation of the films used for bonding. XRD pattern revealed that the films showed (111) preferred grain orientation. Figure 8(A) presents XRD patterns around fcc-(111) diffraction peaks of Ni(20 nm) film and Cu(50 nm) film. The bonding of these films showed the largest T_{ID} in Figure 7(B). Figure 8(B) presents the values of XRD intensity of fcc-(111) plane of Cu films as a function of the Cu film thickness. The intensity decreased remarkably as the Cu thickness decreased. The intensities at thicknesses of less than 20 nm were very low. Diffraction was not observed at 5 nm thickness. This finding demonstrates that the (111) preferred grain orientation was degraded remarkably at Cu thicknesses of less than 50 nm. It is likely that the deterioration of the (111) preferred grain orientation of Cu films reduced the interdiffusion at the Ni–Cu bonded interface in the thin film region of less than 50 nm.

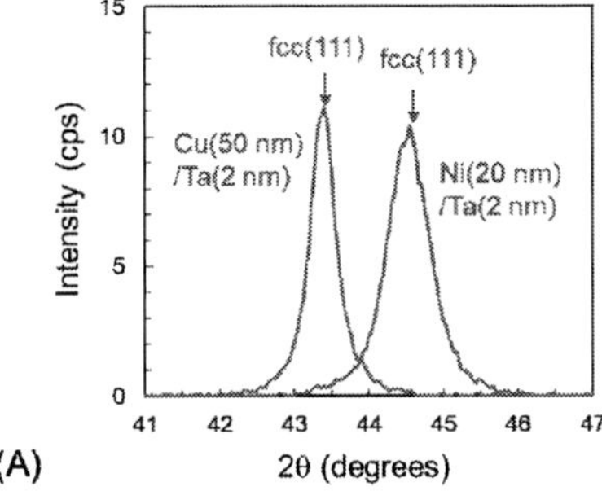
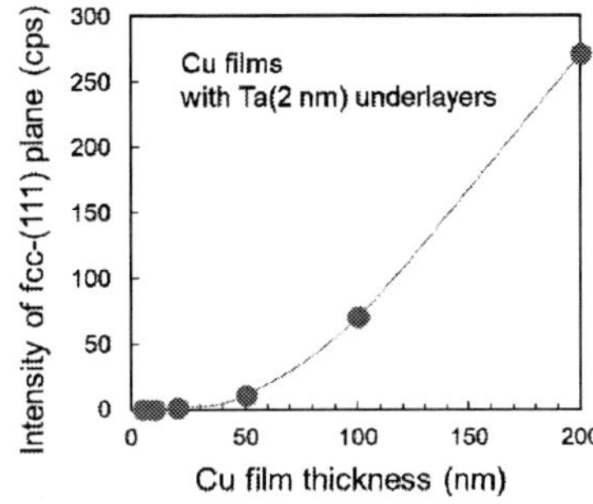

Figure 8. (A) XRD patterns of Ni(20 nm) film and Cu(50 nm) film deposited with the Ta underlayer. (B) Values of the XRD intensity of fcc-(111) plane of Cu films deposited with the Ta underlayer as a function of the Cu film thickness.

Enhancement of Ni–Cu Interdiffusion using Ti Underlayer Films

To support this assumption, Ti underlayers were used underneath Ni(20 nm) and Cu(10, 20 nm) films to change the degree of the (111) preferred grain orientation of these films. Figure 9 presents XRD patterns around the fcc-(111) diffraction peaks for the films. The (111) intensity of Ni(20 nm) with a Ti underlayer was 2.7 times greater than that with a Ta underlayer. The intensity of Cu(20 nm) was also enhanced using Ti underlayers instead of a Ta underlayer. These results indicated that the Ti underlayer, more than a Ta underlayer, enhanced the (111) preferred grain orientation of Ni and Cu films. No marked difference in S_a values was observed in Ni and Cu films between those with Ta and Ti underlayers.

We fabricated Ni(20 nm)–Cu(20 nm) and Ni(20 nm)–Cu(10 nm) bonded films with Ti underlayers and examined the values of T_{ID}. Figure 10 presents the values of T_{ID} for Ni(20 nm)–Cu(20 nm) and Ni(20 nm)–Cu(10 nm) bonded films with Ti underlayers as a function of the Cu film thickness (diamond symbols). Results obtained with Ta underlayers are also shown. The value of T_{ID} of the Ni(20 nm)–Cu(10 nm) bonded interface was enhanced to 5.4 nm, which was three times greater than that of the bonded films with Ta underlayers. The value of T_{ID} of the Ni(20 nm)–Cu(20 nm) bonded interface was also enhanced to 4.9 nm. These results demonstrate that enhancement of the (111) preferred grain orientation increased interdiffusion between Ni–Cu bonded films.

The (111) crystal plane of the fcc crystal lattice shows the highest atomic packing density and the lowest surface energy among all crystal planes (12). Therefore, it is reasonable to infer that the improvement of (111) preferred grain orientation in Ni and Cu films used for bonding enhanced the crystal lattice rearrangement at the bonded interface in Ni–Cu bonded films, resulting in large T_{ID} values. Actually, results obtained for the Au–Ag bonded interface (11) also indicated the (111) preferred grain orientation as effective for enhancing crystal lattice rearrangement at the bonded interface.

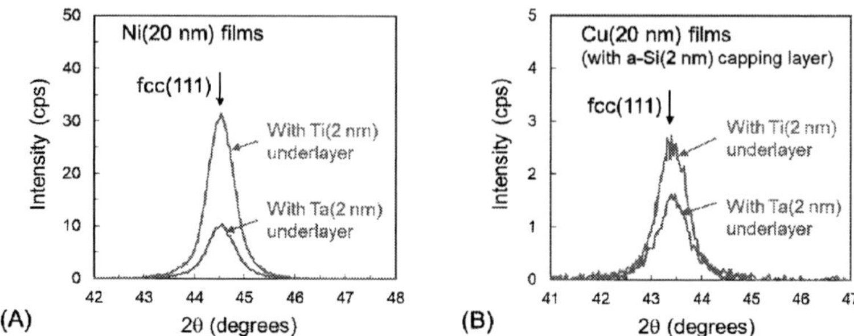

Figure 9. XRD patterns for (A) Ni(20 nm) and (B) Cu(20 nm) films with Ta and Ti underlayers.

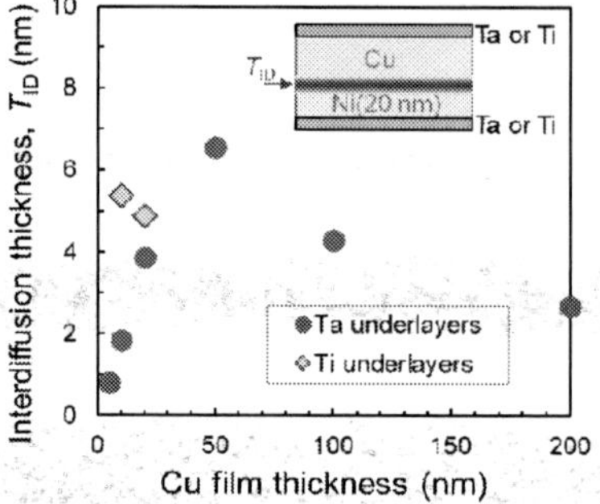

Figure 10. Values of T_{ID} for Ni(20 nm)–Cu(20 nm) and Ni(20 nm)–Cu(10 nm) bonded films with Ti underlayers shown using diamond symbols in Figure 7(B).

Structural analysis was performed to support this discussion. Figure 11 portrays cross-section images of Ni(20 nm)–Cu(10 nm) bonded films observed using scanning transmission electron microscopy (STEM). Panel (A-1) depicts a bright field (BF) image for a bonded film with a Ta underlayer; panel (A-2) presents a high-angle annular dark field (HAADF) image. Panels (B-1) and (B-2) portray those for bonded films with Ti underlayers. No vacancy was observed in either image with a Ta or Ti underlayer. The original interface between Ni and Cu was partially observed. The interface fluctuated because of interdiffusion. A high-resolution image of Ni(20 nm)–Cu(10 nm) bonded films with Ti underlayers shown in Figure 12 portrays crystal lattices formed across the original interface, indicating that crystal lattice rearrangement occurred at the bonded interface. However, large crystal lattices formed over the entire thickness, such as some grains observed in Au–Au or Cu–Cu bonded films shown in Figure 2, were not found in Figure 11. It is reasonable to infer that a non-negligible lattice mismatch of 3% between Cu and Ni, in addition to a small D value of Ni, suppressed advancement of the crystal lattice rearrangement. In Figure 11, the bonded interface in (B-2) was indistinct and blurry compared to that of (A-2), suggesting enhancement of the crystal lattice rearrangement at the bonded interface. Moreover, the grain boundaries in images of (B-1) and (B-2) were clearer than those of (A-1) and (A-2). However, no remarkable difference in STEM images was observed between the bonded films with Ta and Ti underlayers.

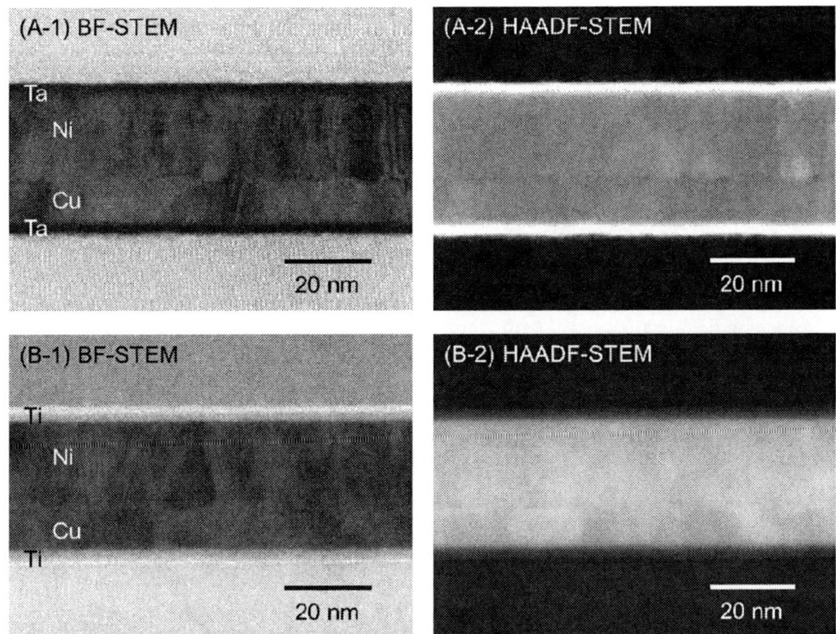

Figure 11. Cross-section STEM images of Ni(20 nm)−Cu(10 nm) bonded films. (A-1) and (A-2): BF and HAADF images for bonded films with Ta underlayers. (B-1) and (B-2) those for bonded films with Ti underlayers.

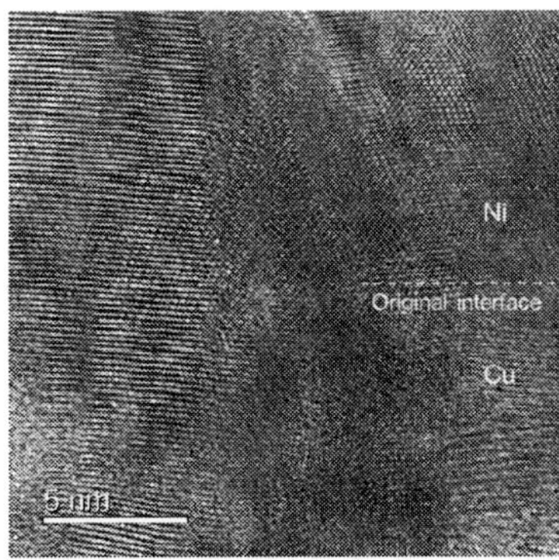

Figure 12. High-resolution STEM image of Ni(20 nm)−Cu(10 nm) bonded films with Ti underlayers.

Figure 13 portrays mapping images of (B) Ni, (C) Cu, and (D) Ti obtained using energy-dispersive X-ray spectroscopy (EDX) analysis of the area shown in the BF image (A) for Ni(20 nm)−Cu(10 nm) bonded films with Ti underlayers. Panels (B) and (C) show the bonded interface between Ni and Cu films as slightly blurry. Moreover, some Ni was observed at the Cu–Ti interface. Some Cu was also observed at the Ni–Ti interface. Surprisingly some Cu and Ni reached the other side of films through grain boundaries. The depth profiles of Ni and Cu compositions, which were evaluated by integrating the signals of Ni and Cu in panels (B) and (C), are shown in Figure 14. Results obtained for Ni(20 nm)–Cu(10 nm) bonded films with Ta underlayers are also shown in the figure.

The amount of Ni at Cu/(Ti or Ta) interface was much greater than that of Cu at the Ni/(Ti or Ta) interface. This difference showed good agreement with that of the D_{inter} values in Table 1. It is noteworthy that no remarkable difference of Ni amount at Cu/(Ti or Ta) interface was observed between with Ti and Ta underlayers. This lack of difference indicates that grain boundary diffusion occurs almost independently of the degree of (111) preferred grain orientation of Ni and Cu films used for bonding. The Ni–Cu composition at the Cu/(Ti or Ta) interface was 50 at%Ni–Cu, corresponding to non-magnetic property. Therefore, the grain boundary diffusion partially contributed to the T_{ID} values, independently of the (111) preferred grain orientation of Ni and Cu films.

A remarkable difference in the Ni composition attributable to the difference of underlayer materials was observed at the bonded interface. In the area shown by the dotted circle in the figure, the Ni content for bonded films with Ti underlayers is less than that of bonded films with Ta underlayers. This difference corresponds to a remarkable difference of M_s values because the value of m/m(Ni) shown in Figure 5(B-2) reduces to become zero as the Ni composition decreases to become lower than 69 at%. Results support that improvement of the (111) preferred grain orientation in Ni and Cu films used for bonding enhances the crystal lattice rearrangement at the bonded interface in Ni–Cu bonded films, resulting in large T_{ID} values.

Conclusion

After Cu film and Ni film were bonded using ADB in vacuum, their interdiffusion at the bonded Cu–Ni film interface was assessed to clarify the relation between the film structure used for bonding and the interdiffusion of the two films at the bonded interface during ADB processing. Results indicated that improvement of the (111) preferred grain orientation in Ni and Cu films used for bonding enhanced the crystal lattice rearrangement at the bonded interface of Ni–Cu bonded films, resulting in extensive interdiffusion of the two films. The representative interdiffusion length evaluated by magnetic characterization was 5.4 nm for the Ni(20 nm)–Cu(10 nm) bonded interface with Ti underlayers. Structural analysis revealed that grain boundary diffusion, in addition to crystal lattice rearrangement, contributed to the interdiffusion length independently of the (111) preferred grain orientations of the Ni and Cu films. It is noteworthy that variation of the interdiffusion length is not related simply to the bonding strength. The bonding strength of all samples used for the examination was great: a blade could not be inserted between the wafers during blade testing. However, it is reasonable to infer that the diffusion length indicates the bonding potential in ADB processing and that it is important, for instance, when bonding wafers with high surface roughness. These results indicate that enhanced bonding performance of ADB can be achieved with a high degree of (111) preferred grain orientation in addition to low surface roughness in

ADB processing using metal films having an fcc crystal structure such as Al, Au, Ag, Cu, Ni, and Pt, although more intensive efforts must be undertaken to clarify the relation between the (111) preferred grain orientation and grain boundary diffusion.

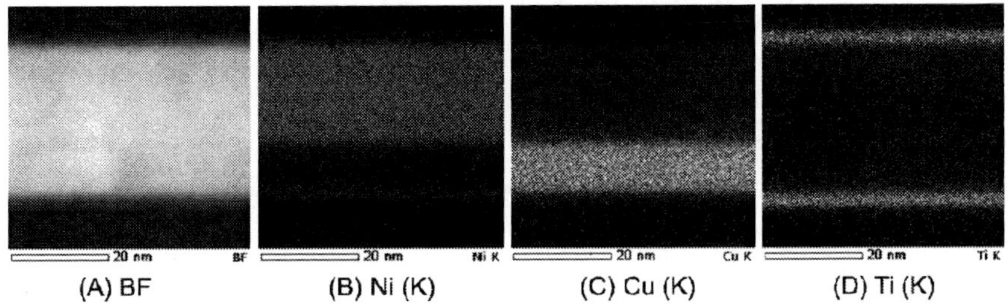

Figure 13. EDX mapping images of (B) Ni, (C) Cu, and (D) Ti of the area shown in (A) as the BF image for Ni(20 nm)−Cu(10 nm) bonded films with Ti underlayers.

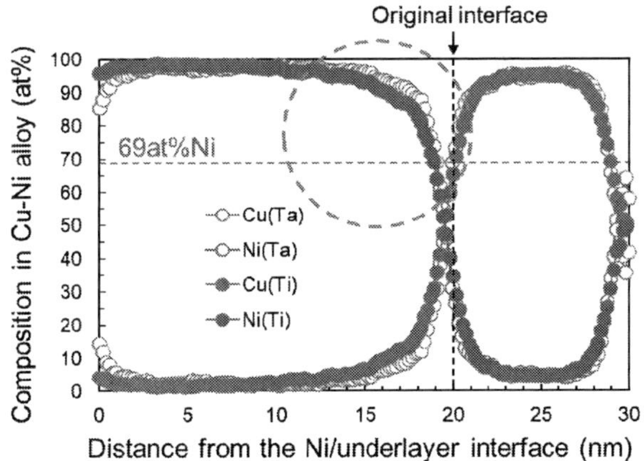

Figure 14. Depth profiles of Ni and Cu compositions evaluated using EDX analysis for Ni(20 nm)−Cu(10 nm) bonded films with Ta and Ti underlayers.

References

1. T. Shimatsu and M. Uomoto, *J. Vac. Sci. Technol.*, **B 28**, 706 (2010).
2. T. Shimatsu and M. Uomoto, *ECS Transactions*, **33**(4), 61 (2010).
3. T. Shimatsu and M. Uomoto, *ECS Transactions*, **64**(5), 317 (2014).
4. T. Suga, K. Miyazawa, and Y. Yamagata, *MRS Int. Meet. Adv. Mater.*, **8**, 257 (1989).
5. T. Suga, Y. Takahashi, H. Takagi, B. Gibbesch, and G. Elssner, *Acta Metall. Mater.*, **40**, s133 (1992).
6. H. Takagi, K. Kikuchi, R. Maeda, T. R. Chung, and T. Suga, *Appl. Phys. Lett.*, **68**, 2222 (1996).

7. E. Higurashi, T. Imamura, T. Suga, and R. Sawada, *IEEE Photonics Technology Letters*, **19**(24), 1994 (2007).
8. The Japan Institute of Metals, *Metal Data Book, Third edition*, Maruzen, Japan, 1993, pp. 20-23.
9. F. Mu, T. Suga, M. Uomoto, and T. Shimatsu, *Proceedings of the 2019 IEEE 69th Electronic Compounds and Technology Conference (ECTC)*, 989 (2019).
10. R. M. Bozorth, *Ferromagnetism*, IEEE Press (Classic Reissue), 1993, pp.308-309.
11. F. Goto, H. Iemura, M. Uomoto, and T. Shimatsu, *244th ECS Meeting, H02 Semiconductor Wafer bonding: Science, Technology and Applications 17*, H02-1612 (2023).
12. L. Vitos, A.V. Ruban, H.L. Skriver, and J. Kolla´r, *Surface Science*, **411**, 186 (1998).

ECS Transactions, 112 (3) 159-172 (2023)
10.1149/11203.0159ecst ©The Electrochemical Society

Oxide-Free SiC-SiC Direct Wafer Bonding and Its Characterization

P. Kerepesi[ab], B. Rebhan[a], M. Danner[a], K. Stadlmann[b], P. Oberhumer[b], J. Duchoslav[c], K. Hingerl[c] and H. Groiss[b]

[a] EV Group, DI Erich Thallner Straße 1, St. Florian/Inn 4782, Austria
[b] Christian Doppler Laboratory for Nanoscale Phase Transformations, Center for Surface- and Nanoanalytics, Johannes Kepler University Linz, Linz 4040, Austria
[c] Center for Surface- and Nanoanalytics, Johannes Kepler University Linz, Linz 4040, Austria

In this study, the feasibility of oxide-free room temperature wafer bonding process was demonstrated for 4H-SiC wafers with *in situ* surface oxide removal. The investigations covered three areas: incoming metrology of the original wafer, characterization of activated single wafer and analysis of bonded wafer pairs. The focus was on compositional, chemical, mechanical and morphological analysis of the surfaces and of the bonded interfaces. Incoming wafers were inspected whether they fulfill the requirements of wafer bonding, and activated wafers were characterized to measure the surface modifications. The quality of the bonded wafers and the bonding energy were verified using scanning acoustic microscopy measurements as well as the Maszara blade test. Furthermore, cross-section transmission electron microscopy was used to investigate the amorphous layer at the bonding interface. The work reported is a demonstration of the capability of different characterization methods regarding SiC-SiC wafer bonding.

Introduction

The global trend for finding alternative semi-conducting materials than silicon is growing rapidly. SiC has some unique properties like a wide band gap, very high thermal conductivity, as well high resistance against electrical field breakdown. This makes it the ideal material for power devices [1]. Such devices, like power MOSFETs, and other power devices can easily operate in the kV range, where the thermal conductivity of SiC can act additionally as heat sink [2]. The potential of such power devices has been demonstrated by several research groups, like applications in power diodes or SiC MEMS where high blocking voltages or high frequency resilience are crucial [3, 4, 5].
There are different requirements for the production process and the final product of SiC-SiC wafer bonding. The manufacturing of devices that are sensitive to high temperature processing – due to broadened doping profiles and induced thermal stresses – requires room temperature bonding with high bond strength, while for electrical devices, it is mandatory that the bonding interface with a thin amorphous layer is oxide-free [6]. Reduced complexity of processes is also an important point for the final production. Hence, the goal of this work was to perform and characterize direct bonding of SiC-SiC without any added/deposited bonding layer. This type of bonded SiC wafers can be used

for power electronics such as for the fabrication of traction inverter for automotive applications, DC/DC converter, on board charger or charging station [7].

Experimental

<u>Specimens</u>

In this research, N-type 100 mm research grade 4H-SiC wafers were used with a thickness of 350 μm and a miscut of 4° toward a <1 1 $\overline{2}$ 0> axis. The wafers were double side polished, and Si-face with epi-ready quality was used for the experiments.

An incoming wafer was characterized without any modification, while the effect (amorphization, modification of chemical composition) of the surface activation was investigated *ex situ* on a single wafer after 157h rest time to ensure a saturated oxide layer. In the case of activated single wafers a metal layers were deposited before to protect the surface during sample preparation. The deposition leads additionally to a clearly recognizable wafer surface in transmission electron microscope (TEM) imaging.

The bonded wafer pair was characterized without any further processing (except TEM specimen preparation).

<u>Wafer Bonding Method</u>

For the wafer bonding processes the standard 100 mm 4H SiC wafers were bonded with their Si-terminated faces to for oxide-free bonds. The wafer bonding process was performed using the EVG® ComBond® system with *in situ* surface oxide removal. The sample processing starts with the *in situ* native oxides removal from both wafer surfaces using an ion beam sputtering process with a beam current of 125 mA, followed by the transfer of both wafers to the bonding module, without breaking the ultra-high vacuum (UHV: ~1 · 10^{-8} mbar), where the wafers are finally bonded at room temperature (RT) using a force of 1,5 kN.

In the case of single wafer activation, the same procedure was applied without the final bonding step.

Characterization methods

Several types of characterization methods were used to investigate the wafers before and after bonding respectively.

There are many different parameters which can be used to specify or describe a wafer. The three most important ones are the surface microroughness, the wafer geometry (bow, warp, TTV) and the surface particle contamination level. The other parameters, which are usually used to specify SiC wafers – like electrical resistivity, doping level, different kind of defect types (micropipe density, etch pit density, scratches, hex plates, polytype ratio etc.), metal ion contamination – could be important for device applications, but do not have major effect on the wafer bonding process and result. As incoming inspection, the surface microroughness of the Si-face of the wafer was measured by Atomic Force Microscope (AFM) and the geometry was investigated by White Light Interferometer (WLI).

In order to investigate the influence of the wafer activation on the microroughness, it was measured after activation and compared to the incoming roughness. During the activation the native oxide layer of the SiC wafer was removed, while also generating an amorphous layer. *Ex situ* spectroscopic ellipsometry (SE) was applied before and after the surface activation to measure the initial oxide layer, the amorphous layer thickness and track the reoxidation. The amorphous layer of an activated, but unbonded wafer was measured by transmission electron microscopy (TEM) in order to compare the results, the two different techniques (SE and TEM). X-ray photoelectron spectroscopy (XPS) was used to compare the chemical composition before and after surface activation. Since SiC is a heteroatomic material and the surface activation works with ion beam bombardment, a selective sputtering occurs on the surface, which can modify the stoichiometry and the chemistry of the surface.

In terms of the bonded wafer pair, Maszara test was performed to measure the bonding energy; and scanning acoustic microscope (SAM) was used to investigate the bonding quality. The post-bond geometry was inspected by WLI; the amorphous layer thickness at the bonding interface and its elemental composition was examined by TEM with Energy-dispersive X-ray spectroscopy (EDX) detector.

The applied methods and the type of the samples are summarized in TABLE I.

TABLE I. Summary of the Sample Types and the Applied Measurement Methods.

Characterization Method	Incoming inspection	Activated single wafer	Bonded wafer pair
Atomic Force Microscopy (AFM)	Surface microroughness	Change of Surface microroughness	—
White Light Interferometry (WLI)	Geometry (Bow, TTV)	–	Geometry (Bow, TTV)
Spectroscopic ellipsometry (SE)	Thickness of native oxide	Amorphous layer, and reoxidized layer thickness	—
X-ray photoelectron spectroscopy (XPS)	Chemical composition of native oxide	Chemical composition of activated surface	—
Scanning Acoustic Microscopy (SAM)	—	—	Bonding quality
Maszara test (blade delamination test)	—	—	Bonding Energy
Transmission electron microscopy with Energy-dispersive X-ray spectroscopy detector (TEM / EDX)	Amorphous layer thickness	Amorphous layer thickness	Amorphous layer thickness, elemental composition of bonding interface

Results

Atomic Force Microscopy (AFM)

The AFM results show high quality wafer surface, only in the middle of the images a minor defect could be observed for both measurement which could come from the initial tip approach on the wafer. The initial surface roughness (Rq) is 0,76 Å (Figure 1a) what is way below the requirement of wafer fusion bonding (< 5 Å), although the surface roughness increased slightly after surface activation, the measured 0,98 Å value (Figure 1b) is still very good. Based on the AFM measurement results a good quality bonding is expected.

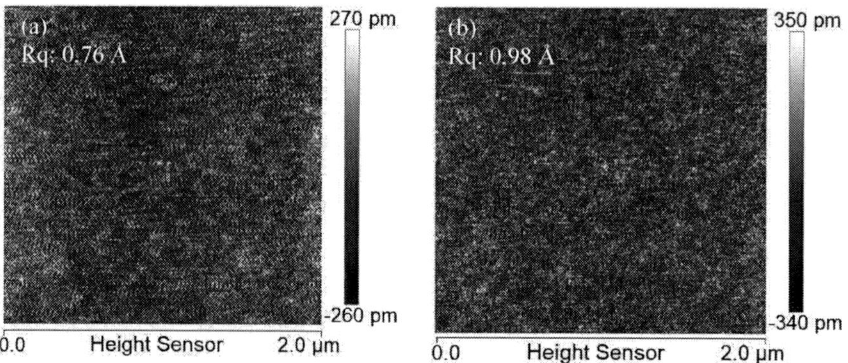

Figure 1. AFM images of 4H-SiC wafer Si-face before (a) and after (b) activation

White Light Interferometer

There are different motivations for WLI measurements of the single wafer and the bonded wafer pair. In the case of the single wafer, the measurement serves as an incoming quality check to measure the wafer geometry (bow) as this is a critical parameter of the wafer for successful wafer bonding. In the case of the bonded wafer pair the geometry measurement serves to check for potential remaining stress in the wafers. Although both wafers are SiC wafers, the activation process could cause a minor thermal impact and the wafers were activated one by one, which can lead to some temperature induced different thermal expansion during bonding.

The single wafer shows 2,6 – 10,7 µm bow, with 14,7 µm overall TTV (Figure 2), so it fulfils the incoming requirement of wafer fusion bonding, which is 30 µm for 100 mm wafer size.

The measurement of the bow for the bonded wafer pair is in the same range as for the single wafer. The measured values are 12,9 µm and 20,7 µm for x-axis and for y-axis respectively. The overall TTV is 22,6 µm with 3 mm edge exclusion (Figure 3). The result shows there is no remaining stress induced due to the potential different wafer temperatures during bonding. This is important from the bonding energy point of view because the extra stress could distort the result of the Maszara test.

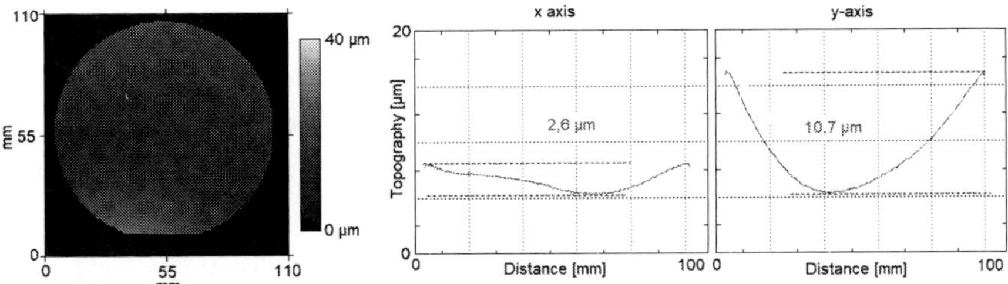

Figure 2. WLI measurement of incoming wafer.

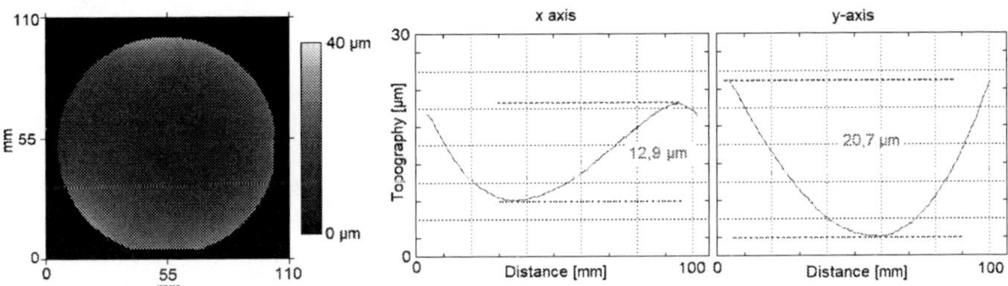

Figure 3. WLI measurement of bonded wafer pair.

Variable Angle Spectroscopic Ellipsometry

VASE method was used to determine the native oxide thickness of the incoming wafer, the amorphous layer thickness of the activated wafer, following the reoxidation process and establishing the required time for a stable surface-oxide condition.

For both measurements the same layer structure model was used for evaluation: SiO_2 on the top, followed by an amorphous Si/C composition and ordinary 4H-SiC as bulk material.

The results are summarized in TABLE II.

TABLE II. VASE measurement results.

Sample	Elapsed time after activation [h]	Average of measured oxide thickness [nm]	Average of measured amorphous layer thickness [nm]	Sum of layer thickness [nm]
Incoming wafer	n/a	0,72	0,00	0,72
Activated wafer	0,5	0,89	0,27	1,16
Activated wafer	88	1,21	0,26	1,47
Activated wafer	157	1,24	0,26	1,49

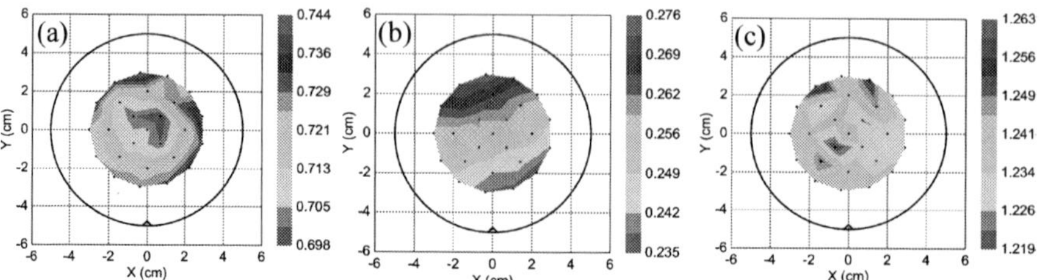

Figure 4. Maps of VASE measurements. Oxide thickness of incoming wafer (a), amorphous layer thickness of activated wafer (b) regrown oxide layer thickness of activated wafer after 157h (c).

The native oxide thickness of the incoming wafer is in the range of 0,70 − 0,74 nm with an average of 0,72 nm compared to the activated wafer where the regrown oxide thickness after 157 h is in the range of 1,22 nm − 1,26 nm with an average of 1,24 nm. This result was not expected and could be explained several ways. Either the activated surface tends to higher rate of oxidation or the native oxide has a different composition compared to the regrown oxide. Regarding to the amorphous layer thickness, it seems to be stable over the time of oxide regrowing, which is a clear conclusion that the original amorphous layer thickness could not be deducted. The fast oxide growing in the first 0,5 h could consume some part of the original amorphous layer.

<u>X-ray photoelectron spectroscopy</u>

In the case of XPS measurement, three types of measurements and evaluations were done, these are respectively the recording the survey spectra, the high-resolution spectra and the angle resolved measurements.

In the case of the wide scan spectra (Figure 5.) all the components (C, Si, O) of the SiC samples were easily detected. Based on these wide scan spectra an elevated oxygen content could be observed, which also fits to the result of the ellipsometry measurement and proofs the assumption, that the thickness and/or the composition of the regrown oxide layer is different compared to the native oxide layer. Also, we can conclude based on these spectra that the stoichiometry of the SiC at the surface was also changed from the original 1,00:1,02 to 1.00:0,95 C:Si ratio. The surplus of Si for the original ratio could be explained, that the native oxide composition contains more or mainly Si compared to C. The surplus C in the activated sample could be explained by the selective sputtering of SiC by Ar. It is also noteworthy, that also a small amount of implanted Ar could be detected.

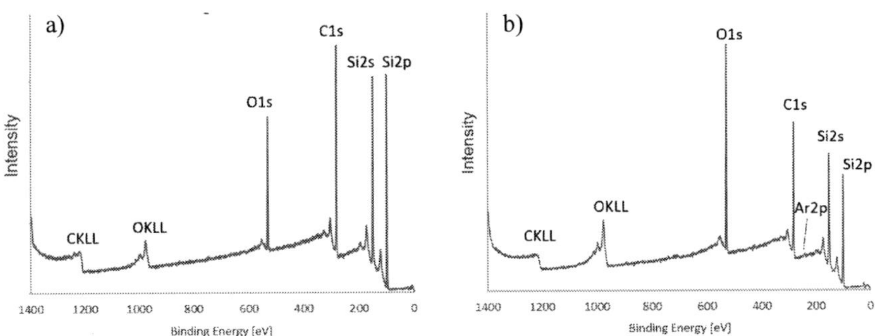

Figure 5. XPS data measured on incoming (a) and on activated wafer (b)

TABLE III. Elemental composition based on wide scan spectrum:

Peak	Incoming wafer		Activated wafer	
	Binding energy [eV]	**Atomic %**	**Binding energy [eV]**	**Atomic %**
O1s	531,04	11,8	530,93	22,5
C1s	282,00	43,6	282,04	39,5
Si2s	150,98	–	150,85	–
Si2p	99,91	44,6	99,42	37,6
Ar2p	–	–	239,98	0,3

The Si 2p region of high resulution spectra (Figure 6.) shows a very different shape for incoming wafer compared to the activated wafer after reoxidation. The oxide peaks at 103,1 eV and 103,8 eV binding energy are absolutelly missing at the incoming wafer while the measured large peak could be resolved for carbide and for oxycarbide peaks. At the same time, the oxycarbide peak is missing from the high reolution spectra of the activated sample. It could be concluded that the native oxide of the SiC wafer is not SiO_2 but some form of Silicon oxycarbide.

The O 1s region of high resolution spectra (Figure 7.) shows a higher oxygen peak for the activated sample as it was already observed at the wide scan spectra.

The C 1s region of high resulution spectra (Figure 8.) consists three components (Carbide Si-C, Oxycarbide SiO_xC_y and Carbon C-C) for the incoming wafer and two components (Carbide Si-C and Carbon C-C) for the activated wafer. Not only the number of components, but also the ratio of the carbide and carbon peak shows significant difference. The carbon peak ratio was increased which can cover the incresed Carbon content of the activated surface due to the selective sputtering of the SiC surface by Ar atoms. In the same time, the oxycarbide peak disappeared, that may indicate the succesful oxide removal.

By investigating the Ar 2p region of high resulution spectra (Figure 9.) the remaining Argon traces could be clearly observed.

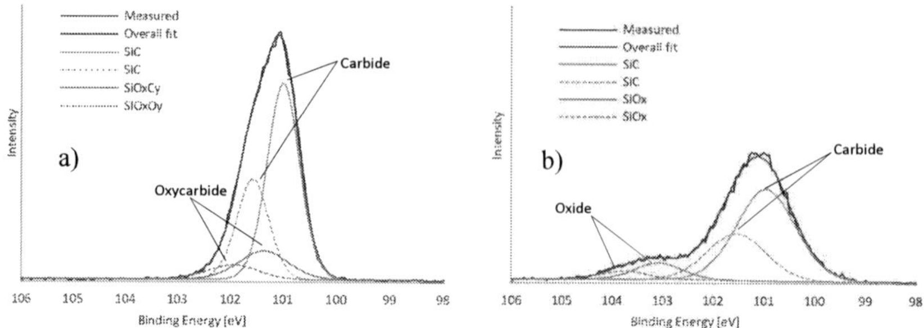

Figure 6. High resolution XPS data and fits for the Si 2p region of incoming wafer (a), and activated wafer (b)

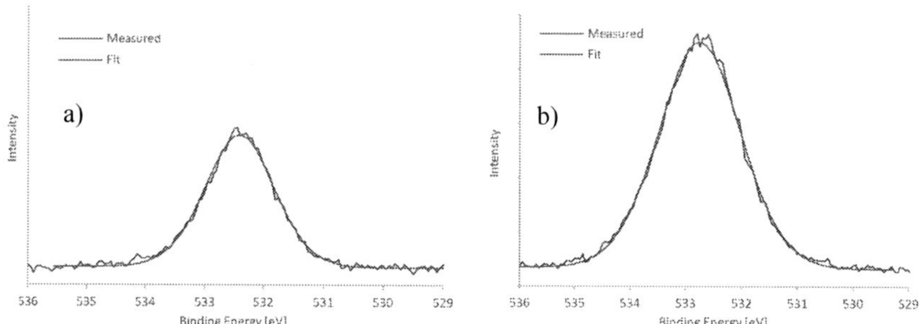

Figure 7. High resolution XPS data and fits for the O 1s region of incoming wafer (a) and activated wafer (b)

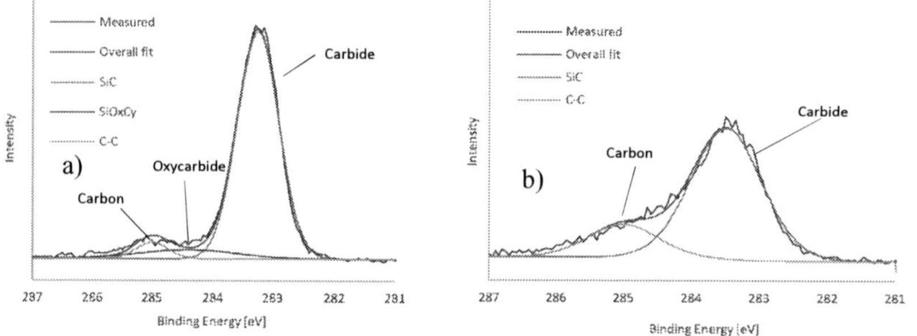

Figure 8. High resolution XPS data and fits for the C 1s region of incoming wafer (a) and activated wafer (b)

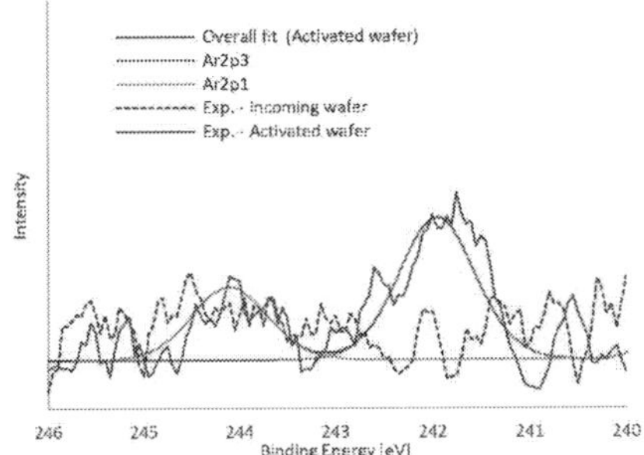

Figure 9. High resolution XPS data and fits for the Ar 2p region of incoming wafer and the activated wafer

TABLE IV. High resolution XPS measurements

Peak	Incoming wafer			Activated wafer		
	Binding energy [eV]	Atomic ratio	Overall atomic ratio	Binding energy [eV]	Atomic ratio	Overall atomic ratio
Ar 2p3	n/a	n/a	0,0%	242,0	n/a	0,4%
Ar2p1	n/a	n/a		244,1	n/a	
O 1s	532,4	n/a	8,1%	532,8	n/a	18,6%
Si 2p1 Carbide	101,6	81,6%	42,0%	101,6	82,2%	36,1%
Si 2p3 Carbide	101,0			101,0		
Si 2p1 SiO_xC_y	102,0	18,4%	9,5%	n/a	0,0%	0,0%
Si 2p3 SiO_xC_y	101,4					
Si 2p1 Oxide	n/a	0,0%	0,0%	103,8	17,8%	7,8%
Si 2p3 Oxide				103,1		
C 1s Carbide	283,3	86,9%	35,1%	283,5	79,8	29,6%
C 1s SiO_xC_y	284,4	4,2%	3,4%	n/a	n/a	n/a
C 1s Carbon	285,0	6,8%	1,9%	285,0	20,2	7,5%

In the angle-resolved mode of XPS (AR-XPS) the photoelectron takeoff angle with respect to the surface typically depends on the depth of the electron's origin according to its attenuation. Therefore, this methode could be used for depth profiling of the sample. The AR-XPS results are visualized in relative depth plot diagrams (Figure 10.), where the order of the different elements and their different chemical states with depth is clearly shown. The weakness of this kind of evaluation is, that it does not provide an exact thickness or depth profile but the positions of the species on the relative depth plot are related to the "average" depth of that species. Its advantage is that it is independent of any model and does not require specific knowledge of the exact composition and their physical constants for the layers. The two diagrams show clearly the different layer structure of the incoming wafer compared to the activated sample e.g., the presence of the implanted argon in the case of the activated sample, and the localization of the Silicon atoms which contributes in the different kind of surface compounds.

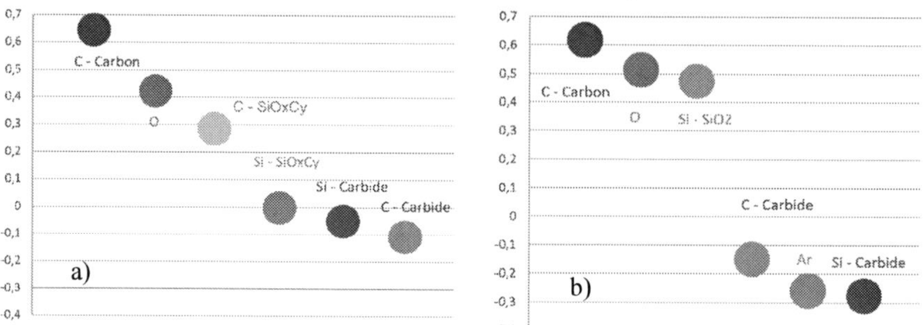

Figure 10. Relative depth plot of the incoming wafer (a) and the actiavetd wafer (b) based on AR-XPS measurement

Scanning Acoustic Microscopy (SAM)

The C-SAM image shows a uniform high-quality bonding interface. Besides the edge bevel caused signal, only minor defects could be observed at 3 o'clock and 9 o'clock position, potentially due to some manual handling error. Otherwise, no particle related voids, no scratch, no delamination, no poorly bonded areas, and no outgassing could be observed. Although the surface particle contamination level of the incoming wafer was not inspected (as one of the most critical quality parameters of the wafer for wafer bonding), this result proofs the wafer quality is according to the requirements and additionally shows overall process maturity.

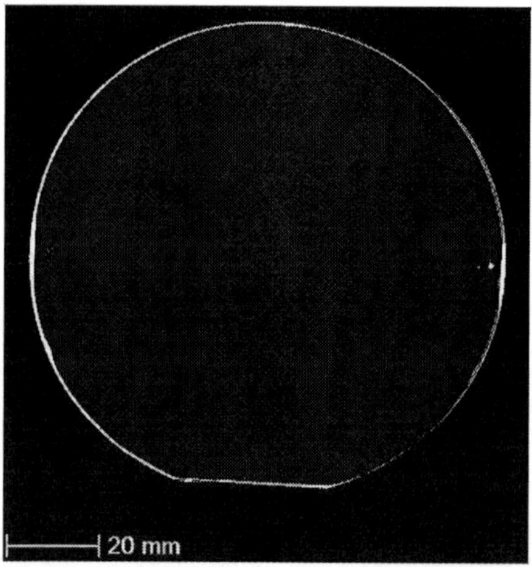

Figure 11. SAM measurement of the SiC-SiC bonding interface

<u>Bonding energy measurement (Maszara test, blade delamination test)</u>

The bonding energy of the bonded wafer pair was measured at four different positions and only a minor difference could be observed.

Although the bonding energy is below the theoretical maximum of the bulk material bonding energy of SiC $(3,5 \text{ J/m}^2)$, it is much higher compared to the lower limit $(0,5 \text{ J/m}^2)$ of bonding energy what is applied in the nanotechnology industry for further processing and also comparable with other similar results from the literature [6].

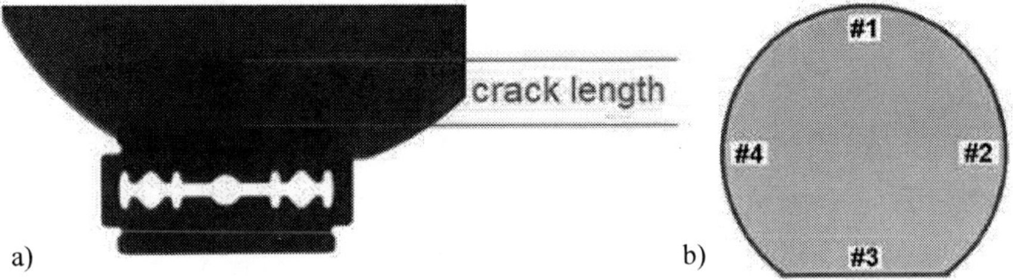

Figure 12: IR image of measuring the crack length (a) and the measurement positions over the bonded wafer pair (b).

TABLE V. Bonding energy measurement results

Position #1		Position #2		Position #3		Position #4		Average
L [mm]	γ [J/m²]	L [mm]	γ [J/m²]	L [mm]	γ [J/m²]	L [mm]	γ [J/m²]	γ [J/m²]
11,2	**1,46**	11,4	**1,36**	11,6	**1,27**	11,2	**1,46**	**1,39**

<u>Transmission Electron Microscopy</u>

TEM images were taken to investigate the oxide thickness of the single wafers (incoming, activated) and the amorphous layer thickness of the bonding interface at the bonded wafer pair.

In the case of the incoming wafer (Figure 13a) the measured oxide thickness is ~1,6 nm, which is more than double of the result of the ellipsometry measurement for the same sample. The measured amorphous layer thickness– what is the sum of the amorphous layer thickness generated by the activation and the regrown oxide thickness – for the activated sample (Figure 13b) is 1,7 nm. This value is comparable with the ellipsometry result.

These results could be explained by the different composition of the oxide layer, which means that it is not possible to apply the same layer structure model in the case of the evaluation of the ellipsometry measurement.

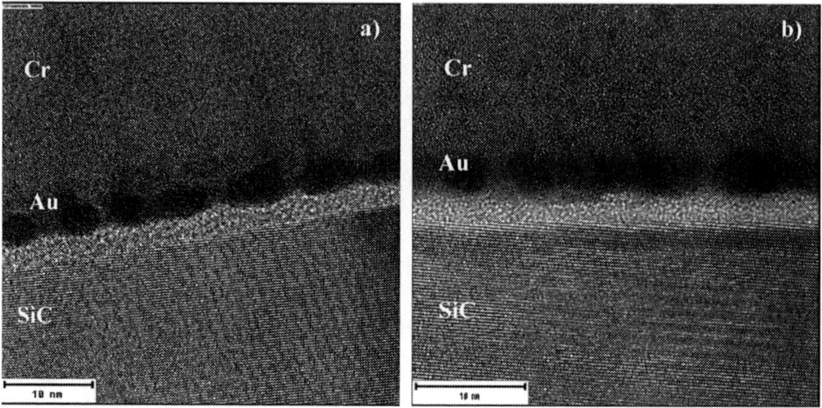

Figure 13. TEM images of incoming wafer (a) and activated wafer after reoxidation (b).

In the case of the bonded wafer pair (Figure 14) the measured amorphous layer thickness is ~2,1 nm, which is very promising from an application point of view where thinner amorphous layer thicknesses are preferred for better electrical characteristic point of view.

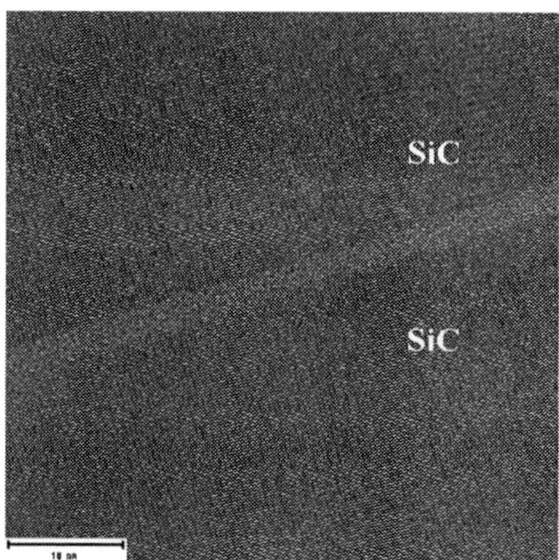

Figure 14. TEM image of the SiC-SiC bonding interface

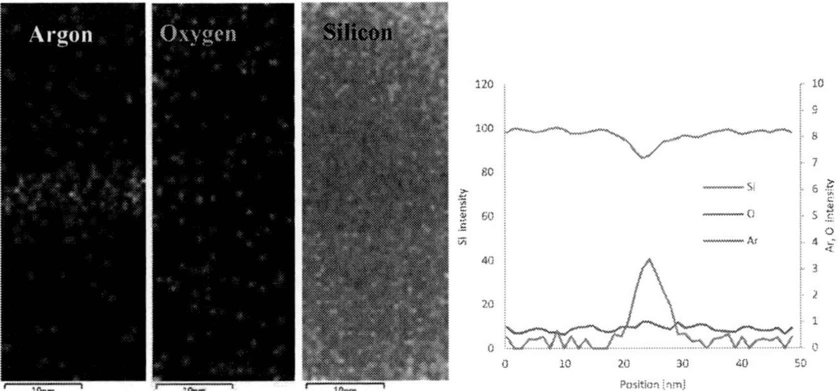

Figure 15. EDX measurement of the bonding interface of a bonded SiC-SiCwafer pair

The elemental analysis of the bonded wafer pair (Figure 15) shows oxide free bonding at the interface as well as some implanted Argon. The ratio of the Silicon is also decreased at the bonding interface which could be explained by the selective sputtering. E.g. in the case of Ar beam the sputtering rate is higher for Si compared to C, therefore in the case of SiC the activated surface will be rich in Carbon rather than Silicon.

Summary

The goal of this study was to demonstrate the feasibility of the bonding process and to gain further insight on the surface chemistry after activation. The incoming wafer was characterized focusing on requirements of the wafer bonding. The quality of the wafer was found excellent for wafer bonding regarding to the surface quality and wafer topography. At the same time a contradiction was found between the oxide thickness measured by TEM and SE. This contradiction was resolved by an unexpected result of the XPS analysis, where it is was observed that the chemical composition of the native oxide is not the expected (in the ellipsometry evaluation model used) SiO_2, but another form of silicon oxycarbides. This can explain the differences, because in the case of ellipsometry the results highly depend on the applied layer structure of the evaluation model (i.e. chemical composition and optical parameters of the different layers).

The surface roughness measurement of the activated wafer verified the activation process, as only a minor increase was observed at surface microroughness after activation. Based on the XPS results, SiO_2 was identified as the chemical composition of the regrown oxide compared to the native oxide. The oxide thickness of the native oxide and the regrown oxide were almost the same based on the TEM images.

The quality of the bonded wafers and the bonding energy were verified using scanning acoustic microscopy (SAM) measurements as well as the Maszara blade test. Furthermore, cross-section TEM showed a bonding interface with a thin amorphous layer and no noticeable additional oxygen containing layer. To gain quantitative elemental distributions of oxygen and argon, energy dispersive x-ray spectroscopy was applied confirming the oxygen free bonding interface and minor amount of implanted Argon.

The work reported is a demonstration of the capability of the different characterization methods regarding SiC-SiC wafer bonding. The characterization methods presented can be further tuned or improved to the peculiarities of SiC characterization, but they already provide a good basis for further investigations of bonded interface characteristics in the function of surface activation process parameters and annealing conditions of the bonded wafer pair.

Acknowledgments

The financial support by the Austrian Federal Ministry of Labour and Economy, the National Foundation for Research, Technology and Development and the Christian Doppler Research Association is gratefully acknowledged.

References

1. T. Suga, F. Mu, M. Fujino, Y. Takahashi, H. Nakazawa and K. Iguchi, 2015 *Jpn. J. Appl. Phys.* 54
2. P.M. Gammon, C.W. Chan, F. Li, F. Gity, T. Trajkovic, V. Pathirana, D. Flandre, V. Kilchytska, Materials Science in Semiconductor Processing, Volume 78, 2018, Pages 69-74
3. S. -H. Ryu, C.Capell, L. Cheng, C. Jonas, A. Gupta, M. Donofrio, J. Clayton, M. O'Loughlin, A. Burk, D. Grider, A. Agarwal, J. Palmour, A. Hefner and S. Bhattacharya, *2012 IEEE Energy Conversion Congress and Exposition (ECCE)*, Raleigh, NC, USA, 2012, pp. 3603-3608
4. U. Usman and M. Nawaz, , Solid-State Electronics, Volume 92, 2014, Pages 5-11
5. R. Maboudian, C. Carraro, D. G. Senesky, C. S. Roper; *Journal of Vacuum Science & Technology A* 1 September 2013; 31 (5)
6. F. Mu, M. Fujino, T. Suga, Y. Takahashi, H. Nakazawa and K. Iguchi, "Wafer bonding of SiC-SiC and SiC-Si by modified surface activated bonding method" 2015 International Conference on Electronics Packaging and iMAPS All Asia Conference (ICEP-IAAC), Kyoto, Japan, 2015, pp. 542-545, doi: 10.1109/ICEP-IAAC.2015.7111073.
7. Tsunenobu Kimoto, "Material science and device physics in SiC technology for high-voltage power devices" Jpn. J. Appl. Phys. 54 040103 (2015), doi: 10.7567/JJAP.54.040103.

ECS Transactions, 112 (3) 173-180 (2023)
10.1149/11203.0173ecst ©The Electrochemical Society

Atomic Diffusion Bonding in Air using Oxide Films

T. Shimatsu[a, b], M. Uomoto[a], H. Fukunaga[a],
H. Makita[c], Y. Suzuki[c], Y. Kozuka[c], A. Muraoka[c], and T. Saito[c]

[a] Frontier Research Institute for Interdisciplinary Sciences (FRIS),
Tohoku University, Sendai, 980-8578, Japan
[b] Research Institute of Electrical Communication (RIEC),
Tohoku University, Sendai, 980-8577, Japan
[c] Canon ANELVA Corporation,
Kurigi 2-5-1, Asao, Kawasaki, 215-8550, Japan

Atomic diffusion bonding (ADB) is a wafer bonding process using thin films. After ADB in air using oxide films was demonstrated, the resultant bonding performance was compared to that obtained ADB in vacuum with the oxide films. Great bonding strength can be obtained at room temperature using ADB in vacuum, whereas ADB in air required post-bonding annealing at temperature above 150 °C to achieve surface free energy at the bonded interface greater than 1 J/m^2. However, ADB in air is a convenient process compared to that in vacuum. For ADB in air using oxide films, we demonstrated that very thin metal films oxidized in air can also be used as oxide films. Particularly, by using amorphous Si films, bonded wafers with a bonded interface consisting of SiO$_2$ amorphous layer can be realized with post-bonding annealing at 150 °C.

Introduction

Atomic diffusion bonding (ADB) of wafers (1,2), along with surface-activated bonding (SAB) (3–6), is a promising process to achieve room-temperature wafer bonding. For ADB processing, thin films are fabricated on two flat wafer surfaces using sputter deposition, with subsequent bonding of the two films on the wafers in vacuum. In addition to thin metal films (1,2), both oxide (7) and nitride (8) thin films are useful for bonding. In fact, any mirror-polished wafer can be bonded in ADB.

We reported the fundamental bonding performances of ADB in vacuum using various oxide films (7,9). Figure 1(A) portrays a schematic illustration of ADB in vacuum using oxide films. Figure 2 portrays cross-section images of Si wafers bonded using (A) 5-nm-thick Al$_2$O$_3$ film on each side (9), and (B) 5-nm-thick ZrO$_2$ film on each side. The images were obtained using scanning transmission electron microscopy (STEM). These images were taken of as-bonded wafers, with no post-bonding annealing. No interface corresponding to the original film surface was observed in either image, indicating the high performance of bonding using these oxide films. Values of the bonding strength estimated using blade-insertion, defined as half the fracture energy, were greater than 2 J/m^2. These values were probably determined by the adhesion strength of these films on wafers rather than that at the bonded interface. We studied

ADB of wafers in vacuum using various amorphous oxide films: Y_2O_3, ZrO_2, TiO_2, Nb_2O_5, Al_2O_3, ZnO, ITO, Ga_2O_3, SiO_2, CuO, GeO_2, and WO_3. Results show that enhancement of structural defects in oxide films enhances their bonding performance significantly. Moreover, surface roughness reduction is important to improve the bonding performance. However, ADB using SiO_2 films is exceptional: the γ of wafers bonded using SiO_2 is very low, probably because of strong diamond-like covalent coupling between Si and O, even with an amorphous structure. The electrical conductivity of the bonded oxide films is negligible, except for conductive oxide films such as ITO. Moreover, incident light can pass through transparent wafers bonded with these oxide films without any marked reduction in intensity. These properties are extremely useful to produce new optical and electrical devices. However, bonding processes conducted in vacuum are expensive and inconvenient in some cases.

For this study, after demonstrating ADB "in air" using oxide films, we compared the resultant bonding performance to that obtained using ADB "in vacuum" with the oxide films. After oxide films were deposited on wafers, bonding was performed in air, as shown in Figure 1(B). We demonstrated that very thin metal films oxidized in air can also be used as oxide films for bonding.

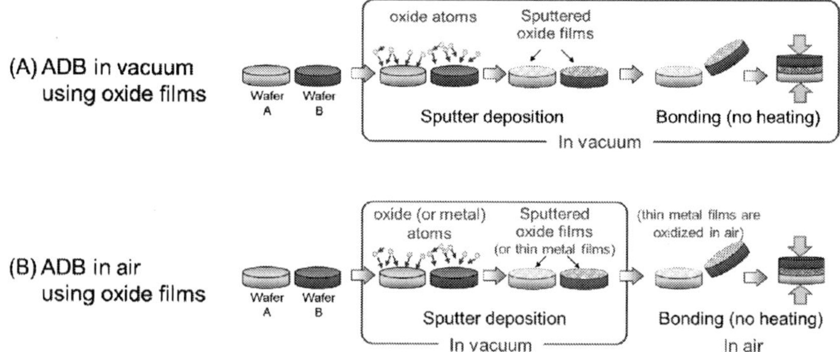

Figure 1. Schematic illustrations of the bonding process using oxide films: (A) ADB in vacuum and (B) ADB in air.

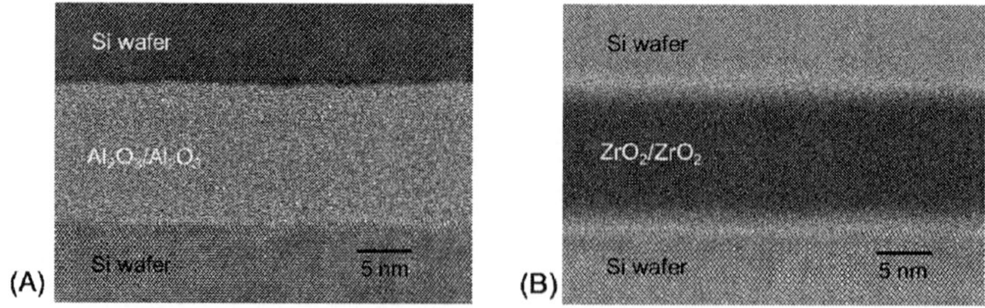

Figure 2. STEM images of Si wafers bonded in vacuum using (A) 5-nm-thick Al_2O_3 film on each side and (B) 5-nm-thick ZrO_2 film on each side.

Experiment Procedures

For this study, mirror-polished synthetic quartz glass wafers of 2-inch (ca. 5.1 cm) diameter were used. The surface roughness S_a of the quartz glass wafers was evaluated as 0.13 nm using atomic force microscopy (AFM). For structural analysis using STEM, we used 2-inch (ca. 5.1 cm) Si(001) wafers with S_a of 0.12 nm. For film deposition, a DC- or RF- magnetron sputtering system was used. Films were deposited directly on two wafer surfaces. Following film deposition, bonding of the two films on the wafers was conducted in air. No heating process or loading force was applied for bonding. Annealing was conducted for bonded wafers using a hot plate in air at 150 °C and at higher temperatures. The annealing time was 5 minutes. Values of the surface free energy at the bonded interface γ were estimated using blade-insertion with Maszara's equation (10). The γ value thus determined corresponds to half the fracture energy in some cases, depending on the structure of the bonded interface. In the blade testing, the de-bonded lengths were measured as soon as the blade-insertion between the wafer to reduce the effect of stress corrosion on the evaluated γ values (11). The values of γ thus determined are approximately those without the corrosion effect γ_0, although γ values are still lower than those of γ_0 (12). Light transmittance at the bonded interface L_t was evaluated at 590 nm wavelength.

Results and Discussion

Bonding in Air Using Oxide Films

As a representative performance of ADB in air using oxide films, Figure 3 presents the values of γ and L_t for quartz glass wafers bonded in air using Y_2O_3 films as a function of Y_2O_3 film thickness on each side. That figure shows results obtained for as-bonded wafers, and those obtained after annealing at 150 °C and 200 °C. The γ values were lower than 0.3 J/m^2 for as-bonded wafers, although L_t values were greater than 99.7% in the film thickness range lower than 5 nm. Annealing at 150 °C enhanced γ significantly more than 1 J/m^2 did. Also, γ of 1.6 J/m^2 with L_t=99.7% was achieved at 5 nm thickness. Annealing at 200 °C enhanced γ further. Table 1 presents the values of γ for quartz glass wafers bonded using 5-nm-thick Y_2O_3 film on each side. Using ADB in air, the γ for as-bonded wafers was small, only 0.25 J/m^2, but low-temperature annealing at 150 °C enhanced γ to 1.6 J/m^2, as described above. Using ADB in vacuum, great bonding strength was achieved for as-bonded wafers: the blade could not be inserted between the wafers. Figure 4 (A) portrays a STEM cross-section image of Si wafers bonded in air using 5-nm-thick Y_2O_3 film on each side, with post-bonding annealing at 150 °C. For comparison, panel (B) portrays a TEM cross-section image of wafers bonded in vacuum, using 5-nm-thick Y_2O_3 film on each side without post-bonding annealing (7). The bonded interface is not visible in panel (B). However, a slightly low-density bonded interface is partially visible in panel (A). The difference of the bonded interface structure is consistent with that of γ presented in Table 1.

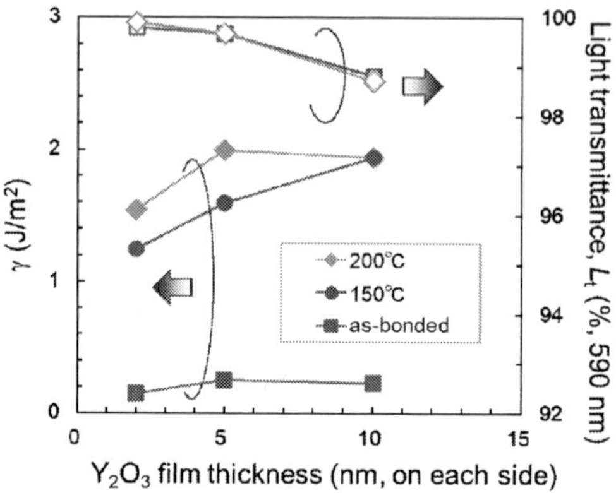

Figure 3. Values of γ and L_t for quartz glass wafers bonded in air using Y_2O_3 films as a function of Y_2O_3 film thickness on each side.

Table 1. Values of γ for quartz glass wafers bonded using Y_2O_3(5 nm) film on each side.

Bonding process	$\gamma\,(J/m^2)$	
	As-bonded	Annealed at 150 °C
In air	0.25	1.6
In vacuum	Unmeasured	Unmeasured

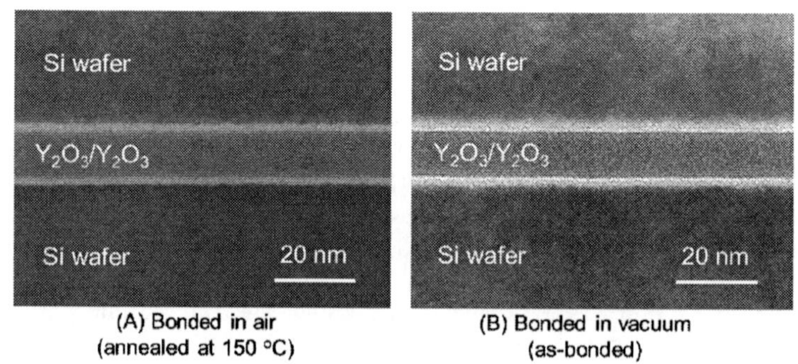

Figure 4. Cross-section images of Si wafers bonded using Y_2O_3 (5 nm) film on each side: (A) STEM image for wafers bonded in air, and (B) TEM image for wafers bonded in vacuum.

It is likely that H_2O gas in air can adsorb on the fresh surface of Y_2O_3 films efficiently and that well-hydrophilic film surfaces can be obtained easily when the deposited oxide films are removed from the vacuum chambers. Annealing is necessary to enhance γ, but low-temperature annealing at 150 °C almost eliminated the bonded interface and enhanced γ remarkably. Structural defects in Y_2O_3 films are likely to have enhanced the bonding performance. Actually, ADB in air was conducted using various oxide amorphous films such as TiO_2, ITO, SiO_2, and WO_3, as is true also for ADB in vacuum. Post-bonding annealing is necessary for ADB in air to achieve γ greater than 1 J/m^2, however, the required annealing temperature is not high, as we have described above. We preliminarily bonded a polyethylene naphthalate (PEN) sheet to quartz glass wafer using ADB in air with Y_2O_3(5 nm) film on each side. In this case, strong bonding strength greater than the breaking strength of the PEN sheet was achieved in the peel test without post-bonding annealing. However, γ values obtained using ADB in air with SiO_2 amorphous films were lower than those using other material films, such as those obtained using ADB in vacuum with SiO_2 films, probably because of strong diamond-like covalent coupling between Si and O even with amorphous structure.

<u>Bonding in Air Using Thin Metal Films</u>

Very thin metal films are oxidized immediately in air when the deposited films are removed from the vacuum chambers to air. These films can also be used for bonding as oxide films. Figure 5 presents the values of γ and L_t for quartz glass wafers bonded in air using thin Zr films as a function of post-bonding annealing temperature. The film thickness on each side used for bonding was defined as δ. Two series of data with δ=0.5 nm and 1.0 nm are presented in the figure. The value of L_t for the as-bonded interface was 100% with δ=0.5 nm and greater than 99% even with δ=1.0 nm, within the accuracy of experiment. This finding indicates that Zr films were oxidized remarkably when the films were exposed to air. The bonding is performed between oxidized film surfaces. The γ values were lower than 0.2 J/m^2 for as-bonded wafers. However, γ values were enhanced by post-bonding annealing. The γ of wafers bonded with δ=1.0 nm achieved 1.3 J/m^2 at the annealing temperature of 150 °C. The L_t value of these bonded wafers reached 99.7% by this annealing. The values of γ and L_t were enhanced further by increasing the annealing temperature to 200 °C. For your reference, almost no oxygen dissociates from the quartz glass wafers in the current annealing temperature range (13).

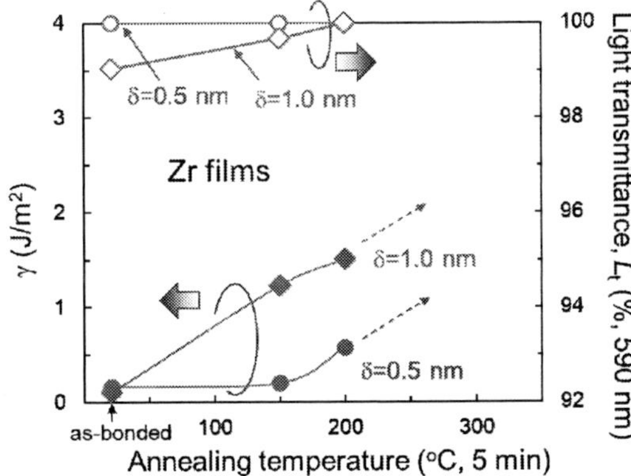

Figure 5. Values of γ and L_t for bonded quartz glass wafers in air using thin Zr films as a function of post-bonding annealing temperature. Two series of data with δ=0.5 nm and 1.0 nm are presented in the figure.

Wafers bonded with an interface layer consisting of SiO_2 can be fabricated with low-temperature post-bonding annealing at 150 °C, which is one important benefit of ADB in air using very thin metal films. Figure 6 presents STEM cross-section images of Si wafers bonded in air using 0.5-nm-thick amorphous Si (a-Si) film on each side with post-bonding annealing at 150 °C: (A) bright-field (BF) image and (B) high-angle annular dark field (HAADF) image. No interface corresponding to the original interface was observed. The bonded interface structure shown in panel (A) was homogeneous, with an amorphous structure. The interface thickness evaluated in (A) was 2.8 nm, although exact measurement was difficult because of the existence of native Si oxide layers on Si wafers. This interface thickness was much greater than the original a-Si film thickness. The bonding strength of as-bonded wafers was weak, as was true also using thin Zr films shown in Figure 5. It is reasonable to infer that thin a-Si films surfaces are oxidized immediately in air when the deposited films are removed from the vacuum chambers to air. Moreover, it is likely that well-hydrophilic film surfaces can be obtained easily by adsorption of H_2O gas in air on the surfaces. Result suggests that the a-Si films bonded in air were oxidized homogeneously by post-bonding annealing at 150 °C. An analysis by blade-testing in atmospheric Ar gas (12) revealed the γ value of this bonded wafers as greater than 1.4 J/m^2. This γ value cannot be obtained by ADB in air using SiO_2 amorphous films with post-bonding temperature of 150 °C at least so far.

We evaluated the structure of this bonded interface further using electron energy loss spectroscopy (EELS) analysis. Figure 7(A) portrays a HAADF STEM image of the sample. Panel (B) portrays mapping images of Si and O obtained from EELS analysis of the region shown by the white line in panel (A). Moreover, the EELS spectra near the Si-L absorption edge obtained along lines a–c shown in (A) are presented in panel (C). In the bonded layer shown in panel (B), the distributions of Si and O are almost homogeneous. The spectra along lines a–c shown in panel (C) are mutually overlapping, reflecting their homogeneous structure. These spectra are good with the spectrum of SiO_2, indicating that a SiO_2 amorphous structure is formed as the interface layer. The results demonstrate that bonded wafers with a bonded interface consisting of SiO_2 amorphous layer was realized with post-bonding annealing at 150 °C, although further examination is necessary to clarify the physical properties of the formed layer.

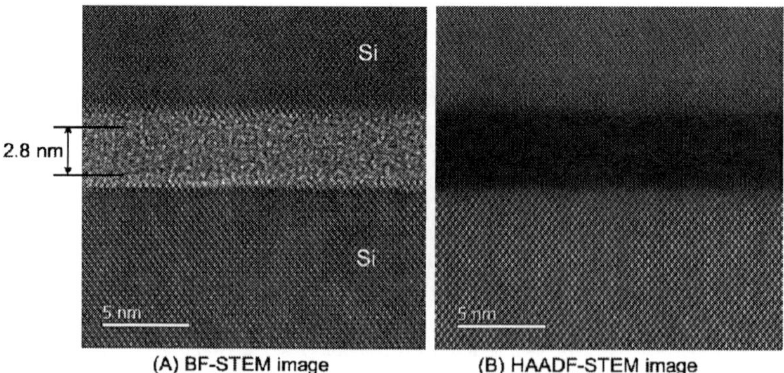

Figure 6. STEM cross-section images of Si wafers bonded using 0.5-nm-thick amorphous Si film on each side with post-bonding annealing at 150 °C: (A) BF (bright-field) image and (B) HAADF image.

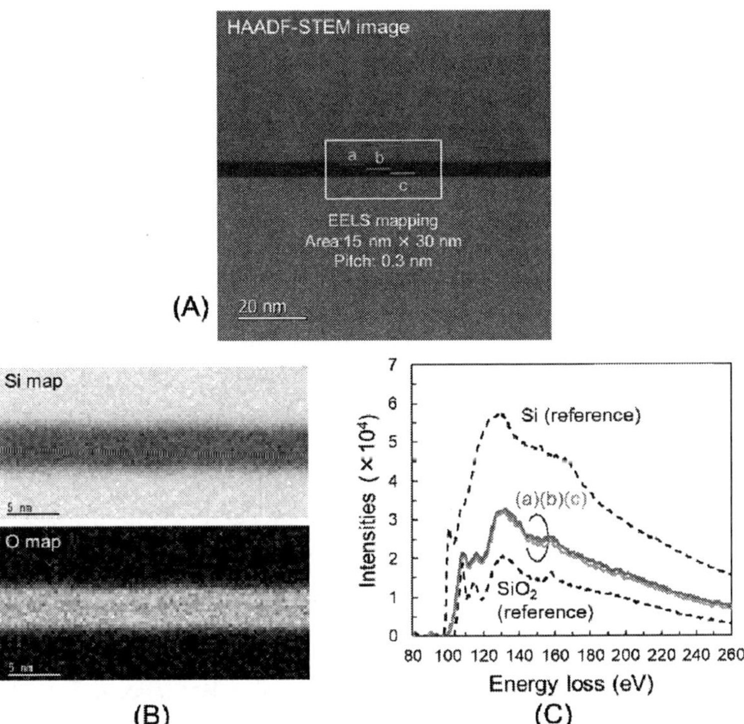

Figure 7. (A) HAADF STEM image of the same sample portrayed in Figure 6. (B) mapping images of Si and O obtained from EELS analysis of the region shown by the white line in (A). (C) EELS spectra near the Si-L absorption edge obtained along lines a–c in (A).

Conclusion

This study demonstrated ADB in air using oxide films. The resultant bonding performance was compared to that obtained ADB in vacuum with the oxide films. Great bonding strength can be obtained at room temperature using ADB in vacuum, whereas ADB in air required post-bonding annealing at temperature above 150 °C to achieve the surface free energy at a bonded interface greater than 1 J/m^2. However, ADB in air is a convenient process compared to that in vacuum. For ADB in air using oxide films, we demonstrated that very thin metal films oxidized in air can also be used as oxide films. Particularly, using amorphous Si films, bonded wafers with a bonded interface consisting of amorphous SiO$_2$ layer can be realized with post-bonding annealing at 150 °C. Any mirror-polished wafer can be bonded using ADB in air, as is true also using ADB in vacuum. For some applications, ADB in air using oxide films is useful if post-bonding annealing at low temperatures is acceptable for bonding processes.

References

1. T. Shimatsu and M. Uomoto, *ECS Transactions*, **33**(4), 61 (2010).
2. T. Shimatsu, M. Uomoto and H. Kon, *ECS Transactions*, **64** (5), 317 (2014).
3. T. Suga, K. Miyazawa and Y. Yamagata, *MRS Int. Meet. Adv. Mater.*, **8**, 257 (1989).
4. T. Suga, Y. Takahashi, H. Takagi, B. Gibbesch, and G. Elssner, *Acta Metall. Mater.*, **40**, s133 (1992).
5. H. Takagi, K. Kikuchi, R. Maeda, T. R. Chung, and T. Suga, *Appl. Phys. Lett.*, **68**, 2222 (1996).
6. E. Higurashi, T. Imamura, T. Suga, and R. Sawada, *IEEE Photonics Technology Letters*, **19**(24), 1994 (2007).
7. T. Shimatsu, H. Yoshida, M. Uomoto, T. Saito, T. Moriwaki, N. Kato, Y. Miyamoto, and K. Miyamoto, *Proceedings of Seventh Low Temperature Bonding for 3D Integration (LTB-3D 2021)*, p.51 (2021).
8. M. Uomoto, H. Yoshida, T. Shimatsu, T. Saito, T. Moriwaki, N. Kato, Y. Miyamoto, and K. Miyamoto, *Proceedings of Seventh Low Temperature Bonding for 3D Integration (LTB-3D 2021)*, p.45 (2021).
9. T. Shimatsu, M. Uomoto, T. Saito, T. Moriwaki, and N. Kato, *Proceedings the Conference on Wafer Bonding for Microsystems, 3D- and Wafer Level Integration (WaferBond22)*, pp.19-22 (2022).
10. M. P. Maszara, G. Goetz, A. Cavigila, and J. B. McKitterick, *J. Appl. Phys.*, **64**, 4943 (1988).
11. F. Fournel, L. Continni, C. Morales, J. Da Fonseca, H. Moriceau, F. Rieutord, A. Barthelemy, and I. Radu, *J. Appl. Phys.*, **111**, 104907 (2012).
12. H. Iemura, F. Goto, M. Uomoto, and T. Shimatsu, *244th ECS Meeting, H02 Semiconductor Wafer bonding: Science, Technology and Applications 17*, H02-1613 (2023).
13. G. Yonezawa, Y. Takahashi, Y. Sato, S. Abe, M. Uomoto, and T. Shimatsu, *ECS Transactions*, **86** (5), 233 (2018).

ECS Transactions, 112 (3) 181-190 (2023)
10.1149/11203.0181ecst ©The Electrochemical Society

High Cleanliness and High Hydrophobic/Hydrophilic Contrast Done by Direct Wafer Bonding for Die-to-Wafer Self-Assembly

P. Montméat, T. Enot, A. Bond, A. Thiolon, E. Bourjot and F. Fournel

Univ. Grenoble Alpes, CEA, LETI, F-38000 Grenoble Department of Chemistry,

We propose an innovative process with a high hydrophilic contrast for die-to-wafer self-assembly bonding. Dies and target wafer bonding surfaces first undergo a photolithography process to define bonding sites with a 15 µm step. An efficient cleaning is then performed for direct bonding surface preparation. A carrier is bonded to the bonding site to temporarily protect it during the hydrophobic treatment. After it, water contact angles of 18° and 110° are measured on bonding sites and on hydrophobic area, respectively. Finally, the self-assembly process compatibility is demonstrated with 8x8 mm² dies achieving alignment accuracy of less than 1 µm and excellent bonding interface quality.

Introduction

Die-to-wafer assembly is a promising technology for 3D-integration in terms of yield. However, achieving high placement accuracy and throughput with a pick and place process is challenging. To overcome these issues, self-assembly and collective transfer for die-to-wafer have been proposed [1].

A self-assembly process relies on small liquid drops to align a die on a target site through capillary forces. Capillary forces occur due to surface tension in liquids (see **figure 1**). The liquid strives to minimize its liquid/air interface and reaches an equilibrium state with minimum energy. This mechanism enables the self-alignment of the silicon die on its bonding site. Deionized water is often chosen as realignment vector [2] because (i) it is easy and safe to handle, (ii) it exhibits a high surface tension compared with others liquids and (iii) its evaporation is easily controlled in a monitored environment and (iv) supports direct bonding mechanisms [3]. Alternatively, aqueous HF solutions can also be used [4], where HF is assumed to enhance the bonding adherence. Once the water droplet has evaporated, direct bonding takes place. Direct bonding refers to a spontaneous adhesion of two surfaces without any intermediate material. The success of such bonding largely depends on the quality of the two involved surfaces. Particles, organic or metallic elements contamination can strongly degrade the bonding quality [5]. For example, a 1-µm particle causes an unbonded region approximately 1 cm in diameter for a 700 µm thick wafer [6]. Thus, meticulous surface cleaning is mandatory to ensure satisfactory wafer assembly. Various cleaning methods are also available to remove most contaminants from silicon wafer surfaces [7]. Silicon oxide surfaces often exhibit hydrophilic behaviour and bonding process has mainly been developed for such surfaces with water contact angles less than 10°. Large non-uniformities in surface flatness can also lead to bonding defects, and a surface roughness of less than 0.5 nm is mandatory for a defect-free bonding. Finally, post-bonding thermal treatments are often required to reinforce the adherence of the stack [8].

Self-alignment is only possible if water is perfectly confined in the bonding site. Poor containment would result in overflow and misalignment. Water containment is ensured by a chemical contrast between hydrophilic and hydrophobic areas. Additionally, a topographical contrast is often created between both types of areas. The chemical contrast is achieved by coating hydrophobic material around the hydrophilic bonding site. Fluorocarbon films, such as fluorinated polymers, are excellent choices among hydrophobic materials due to their coating ease and high hydrophobicity with a water contact angle greater than 90° [7, 9, 10]. The topographic contrast is achieved by incorporating a step that surrounds the bonding site. The combination of chemical and topolographical contrasts maximizes water containment [11].

Numerous research teams are currently working on the manufacturing of dies and target bonding site wafers. All these developments aim to define the direct bonding site by lithographic methods [11, 12]. **Figure 1** shows a standard photolithography process flow for preparing target wafers and dies.

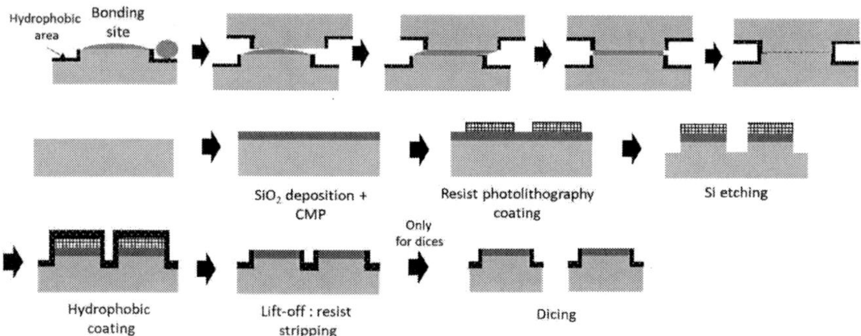

Figure 1: self-assembly bonding (top row), lithography and lift-off processes for the manufacturing of highly contrasted hydrophobic/hydrophilic surfaces (middle and bottom rows)

After the deposition and polishing of SiO_2, photolithography then etching processes are used to create a height variation in silicon, which is necessary to generate a topographic contrast. To achieve chemical contrast, a hydrophobic organic material is deposited. The resist and hydrophobic material on top of the bonding site are removed using a lift-off technique. This results in an array of hydrophilic SiO_2 assembly areas with hydrophobic regions around. Additionally, dicing is carried out to obtain dies.

To ensure high bonding quality, it is crucial to have extremely clean surfaces. Therefore, during the resist stripping step, all particles and organic traces must be thoroughly eliminated. This poses a significant challenge as the organic resist needs to be removed while preserving the organic hydrophobic material. The use of highly aggressive and efficient stripping and cleaning solutions is not viable to achieve the desired cleanliness of bonding surfaces. Consequently, an alternative process to standard lift-off needs to be developed.

We thus evaluate an innovative process that involves temporarily protection of the bonding site for the hydrophobic treatment. A typical flow is presented in **Figure 2**. A standard photolithography and etching process is used to create steps at the edges of the bonding site. An efficient stripping based on plasma and wet cleaning prepares the surface for bonding. This surface is then bonded with another temporary wafer which creates cavities with the surrounding of the bonding site. The resulting stack is immersed in a hydrophobic material solution which penetrates into the cavities. The protection wafer is subsequently dismounted. As a result, bonding sites are surrounded with hydrophobic areas and are ready for a self-assembly bonding process. This new process enables the manufacturing of both the target and dies.

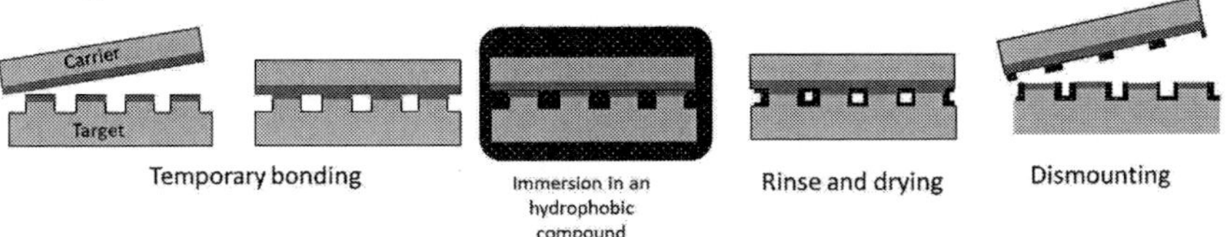

Figure 2: temporary bonding and dipping process

The first part of the paper focuses on describing the manufacturing of the temporary protection, the self-assembly procedure and the characterization methods. The second section presents the results of collective bonding achieved using a target wafer and dies manufactured with the temporary protection.

Experimental

<u>Dies and target wafer manufacturing</u>

All experiments are conducted in a clean room environment on 200 mm p-type (100) silicon wafers. To manufacture the temporary carrier, a silicon wafer is oxidized to produce a 500 nm thick SiO_2 film. The wafer is then edge trimmed to a width of 5 mm and a depth of 250 µm. Trimming is carried out using a 100 µm wide blade on a Disco Full Dicing tool. This silicon temporary carrier is wet cleaned (CARO and SC1) prior to direct bonding.

A 2 µm thick silicon oxide layer is deposited and polished on top of another silicon wafer. In the first photolithography step, two verniers are defined for alignment measurements. A second photolithography step and etching processes are used to have a 13 µm step height in the silicon, which is necessary to establish a physical contrast. Bonding sites have 8 x 8 mm^2 dimensions. Oxygen plasma and wet cleaning are employed to achieve a clean surface for direct bonding. Both wafers of interest are prepared with this procedure: the target (or receiver) wafer and the die wafer. The target wafer comprises 40 bonding sites, while the die wafer consists of 80 dies.

These wafers are directly bonded with the temporary carriers. The bonding can be carried out either in a clean room atmosphere or under vacuum with an EVG Gemini bonding module. No annealing is performed to ensure an easy carrier dismounting. The selection of the hydrophobic compound is also a main topic of interest. Although fluorinated materials are often used due to their excellent hydrophobic or anti-sticky properties [9, 13, 14, 15], these materials are part of per and polyfluoroalkyl substances (PFAS) [16, 17] and have become a global threat to human health and environment. These substances are currently or will soon be regulated under the Registration, Evaluation, Authorisation and Restriction of Chemicals (REACH). Nowadays, many chemical suppliers intend to replace PFAS by more environmentally friendly ones. Therefore, we chose to also evaluate a fluorine-free solution with hydrophobic properties. The previous manufactured stacks (target and die wafers) are then soaked in this solution. After spin drying, bonded stacks are dismounted. Saw dicing is used to separate dies using a Disco Full Dicing tool with a 100 µm wide blade. The resulting dies have 10.2 x 10.2 mm² dimensions, which corresponds to 8 x 8 mm² bonding sites with 200 µm wide wings.

Collective bonding

A collective bonding is performed on a homemade bench, where 40 bondings are conducted simultaneously (**Figure 3**). Deionized water droplets of 3 µL are dispensed onto the die bonding sites. Just before bonding, dies are placed in a silicon chip holder for collective cleaning. After dies are brought into contact with and transferred onto the target wafer, the stack is dried overnight then heated for 2 hours at 200°C.

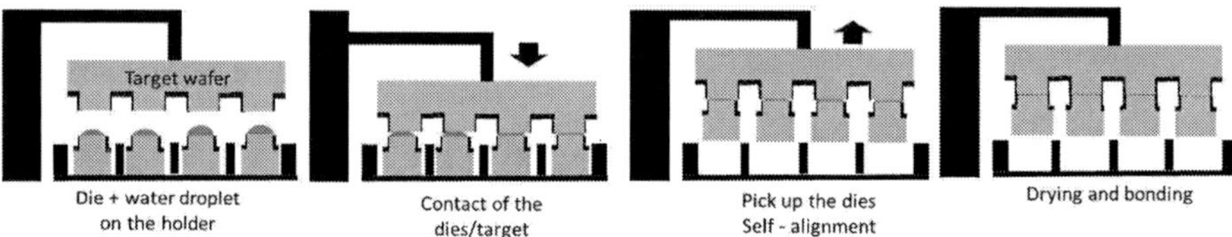

Figure 3: collective bonding

Characterizations

The water contact angle is measured with a DSA Kruss equipment, with a 3 µL water volume. A surface is considered to be definitely hydrophobic when the water contact angle (WCA) is higher than 90°, while a hydrophilic surface has a WCA of less than 20°. Atomic Force Microscopy (AFM) is used to investigate surface morphology and roughness using a Dimension Fastscan apparatus from Bruker, operating in tapping mode. The bonding site roughness is characterized using Root Means Square (RMS) statistics from 1 µm² scan fields. The quality of temporary and self-assembly bondings is evaluated using an acoustic microscope. A full automatic acoustic microscope from PVA-Tepla, with a 140 MHz acoustic head frequency, is used with an image resolution of 40 µm/pixel. A bonding interface is considered "defect free" when the defective surface area does not exceed 1% of the die surface. The alignment of each die is assessed using an infrared microscope. If the alignment is less than 1 µm, it is considered as being a successful self-assembly.

Results

Temporary bonding and dipping:
A die wafer is bonded with a carrier. Acoustic picture examples of the bonded dies are shown in **Figure 4**. When the bonding is performed in the clean room atmosphere, many white spots indicating bonding defects are observed at bonding locations. In contrast, bonding quality is excellent when performed under vacuum.

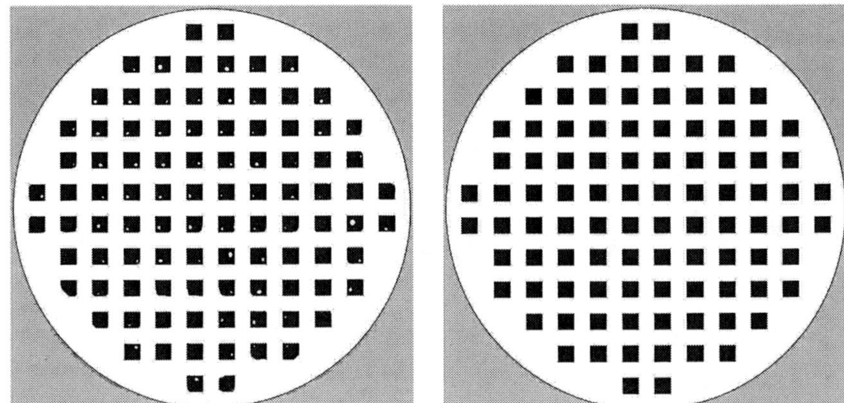

Figure 4: acoustic pictures of a 200 mm diameter stack obtained with an atmospheric direct bonding (left) and a vacuum direct bonding (right). White spots show un-bonded regions.

Bonding defects for atmospheric bonding are probably due to peculiar bonding wave propagation on each bonding site. Indeed a key parameter in direct bonding is the propagation of the bonding wave between both surfaces. When bonding two silicon wafers in the atmosphere, the bonding is typically initiated by the operator at a specific locations, either at the edge or at the center of the wafer. This way, only one bonding wave propagates, resulting in defect free bonding. However, when a wafer is bonded onto a surface with steps, it is challenging to control the bonding initiation at each step and multiple bonding waves may be self-initiated at different surface locations. When bonding waves meet, air bubbles can be trapped, resulting in bonding defects. Under vacuum, multiple bonding waves may still appear but no gases are trapped when two bonding waves meet, resulting in defect free bonding. In the present study, all subsequent bondings are performed under vacuum. The stack is then dipped into the hydrophobic solution. Infrared images show that the liquid filled the gap between the two wafers within 3 minutes. After spin-drying, the acoustic picture of the stack does not reveal any detachment of bonded areas. The dismounting of the bonded structure was easy, without target, die or carrier wafer breakage. As a quick proof of hydrophobic treatment, the treated wafers (target and carrier) are dipped in water. The resulting pictures of the various wafers are shown in **Figure 5**.

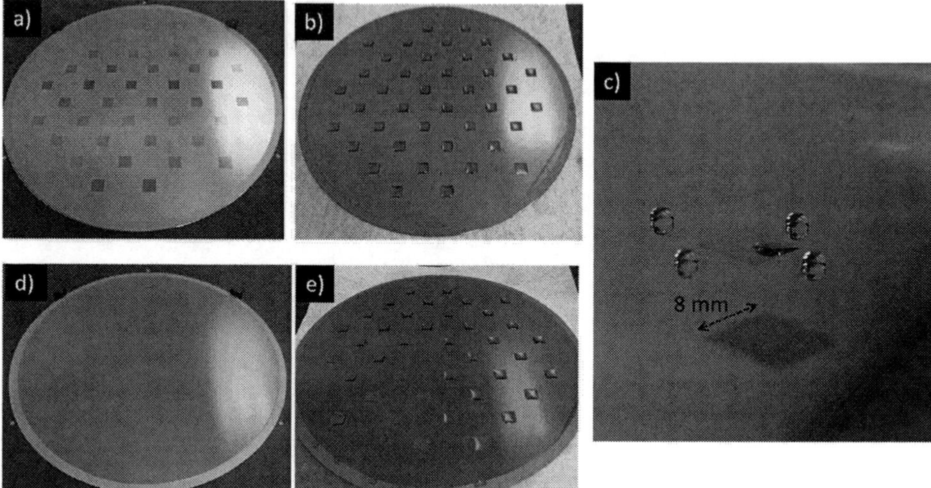

Figure 5: snapshots of a) a starting target wafer, b) a target wafer treated by the hydrophobic solution then dipped into water, c) water droplets onto a bonding site and surrounding areas, d/ a starting carrier wafer, e) a carrier wafer treated by the hydrophobic solution and then dipped in water (wafer diameters are 200 mm)

Water containment on the die or target wafers are clearly observed on the bonding sites while water de-wetting occurs elsewhere. The 40 bonding sites of the target wafer exhibit a WCA between 10° and 20°. A WCA of 110° is measured on the other part of the wafer as shown in **Figure 6**. The same behavior is observed on the carrier wafer, where the protection and hydrophobic treatment define hydrophilic squares surrounded by hydrophobic areas. After an O_2 plasma and wet cleaning, the hydrophobic film is removed and the carrier can be reused.

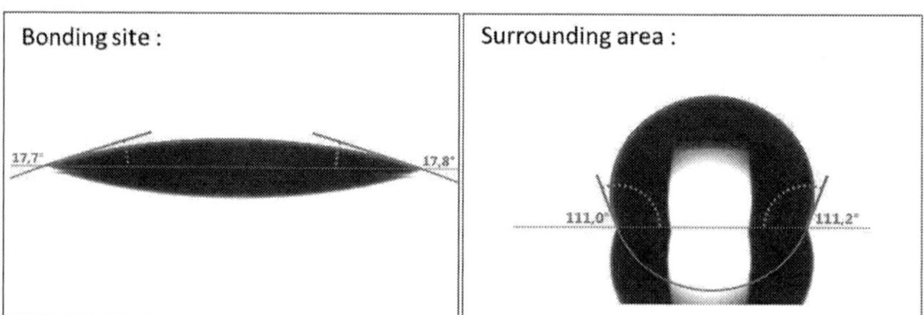

Figure 6: water contact angle measurements

AFM snapshots of treated wafers are provided in **Figure 7**. The RMS roughness of the bonding site is 0.18 nm, which is the initial roughness of the 2 μm thick oxide film after polishing.

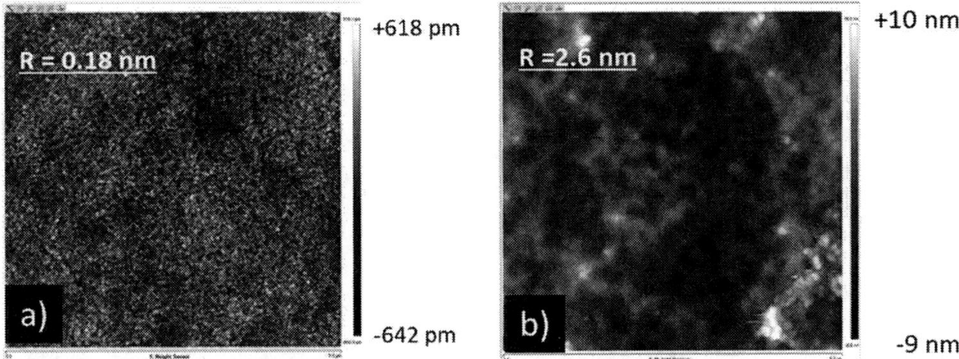

Figure 7: 1 x 1 µm² AFM snapshots of a) a bonding site after hydrophobic treatment, b) a region between two bonding sites after the hydrophobic treatment.

The unprotected region exhibits a significantly higher topography, with RMS roughness higher than 2 nm. The high water contact angle and the AFM snapshot confirm the presence of the hydrophobic material on unprotected areas surrounding bonding sites.
The bonding site protection is effective against liquid ingress, while the rest of the target wafer is completely covered and treated with the hydrophobic compound.
Die and target wafers treated with the hydrophobic solution are tested in a collective self-assembly bonding process.

<u>Collective self-assembly bonding</u>

A collective self-assembly bonding process is carried out with 40 dies bonded onto a target wafer using the method described earlier. The main results are summarized in **Table 1**.

Bonded dies in %	Bonded die without defect in %	Bonded die with alignment < 1 µm in %	Bonded die with alignment 1 µm < < 2 µm in %	Bonded die with alignment > 5 µm in %
50 %	90 %	85%	15 %	0 %

Table 1: results of collective bonding

The percentage of transferred and bonded dies is 50 %. After annealing at 200°C, acoustic pictures of bonded dies (cf. **Figure 8**) reveal that the transfer and bonding yield is not very good, with a majority of missing die located in the lower part of the wafer. The partial failure of die transfer to the target wafer could be attributed to the high hydrophilicity of the bonding site (water contact angle less than 20°). When a 3 µL water droplet is deposited on such a surface, it spreads over the entire surface with minimal height. During collective bonding (cf. **Figure 9**), perfect contact between the target wafer and all water droplets heavily relies on the flatness of the bonding bench. The flatness between the target and the die wafer is around 200 µm, which is inadequate for complete transfer of all 40 dies. The dies in the lower part of the holder do not come into contact with the target wafer during the approach. Improving the bonding bench would require an automatic tool that provides control over the levelling and flatness of the wafer during approach.

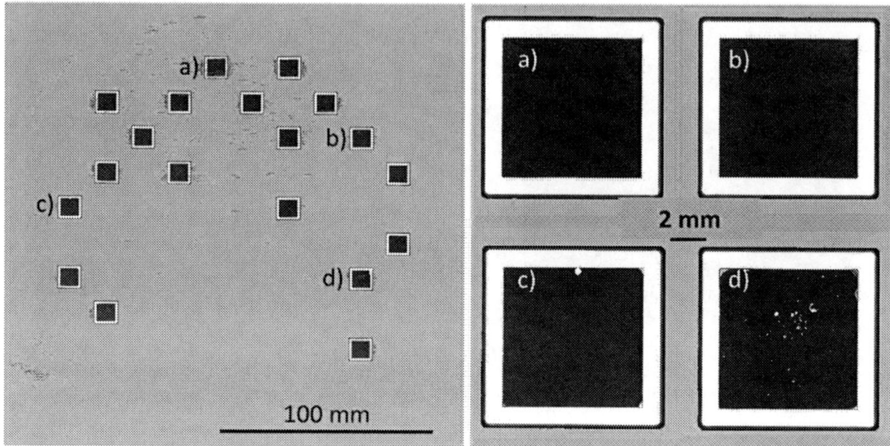

Figure 8: acoustic pictures of the die-to-wafer collective bonding (left) and zooms on some bonded dies (right). White areas refer to un-bonded zones. The edge around the die is the so-called die wing.

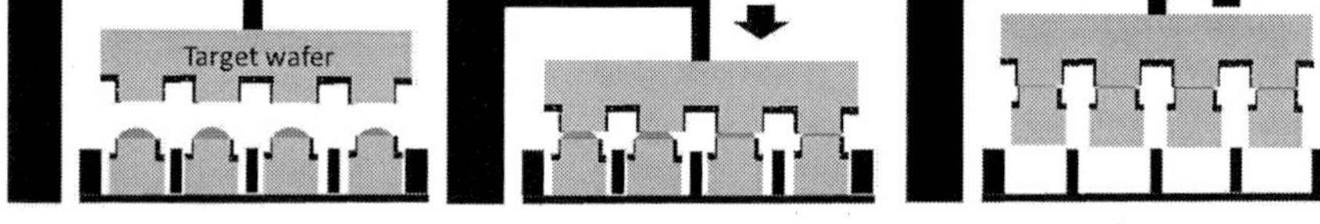

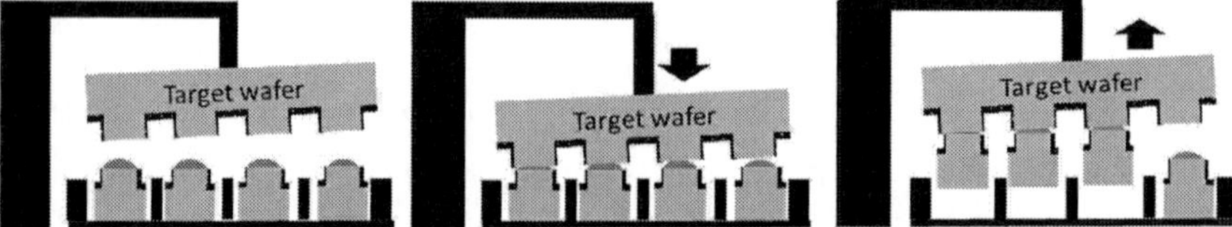

Figure 9: impact of flatness on dies transfer

The percentage of bonded dies with alignment less than 1 µm is 85 %, indicating successful self-alignment. The hydrophobic/hydrophilic contrast created through the bonding protection is effective in facilitating the self-alignment of the die on the bonding site.

When annealed at 200°C, 90% of bonded dies are bonded without defects. Acoustic picture of some selected dies are provided in figure 8. In comparison, using a standard lift-off process for the manufacturing of the die and target wafers resulted in an average of only 70% defect-free dies from 10 different collective bondings. This highlights the excellent quality of the surface preparation after the temporary bonding and dipping, which maintains a perfectly clean surface compatible with direct bonding. The main cause of defects at 200°C is resist particles, as organic resists can be oxidized during annealing, trapping gas at the bonding interface and resulting in larger bonding defects. This is successfully suppressed using the current temporary direct bonding process.

Conclusion

In conclusion, this study presents an innovative process for manufacturing highly clean and strong hydrophobic/hydrophilic contrasted surfaces through temporary direct wafer bonding for die-to-wafer self-assembly. Instead of relying on a lift-off process, typically used to prepare such surfaces, the approach involves temporarily protection of the hydrophilic bonding sites during hydrophobic treatment by bonding a carrier to sites and immersing the stack in a hydrophobic solution. The temporary bonding process enables the manufacturing of target as well as die wafers and this method yields clean bonding sites that are suitable for subsequent self-assembly direct bonding. The hydrophobic treatment employs a free-fluorine compound. Additionally, an excellent alignment yield is achieved in collective self-assembly bonding, with die to wafer alignment below 1 μm for over 80 % of the bonded dies. The bonding interface quality is also superior to that obtained with a lift-off process. Further improvement in bonding yield could be achieved through the development, by tool suppliers, of automatic bonders specifically designed for self-assembly processes.

Acknowledgments

The authors acknowledge financial support from INTEL Corporation, United States

References

1. Y. Yamada, H. Kikuchi and M. Koyanagi, Proc. Int. Electron Dev. Meet. pp. 359–362 (2005).
2. L. Sanchez, L. Bally, B. Montmayeul, F. Fournel, J. Dafonseca, E. Augendre, L. Di Cioccio, V. Carron, T. Signamarcheix, R. Taibi, S. Mermoz and G. Lecarpentier, Electronic Components and Technology Conference, pp 1960-1964, (2012)
3. F. Fournel, C. Martin-Cocher, D. Radisson, V. Larrey, E. Beche, C. Morales, P. A. Delean, F. Rieutord, and H. Moriceau, ECS J. Solid State Sci. Technol. 4, P124 (2015).
4. T. Fukushima, E. Iwata, K.-W. Lee, T. Tanaka, and M. Koyanagi, Electronic Components and Technology Conference, pp 1050-1055, (2010)
5. T. Abe, Wafer bonding technique for Silicon-On-Insulator technology, Solid State Technology, (1990)
6. V. Lehmann, W. K. Ong, U. Gösele, R. Stengl, K. Mitani, Semiconductor wafer Bonding, Adv. Mater. 2, N°8, (1990)

7. W. Kern, Handbook of Silicon Wafer Cleaning Technology 2nd edn, William Andrew Publishing, (2007)
8. F. Fournel, L. Continni, C. Morales, J. Da Fonseca, H. Moriceau, F. Rieutord, A. Barthelemy and I. Radu, Journal of Applied Physics 111, 104907, (2012°
9. T. Fukushima, H. Hashiguchi, H. Yonekura, H. Kino, M. Murugesan, J.-C. Bea, K.-W. Lee, T. Tanaka and M. Koyanagi et al, Micromachines, 7, 184, (2016)
10. A. Jouve, L. Sanchez, C. Castan, M. Laugier, E. Rolland, B. Montmayeul, R. Franiatte, F. Fournel, S. Cheramy, IEEE 69th Electronic Components and Technology Conference, pp 225-234, (2019)
11. A. Bond , E. Bourjot, S. Borel, T. Enot, P. Montméat, L. Sanchez, F. Fournel and J. Swan, 2022 IEEE 72nd Electronic Components and Technology Conference, San Diego, CA, USA, pp. 168-176, (2022)
12. S. Mermoz, L. Sanchez, L. Di Cioccio, J. Berthier, E. Deloffre, P. Coudrain and C. Fretigny, 2013 IEEE 15th Electronics Packaging Technology Conference, pp 162-167, (2013)
13. P. Montméat, T. Enot, G. Enyedi, M. Pellat, J. Thooris and F. Fournel, International Journal of Adhesion and Adhesives, Volume 82, , Pages 100-107, (2018)
14. S. Brault, O. Garel, G. Schelcher, N. Isac, F. Parrain and A. Bosseboeuf , MEMS packaging process by film transfer using an anti-adhesive layer. Microsyst Technol, 16(7), (2010)
15. M. Pei, L. Huo, X. Zhao, S. Chen, J. Li, Z. Peng, K. Zhang, H. Zhou, P. Liu, Applied Surface Science Volume 507, 30, 145138, (2020)
16. E. Hovland Steindal and M. Grung, Integrated Environmental Assessment and Management, Volume 17, Number 4, pp. 835–851, (2020)
17. Z. Y.Yong, K. Y. Kim and J.-E. Oh, Environmental Pollution Volume 268, Part B, 115395, (2021)

ECS Transactions, 112 (3) 191-198 (2023)
10.1149/11203.0191ecst ©The Electrochemical Society

Crystal Lattice Rearrangement Occurred at Au/Ag Bonded Interface in Atomic Diffusion Bonding in Vacuum

F. Goto[a,b], H. Iemura[a,b], M. Uomoto[a], and T. Shimatsu[a,c]

[a] Frontier Research Institute for Interdisciplinary Sciences (FRIS),
Tohoku University, Sendai, 980-8578, Japan
[b] Department of Electronic Engineering, Graduate School of Engineering,
Tohoku University, Sendai 980-8579, Japan
[c] Research Institute of Electrical Communication (RIEC),
Tohoku University, Sendai, 980-8577, Japan

The crystal lattice rearrangement which occurs at the bonded interface of two films during atomic diffusion bonding processing in vacuum was examined using Au and Ag films. Results revealed that remarkable crystal lattice rearrangement occurs at the bonded interface of Au−Ag bonded films at room temperature. Grains formed continuously across the original interface over the entire thickness of the bonded films. Also, the (111) preferred grain orientation was effective at enhancing the crystal lattice rearrangement. The crystal lattice rearrangement did not accompany remarkable interdiffusion of Au and Ag at the interface, even though the crystal lattice formed continuously across the original interface. In addition to crystal lattice rearrangement, grain boundary diffusion plays an important role in bonding processes, enhancing the interdiffusion between Au and Ag films. Grain boundary diffusion is likely to be effective to fill the gaps in the boundaries of grains formed by crystal lattice rearrangement.

Introduction

Atomic diffusion bonding (ADB) of wafers using thin metal films (1–3) is a promising route to achieving room-temperature wafer bonding along with surface-activated bonding (SAB) (4–7). For ADB processing, thin metal films are fabricated on two flat wafer surfaces using sputter deposition, with subsequent bonding of the two films on the wafers in vacuum. This bonding technique is applicable to any mirror-polished wafer, with bonding using almost any metal film. When two film surfaces mutually contact at room temperature during ADB, crystal lattice rearrangement occurs, thereby enhancing the bonding performance. Figure 1 portrays cross-section images of the bonded interface observed using transmission electron microscopy TEM: (A) using 20-nm-thick Au film on each side, and (B) using 20-nm-thick Ag film on each side. These are structures bonded in vacuum without post-bonded annealing. As shown in panel (A), the original bonded interface disappears; also, some crystal grains formed over the entire thickness. In panel (B), no interface that corresponded to the original Ag surfaces is visible. The unique image of diagonal stripes resulted from the formation of a twin structure over the entire thickness. During ADB processing, crystal lattice rearrangement occurs when two film surfaces mutually contact at room temperature, as depicted schematically in Figure 2.

The bonded structure was found to be related closely to the self-diffusion coefficient at 300 K, D, for metals used for bonding. Remarkable crystal lattice rearrangement occurs at the bonded interface using metal films with fcc or hcp structure having large D (1,2). It is reasonable to infer that the crystal lattice rearrangement is related to the film structure such as the crystallographic grain orientation, in addition to D values. Moreover, it has not been clarified to date how much interdiffusion of the two metal films occurs at the bonded interface by crystal lattice rearrangement phenomena. Generally, films of the same material used for bonding are fabricated on two flat wafer surfaces. Therefore, few methods are available for examining the crystal lattice rearrangement mechanism.

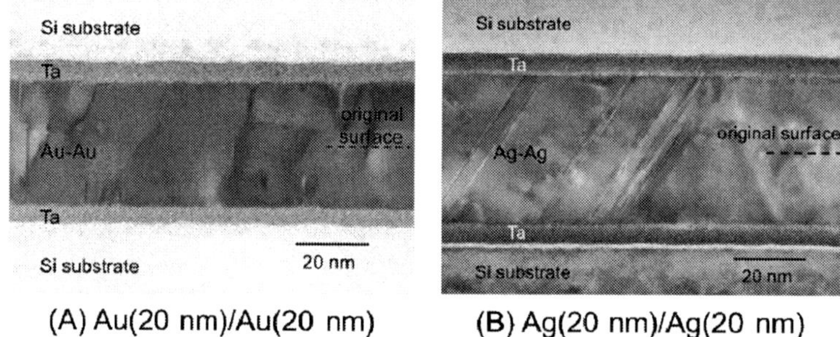

(A) Au(20 nm)/Au(20 nm)   (B) Ag(20 nm)/Ag(20 nm)

Figure 1. TEM cross-section images of Si wafers bonded in vacuum using (A) 20-nm-thick Au film on each side and (B) 20-nm-thick Ag film on each side.

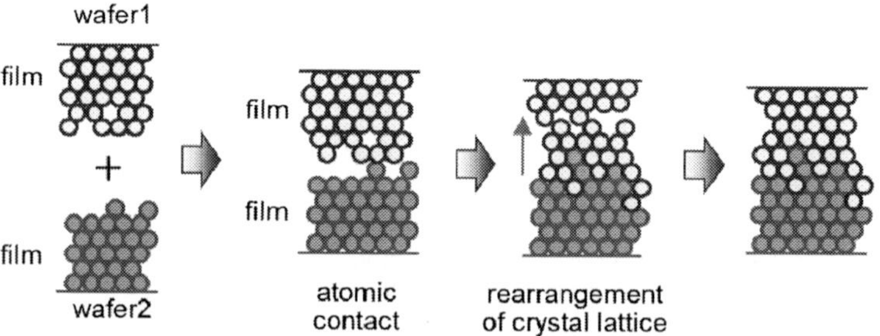

Figure 2. Schematic illustration of crystal lattice rearrangement occurring at the bonded interface of two films.

For this study, we examined the crystal lattice rearrangement which occurs at the bonded interface between Au and Ag films in vacuum. Physical properties of Au and Ag are presented in Table 1. The Au and Ag have an fcc crystal structure and show solid solution in the whole Au–Ag composition range. Values of the lattice constant of Au and Ag are almost identical such that the lattice mismatch of these materials is very slight: less than 0.1%. This is a specific and very important character of Au and Ag because the lattice strain energy does not increase when the substitution of Au and Ag atom occurs in fcc crystal lattice during the crystal lattice rearrangement. Moreover, the values of D of

Au and Ag are large. Furthermore, remarkable crystal lattice rearrangement occurs at the bonded interface of Au–Au and Ag–Ag films, as shown in Figure 1. The values of interdiffusion coefficient D_{inter} of Au to Ag, D_{inter}(Au to Ag), are slightly smaller than the others (D_{inter}(Ag to Au)) but still larger than the D value of Cu ($=1.4 \times 10^{-41}$ m^2/s): remarkable crystal lattice rearrangement occurs at the Cu–Cu interface (1,2).

For this study, the bonded interface structure of Au–Ag bonded films and depth profiles of Au and Ag atoms were examined. To examine the effects of films structure on the crystal lattice rearrangement at the bonded interface between Au and Ag films, Au–Ag bonded films with Ta and Ti underlayers were fabricated. The resultant difference is discussed.

Table 1. Physical properties of Au and Ag. The value of D and D_{inter} at 300 K were calculated using the Arrhenius equation with the frequency factor and the activation energy (8).

Metals	Au	Ag
Crystal structure	fcc	
Lattice constant (nm)	0.40785	0.40862
Atomic weight	196.97	107.87
Density (g/cm^3)	19.30	10.49
Self-diffusion coefficient D (m^2/s, 300 K)	1.6×10^{-36}	8.3×10^{-38}
Interdiffusion coefficient D_{inter}(Au to Ag) (m^2/s, 300 K)	5.7×10^{-40}	
Interdiffusion coefficient D_{inter}(Ag to Au) (m^2/s, 300 K)	4.0×10^{-35}	

Experiment Procedures

For this study, Si(001) wafers of 2-inch (ca. 5.1 cm) diameter were used. The Si wafer surface roughness was evaluated as 0.12 nm using atomic force microscopy (AFM). A DC-magnetron sputtering system was used for film deposition. We fabricated two Au and Ag bonded films: one with Ti underlayers in both Au and Ag films; and the other with Ta underlayers in both films. We fabricated 20-nm-thick Au and Ag films on two flat wafer surfaces using sputter deposition, with Ti or Ta films underneath, with subsequent bonding of the two films on the wafers in vacuum. No substrate heating was conducted during deposition or during bonding processes.

Results and Discussion

Grain orientations of Au and Ag films used for bonding

X-ray diffraction (XRD) analysis revealed that Au(20 nm) and Ag(20 nm) films used for bonding show the preferred (111) grain orientation parallel to the films plane. Figure 3 presents the XRD pattern of (111) diffraction: (A) Au films and (B) Ag films deposited with Ta and Ti underlayers, respectively. For Ag films, we deposited 5-nm-thick Cr capping layer on top of Ag films to avoid cohesion of Ag film surfaces occurring by exposure of Ag surfaces to air. The film thickness of underlayers was 5 nm, but the Ti film thickness for Au film was 2 nm: a preliminary study revealed that 2-nm-thick Ti film enhanced the (111) orientation of Au film compared to that using 5-nm-thick Ti film. The XRD intensity of Au(111) with the Ta underlayer was slightly higher than that with the Ti film underlayer, but no remarkable difference was observed. Rocking curve analysis revealed the value of the distribution of the <111> crystal axis, $\Delta\theta_{50}$, of Au films with the Ta underlayer as 3.0°, which was also identical to that with the Ti underlayer (=3.2°). By contrast, a remarkable difference in XRD caused by underlayer material films was observed in Ag films. The XRD intensity of Ag(111) with the Ti underlayer was high, with $\Delta\theta_{50}$ of 4.1°. However, the XRD intensity of Ag(111) with the Ta underlayer was very weak. For that reason, we were unable to estimate the value of $\Delta\theta_{50}$. This finding indicated that the (111) preferred grain orientation of Ag films with Ta underlayer was remarkably lower than in the film with the Ti underlayer.

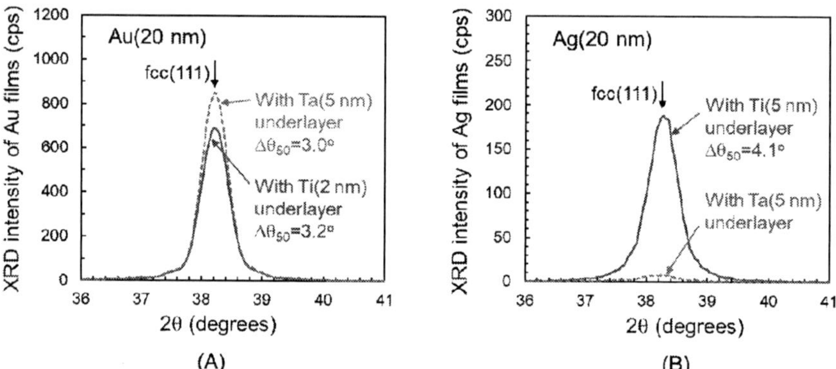

Figure 3. XRD pattern of (111) diffraction of (A) Au films and (B) Ag films deposited with Ta and Ti underlayers used for bonding.

We bonded these Au and Ag films in vacuum. The blade could not be inserted between the wafers in either sample, indicating that great bonding strength was achieved in these bonded wafers. Figure 4 portrays cross-section images with a low-magnification for Au−Ag bonded films observed using scanning transmission electron microscopy (STEM). Panel (A-1) is a bright field (BF) image of bonded films with Ta underlayers; (A-2) is a corresponding high-angle annular dark field (HAADF) image. Panels (B-1) and (B-2) are those bonded films with Ti underlayers. No vacancy was observed at the bonded interface in either sample. Moreover, the Au and Ag film morphologies were mutually continuous across the original interface, as shown in BF images of (A-1) and (B-1). This continuity of morphologies suggests that crystal lattice rearrangement occurred in both samples over the whole bonded area. Many grain boundaries formed crossing the original interface were observed clearly in (B-1) and (B-2). However, the grain boundaries observed in (A-1) and (A-2) were unclear. A few grain boundaries across the original interface were also observed in these images. It is noteworthy that the bonded Au−Ag films observed in HAADF images shown in (A-2) and (B-2) consist of two layers: the upper bright side and dark lower side layers. These two layers are expected to be attributable mainly to the different atomic weights of Au and Ag, suggesting that Au and Ag films did not inter-diffuse remarkably in both samples, although crystal lattice rearrangement changed the crystallographic structure remarkably.

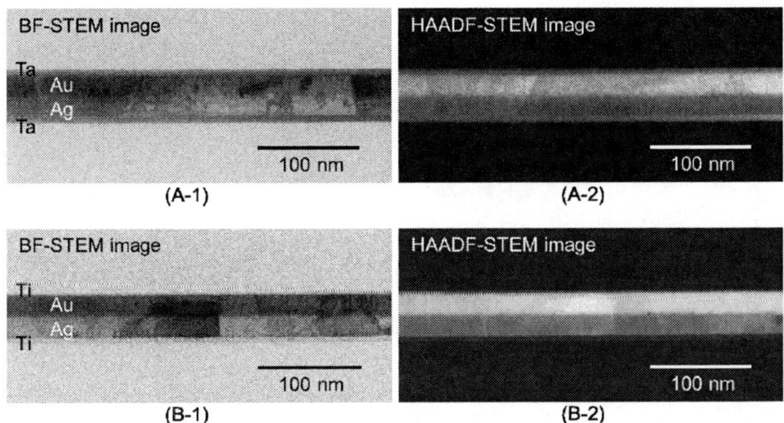

Figure 4. STEM cross-section images with a low-magnification of Au–Ag bonded films: (A-1) and (A-2) depict BF and HAADF images for bonded films with Ta underlayers; (B-1) and (B-2) portray those for bonded films with Ti underlayers.

Figure 5 portrays high-magnification STEM images of Au–Ag bonded films. Panels (A-1) and (A-2) are BF and HAADF images for bonded films with Ta underlayers. Panel (A-3) is an enlarged image of an area (a) in (A-1). Panels (B-1) and (B-2) portray bonded films with Ti underlayers; panel (B-3) shows an enlarged image of an area (b) in (B-1). For bonded films with Ta underlayers, the (111) crystal plane was observed over the entire film thickness, as shown in (A-1) and (A-3), supporting that the remarkable crystal lattice rearrangement occurred at the bonded interface. The Ag film with Ta underlayer showed no clear (111) preferred grain orientation, as shown in Figure 3(B). However, the (111) crystal plane of bonded Au–Ag crystal lattice was parallel to the film plane as observed in almost all areas. This finding indicated that the crystal lattice rearrangement started from the surface of the (111) crystal plane of Au film, probably because the (111) crystal plane shows the highest atomic packing density and the lowest surface energy compared to other crystal planes (9). This finding suggests that the (111) preferred grain orientation is effective for enhancement of the crystal lattice rearrangement. Although the crystal lattices of Au and Ag layers were identical across the original interface because of the crystal lattice rearrangement, the contrast between the upper-half and lower-half areas in panel (A-3) is expected to be attributable mainly to the different atomic weights of Au and Ag. For bonded films with Ti underlayers, the (111) crystal plane observed across the original bonded interface, as shown in panels (B-1) and (B-3). Some grains were formed continuously across the original interface over the entire thickness of the bonded films, as is true also with Ta underlayers. The HAADF image shown as (B-2) suggests that the upper and the lower layers consisted respectively of Au and Ag atoms, although crystal lattice formed continuously over the entire film thickness, as is true also with Ta underlayers.

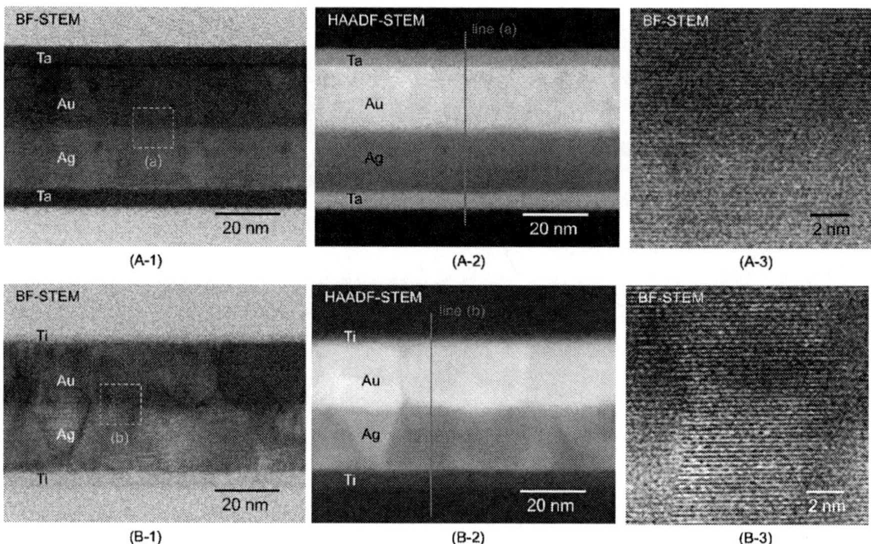

Figure 5. High-magnification STEM images of Au−Ag bonded films: (A-1) and (A-2) BF and HAADF images for bonded films with Ta underlayers; (A-3) an enlarged image of area (a) in (A-1). Panels (B-1) and (B-2) show those for bonded films with Ti underlayers; (B-3) portrays an enlarged image of area (b) in (B-1).

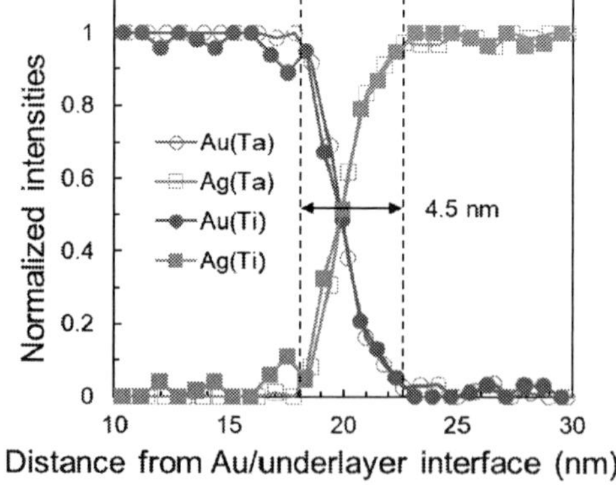

Figure 6. Depth profiles of Au and Ag for bonded films with Ta and Ti underlayers evaluated using EELS analysis along lines (a) and (b) in Figure 5.

Depth profiles of Au and Ag were evaluated using electron energy loss spectroscopy (EELS) analysis along lines (a) and (b) in panels (A-2) and (B-2). The results are presented in Figure 6. Interdiffusion at the Au–Ag bonded interface was not remarkable even though the crystal lattice formed continuously across the original interface. No significant difference caused by the difference of underlayer materials was found, although the interdiffusion for bonded films with Ti underlayers tended to be slightly thicker than that with Ta underlayers. The interdiffusion length estimated, as the figure shows, was 4.5 nm, but the real diffusion length is expected to be shorter: probably a few nanometers. In fact, the estimated width using EELS analysis is 1–2 nm larger than the actual width because of the electron beam dispersion in the sample.

It is noteworthy that the boundary between the upper-half and lower-half areas shown in Figure 5(B-2) fluctuated. Figure 7 portrays high-resolution images of an area across the original interface of Au–Ag bonded films with Ti underlayers: (A) BF-STEM and (B) HAADF-STEM images. The Au and Ag films are expected to have a flat film surface before bonding. However, in the area enclosed in the dotted circle, the interface was not straight. Some diffusion of Ag atoms into Au was observed clearly at around the grain boundaries. This finding indicated grain boundary diffusion at the bonded interface. Actually, the peak and valley locations at the fluctuated boundary between the upper and lower half areas were near the grain boundaries in Figure 5(B-2). These results indicate that grain boundary diffusion, in addition to crystal lattice rearrangement, plays an important role in ADB.

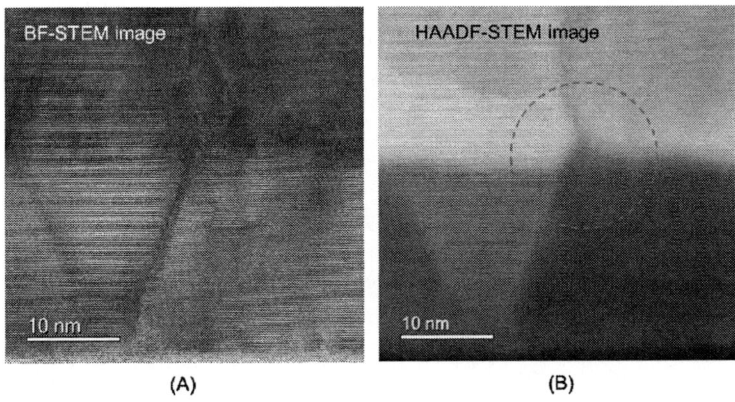

Figure 7. High-resolution images of an area across the original interface of Au–Ag bonded films with Ti underlayers: (A) BF-STEM and (B) HAADF-STEM images.

Conclusion

Our results revealed that remarkable crystal lattice rearrangement occurred at the bonded interface of Au–Ag bonded films at room temperature. Grains were formed continuously across the original interface over the entire thickness of the bonded films. Results suggest that the (111) preferred grain orientation was effective to enhance the crystal lattice rearrangement. It is noteworthy that crystal lattice rearrangement did not accompany any remarkable interdiffusion of Au and Ag atoms at the interface, even though the crystal lattice formed continuously across the original interface. However, the results demonstrated that grain boundary diffusion played an important role in ADB processes in addition to crystal lattice rearrangement, consequently enhancing the interdiffusion between Au and Ag films. The grain boundary diffusion is likely to be effective to fill the gaps in the boundaries of grains formed by crystal lattice rearrangement, resulting in structural relaxation over the whole films, although more intensive efforts must be undertaken to clarify the bonding mechanism at the bonded interface.

References

1. T. Shimatsu and M. Uomoto, *J. Vac. Sci. Technol.*, **B 28**, 706 (2010).
2. T. Shimatsu and M. Uomoto, *ECS Transactions*, **33**(4), 61 (2010).
3. T. Shimatsu and M. Uomoto, *ECS Transactions*, **64**(5), 317 (2014).
4. T. Suga, K. Miyazawa, and Y. Yamagata, *MRS Int. Meet. Adv. Mater.*, **8**, 257 (1989).
5. T. Suga, Y. Takahashi, H. Takagi, B. Gibbesch, and G. Elssner, *Acta Metall. Mater.*, **40**, s133 (1992).
6. H. Takagi, K. Kikuchi, R. Maeda, T. R. Chung, and T. Suga, *Appl. Phys. Lett.*, **68**, 2222 (1996).
7. E. Higurashi, T. Imamura, T. Suga, and R. Sawada, *IEEE Photonics Technology Letters*, **19**(24), 1994 (2007).
8. The Japan Institute of Metals, *Metal Data Book, Third edition*, Maruzen, Japan, 1993, p. 20.
9. L. Vitos, A.V. Ruban, H.L. Skriver, and J. Kolla´r, *Surface Science*, **411**, 186 (1998).

ECS Transactions, 112 (3) 199-206 (2023)
10.1149/11203.0199ecst ©The Electrochemical Society

Blade Test in Atmospheric-Pressure Ar Gas
to Characterize Bonded Interface Fabricated Using Atomic Diffusion Bonding

H. Iemura[a,b], F. Goto[a,b], M. Uomoto[a], and T. Shimatsu[a, c]

[a] Frontier Research Institute for Interdisciplinary Sciences (FRIS),
Tohoku University, Sendai, 980-8578, Japan
[b] Department of Electronic Engineering, Graduate School of Engineering,
Tohoku University, Sendai 980-8579, Japan
[c] Research Institute of Electrical Communication (RIEC),
Tohoku University, Sendai, 980-8577, Japan

A blade test was applied in atmospheric-pressure Ar gas for wafers bonded using atomic diffusion bonding processing. We assessed the variation of the values of surface free energy at the bonded interface γ calculated, for convenience, from the debonding length. For interfaces bonded using thin Zr and Ti films, γ measured in Ar maintained the initial value $\gamma_0(Ar)$ in the initial region of observation time t and started decreasing as t increased further. Results indicate that $\gamma_0(Ar)$ corresponds to the value without water stress corrosion effects. The initial value of γ measured in air with a higher blade insertion-speed was almost equal to $\gamma_0(Ar)$. Result obtained for wafers bonded using Al_2O_3 films were almost identical to those obtained using metal films. However, γ for wafers bonded using ZrO_2 films did not maintain their initial values. They decreased gradually as t increased, even in Ar, suggesting high water stress corrosion effects.

Introduction

Atomic diffusion bonding (ADB) of wafers using thin films is a promising process to achieve room-temperature wafer bonding (1–3) in addition to surface-activated bonding (SAB) (4-7). For ADB processing, thin oxide (8,9) and nitride (10,11) films are useful for bonding, as are thin metal films (1-3).

For blade testing, a conventional method used to examine the surface free energy at the bonded interface γ, the debonding length L is measured after a thin blade is inserted between bonded wafers. The value of γ is calculated using L values. However, in some bonded wafers, the L value changes gradually with increasing observation time after blade insertion. For instance, Figure 1(A) presents the γ values of quartz glass wafers bonded using Zr film as a function of the Zr film thickness on each side. The value of γ was calculated using Maszara's equation (12). Zr is a representative material films used for ADB, as is true also for Ti. As shown in panel (A), high bonding strength is obtained: the blade cannot be inserted between the wafers at thicknesses greater than 1 nm. However, with reduced thickness from 1 nm, the blade can be inserted between the wafers; γ as evaluated using L tends to be lower with decreasing film thickness. Some time decay of γ value (i.e. an increase in the L value) is generally observed, particularly for thicknesses of 0.4–1 nm, as is true also for Ti films.

Figures 1(B-1) and (B-2) respectively portray representative cross-section images observed by transmission electron microscopy TEM for quartz glass wafers bonded using Zr(0.4 nm) on each side and those using Zr(20 nm) on each side. The bonded interface disappeared in the Zr–Zr bonded interface. Therefore, it is reasonable to infer that the blade edge can be inserted between the wafers by cracking the Zr–Zr bonded films. For a bonded interface such as Si/SiO_2 or SiO_2/SiO_2, stress corrosion caused by oxygen and water gases in air is well-known to affect the L value, as do the γ values (13–15). Therefore, the experimentally observed time decay of γ is probably caused by water stress corrosion occurring at the bonded interface during blade testing. This problem is left without detailed discussion. The γ values we have reported earlier (3,16) were evaluated using L values measured two minutes after blade insertion. Because the thus determined γ values were still greater than the surface energy of Zr at thicknesses greater than 0.4 nm. Moreover, no decay of bonding strength has been observed in actual applications for device fabrication.

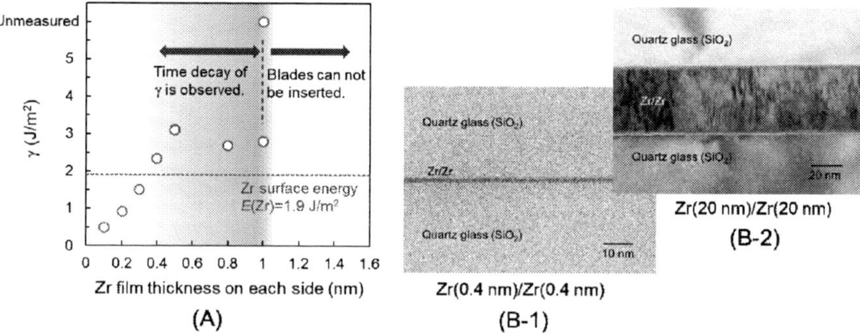

Figure 1. (A) Values of γ of quartz glass wafers bonded using Zr film as a function of the Zr film thickness on each side. (B-1) Cross-section images observed using transmission electron microscopy TEM for quartz glass wafers bonded using Zr(0.4 nm) on each side and (B-2) using Zr(20 nm) on each side.

Recent reports have described successful bonding using oxide films (8,9). Wafers bonded using oxide films show remarkable time decay of γ compared to those using metal films. The water stress corrosion effect on the evaluation of bonding strength is not negligible. One report (17) described that γ value evaluated in vacuum was remarkably higher than that in air for Al_2O_3–Al_2O_3 films bonded using SAB method.

For this study, a blade test was applied in Ar gas at atmospheric pressure for wafers bonded using ADB processing. Bonded interfaces of two kinds were examined: interfaces bonded using thin metal films and those bonded using oxide films. Using Maszara's equation (12) for convenience, we assessed the variation of γ values calculated from L values.

Experiment Procedures

Mirror-polished synthetic quartz glass wafers of 2-inch (ca. 5.1 cm) diameter were used. Their surface roughness was evaluated as 0.13 nm using atomic force microscopy (AFM). An ultra-high vacuum (UHV) magnetron sputtering system was used for film deposition. Films were deposited directly onto two quartz glass wafer surfaces. Subsequent bonding was accomplished in the same vacuum. No substrate heating was applied during deposition or during bonding processes. Bonded wafers of two kinds were prepared for examination. Some wafers were bonded in vacuum using thin metal films: thin Ti and Zr films were used as representative materials films. Other wafers were bonded in vacuum using oxide films: thin ZrO_2 and Al_2O_3 films were used for this study.

We fabricated a highly airtight measurement chamber made of Al alloy compatible to that of the vacuum chamber. Its internal volume was 140 cm^3. Measurements were taken in a clean room with a moisture level of 50%. After a bonded wafer was set in the chamber, we inserted a blade between the wafers in air. The chamber surface was sealed with a glass plate using a sealing method used for the vacuum chamber. Then Ar gas at atmospheric pressure with impurities of less than 1 ppm was introduced into the chamber and flowed continuously with a flow rate of 0.8 liters per minute. We replaced the air in chamber with Ar gas at atmospheric pressure with replacement time t_r. The standard value of t_r was 600 s. Then the blade edge was advanced further in Ar gas. After a new crack-edge was formed in Ar gas by advancing the blade edge, we started the measurement of time dependence of the variation of de-bonded length L. We observed the bonded interface through a glass plate using a CMOS video camera and evaluated the L value on images obtained from the video sequence. For blade insertion, a razor blade (100 µm thickness) was advanced with the blade insertion speed S_b. Values of S_b were set as 50, 70, 100, and 200 µm/s.

Results and Discussion

<u>Bonded Wafers using Thin Metal Films</u>

Figure 2(A) presents values of γ for quartz glass wafers bonded using Zr(1 nm) film on each side as a function of measurement time t. Two data series are shown: those measured in Ar and in air. The values of t_r and S_b were 600 s and 100 µm/s. The surface energy of Zr (18), $E_s(Zr)$, is also presented as a dotted line for comparison. As t increased, γ measured in air decreased remarkably from the initial value $\gamma_0(air)$ of 4.1 J/m^2. Also, γ was nearly saturated: 2.9 J/m^2 at t=15 s. The values of γ measured in Ar were higher than those in air. The initial value of γ in Ar was 4.1 J/m^2, which was identical to that in $\gamma_0(air)$. However, γ in Ar maintained the value of $\gamma_0(Ar)$ until t=400 s; it then started decreasing. At t=1800 s, we stopped the Ar gas flow and introduced air into the measurement chamber. This intruded air led to a marked γ reduction; γ was saturated to a value that was almost equal to that of the saturated value in air.

Similar behaviors were observed for quartz glass wafers bonded using Ti(0.7 nm) film on each side, as shown in Figure 2(B). The values of t_r and S_b were equal to those shown in panel (A). The surface energy of Ti (18), E_s(Ti), is also shown as a dotted line for comparison. As t increased, γ measured in air decreased remarkably from γ_0(air) of 3.1 J/m^2. Also, γ was nearly saturated at 2.2 J/m^2 at t=200 s. For γ measured in Ar, the value of γ_0(Ar) was 3.6 J/m^2. This value was higher than that of γ_0(air), which differed from the result obtained using the Zr(1 nm) films shown in panel (A). However, γ in Ar maintained the value of γ_0(Ar) until t=400 s also in this sample; it then started decreasing. Other behavior was similar to that shown in panel (A).

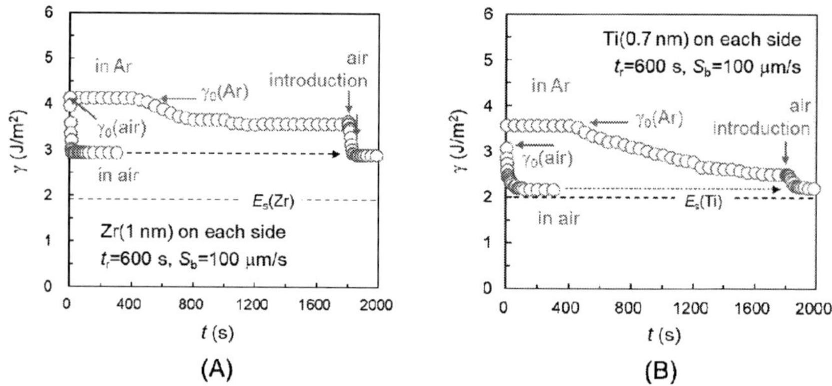

Figure 2. (A) Values of γ as a function of observation time t for quartz glass wafers bonded using Zr(1 nm) film on each side, measured in Ar gas and in air. (B) Results for quartz glass wafers bonded using Ti(0.7 nm) film on each side.

Figures 3(A)–(D) portray images in the blade test in atmospheric-pressure Ar gas for the bonded wafers during the evaluation shown in Figure 2(A). The images were obtained from video sequences. At t=0 s shown in panel (A), the crack-edge in Ar gas formed by advancing the blade-end in Ar gas is indicated by a solid-line arrow. The crack-edge location formed in air, before advancing the blade edge in Ar gas, is indicated by a dotted-line arrow. It is noteworthy that the area between the crack edges formed in Ar and that in air showed slight metallic reflection at t=0 s. The length of the metallic-colored area was defined as L_m, as shown in panel (A). L_m decreased gradually with increasing t, as shown in panel (B) at t=100 s and became zero at t=400 s, as shown in panel (C). This pattern of decrease indicates that metallic surfaces formed by the crack-advancement in Ar gas are oxidized gradually by the impurity gases of O_2 and H_2O in atmospheric-pressure Ar gas. It is noteworthy that L maintained a constant value in the time range from t=0 to 400 s, corresponding to a constant γ (equal to γ_0(Ar)) in this time range in Figure 2(A). However, L started increasing gradually as t increased from 400 s. This gradual increase supports that water stress corrosion occurs at the crack front because of oxidation of cracked Zr metal films used for bonding by impurity gases in atmospheric-pressure Ar gas. These results indicate that water stress corrosion occurs at the crack front during measurement in air. The gradual reduction of γ in Ar shown in Figures 2(A) and (B) resulted from oxidation of Zr and Ti films with impurities of O_2 and

H_2O in Ar gas. The value obtained without oxidation effects is $\gamma_0(Ar)$. In fact, $\gamma_0(Ar)$ did not increase concomitantly with increasing blade-insertion speed.

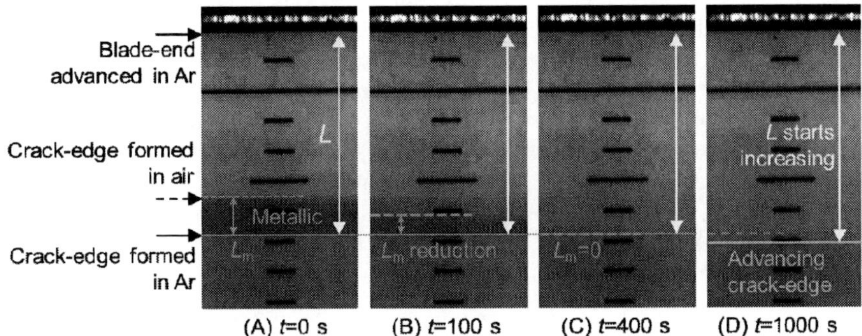

Figure 3. Images obtained from video sequences in the blade test in Ar gas for the bonded wafers characterized in Figure 2(A).

For the wafers bonded using Zr(1 nm) shown in Figure 2(A), γ was measured at different conditions. The results are shown in Figure 4. The value of t_r was 30 s in this measurement. Two series of data measured with S_b=70 μm/s and 100 μm/s, respectively in Ar and in air, are presented in the figure. The horizontal axis is more expanded than those in Figure 2. In atmospheric-pressure Ar, the values of $\gamma_0(Ar)$ in both series of data were about 4.1 J/m^2. No remarkable difference was found between the measurement conditions of S_b of 70 μm/s and 100 μm/s, within the accuracy of experiment. The values of γ in both series show constant values of $\gamma_0(Ar)$ in the t range up to 40 s. As t increased further, γ in both series started decreasing. This finding supported that $\gamma_0(Ar)$ of 4.1 J/m^2 was the intrinsic value without oxidation effects. By contrast, the values of γ measured in air decreased remarkably as t increased in both series of data. The initial γ value ($\gamma_0(air)$) measured with S_b=100 μm/s was about 4.1 J/m^2. This value was identical to that of $\gamma_0(Ar)$, as was true also for the result shown in Figure 2(A) measured with t_r of 600 s. However, the value of $\gamma_0(air)$ measured with S_b=70 μm/s was 3.3 J/m^2, which was lower than that measured with S_b=100 μm/s. This finding indicates that $\gamma_0(air)$ measured with a higher blade insertion-speed was almost equal to the intrinsic value without oxidation effects. This near equivalence is probably attributable to the fact that, by increasing S_b, the advancing crack speed becomes higher than the oxidation speed at the crack front in air.

<u>Bonded Wafers using Oxide Films</u>

Figure 5 portray cross-section images observed using scanning transmission electron microscopy (STEM) for Si wafers bonded using (A) Al_2O_3(5 nm) on each side (9), and (B) ZrO_2(5 nm) film on each side. The bonded interface was not apparent in either image. Therefore, for blade-testing of wafers bonded using these material films, it is reasonable to infer that the blade edge can be inserted between the wafers by cracking these bonded oxide films. Figure 6 presents values of γ for quartz glass wafers bonded using oxide thin films as a function of t: (A) using Al_2O_3(2 nm) film on each side, and (B) using ZrO_2(0.5 nm) film on each side. The measurement conditions of these samples were the same:

t_r=600 s and S_b=100 μm/s. The bonding conditions were almost identical to those shown in Figure 5. In both Figures 6(A) and (B), the values of γ measured in Ar were much higher than those measured in air. Actually, γ in Ar for wafers bonded using Al_2O_3(2 nm) films maintained the initial value γ_0(Ar) of 2.5 J/m^2 until t=150 s; then it started decreasing. This pattern of decrease suggests that γ_0(Ar) corresponds to the value obtained without the effects of water stress corrosion. However, γ in Ar for wafers bonded using ZrO_2(0.5 nm) films did not maintain the initial value γ_0(Ar): γ decreased gradually as t increased, even in Ar. This difference suggests that the water stress corrosion effects on the values of γ were not suppressed, even in Ar. Moreover, values of γ measured in Ar were remarkably larger than those measured in air. This finding suggests that ZrO_2 showed remarkable water stress corrosion.

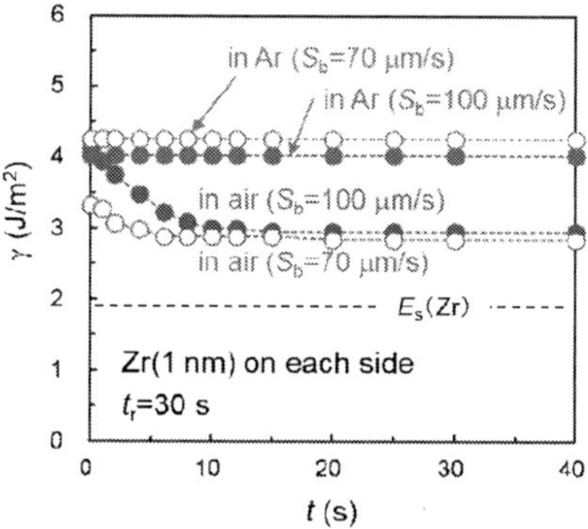

Figure 4. Values of γ as a function of observation time t for quartz glass wafers bonded using Zr(1 nm) film on each side. Two series of data with S_b=70 μm/s and 100 μm/s measured respectively in Ar and in air are shown.

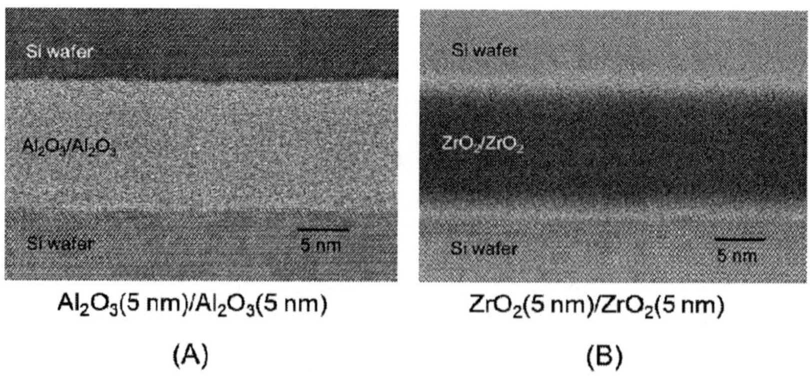

Figure 5. STEM cross-section images for Si wafers bonded using (A) Al_2O_3(5 nm) film on each side and (B) ZrO_2(5 nm) film on each side.

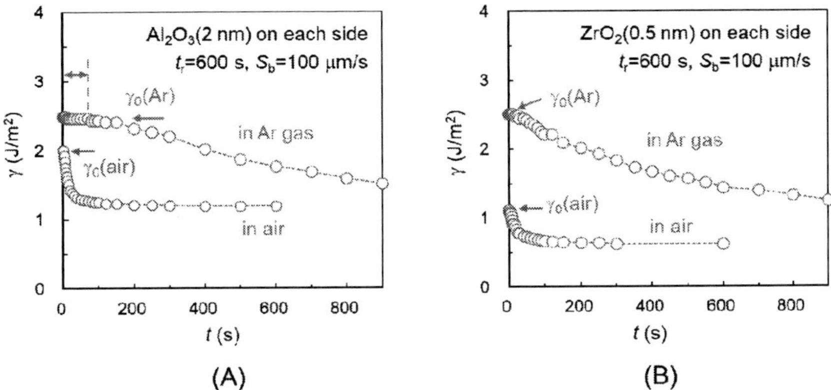

(A)   (B)

Figure 6. Values of γ for quartz glass wafers bonded using oxide thin films as a function of t: (A) using Al_2O_3(2 nm) film on each side and (B) using ZrO_2(0.5 nm) film on each side. The bonding conditions were almost identical to those shown in Figure 5.

Conclusion

A blade test was applied in atmospheric-pressure Ar gas for wafers bonded using ADB processing. For interfaces bonded using thin Zr and Ti films, which are film materials typically used for ADB, γ measured in Ar gas maintained its initial value γ_0(Ar) in the initial t region and started decreasing as t increased further. Results indicated that γ_0(Ar) corresponds to the value without water stress corrosion effects. Results also demonstrated that the initial value of γ measured in air was almost equal to γ_0(Ar), probably because the speed of crack advancement becomes higher than the oxidation speed at the crack front in air. For interfaces bonded using oxide films, results showed material dependence on the oxide films. For wafers bonded using Al_2O_3 films, water stress corrosion effects on γ were observed like those found when using metal films, indicating that γ_0(Ar) corresponds to the value without water stress corrosion effects. However, γ for wafers bonded using ZrO_2 films did not maintain the initial value. In fact, its value decreased gradually as t increased, even in Ar, probably because ZrO_2 shows remarkable water stress corrosion. More intensive effort are necessary to clarify the mechanisms of water corrosion effects on the evaluation of bonding strength for wafers bonded using ADB processing.

References

1. T. Shimatsu and M. Uomoto, *J. Vac. Sci. Technol.*, **B 28**, 706 (2010).
2. T. Shimatsu and M. Uomoto, *ECS Transactions*, **33**(4), 61 (2010).
3. T. Shimatsu and M. Uomoto, *ECS Transactions*, **64**(5), 317 (2014).
4. T. Suga, K. Miyazawa, and Y. Yamagata, *MRS Int. Meet. Adv. Mater.*, **8**, 257 (1989).

5. T. Suga, Y. Takahashi, H. Takagi, B. Gibbesch, and G. Elssner, *Acta Metall. Mater.*, **40**, s133 (1992).
6. H. Takagi, K. Kikuchi, R. Maeda, T. R. Chung, and T. Suga, *Appl. Phys. Lett.*, **68**, 2222 (1996).
7. E. Higurashi, T. Imamura, T. Suga, and R. Sawada, *IEEE Photonics Technology Letters*, **19**(24), 1994 (2007).
8. T. Shimatsu, H. Yoshida, M. Uomoto, T. Saito, T. Moriwaki, N. Kato, Y. Miyamoto, and K. Miyamoto, *Proceedings of the Seventh International Workshop on Low Temperature Bonding for 3D Integration (LTB-3D 2021)*, 51 (2021).
9. T. Shimatsu, M. Uomoto, T. Saito, T. Moriwaki, and N. Kato, *Proceedings of the Conference on Wafer Bonding for Microsystems, 3D and Wafer Level Integration (WaferBond22)*, pp.19-22 (2022).
10. M. Uomoto, H. Yoshida, T. Shimatsu, T. Saito, T. Moriwaki, N. Kato, Y. Miyamoto, and K. Miyamoto, *Proceedings of the Seventh International Workshop on Low Temperature Bonding for 3D Integration (LTB-3D 2021)*, 45 (2021).
11. A. Muraoka, H. Makita, T. Saitoh, M. Uomoto, and T. Shimatsu, *Proceedings of the Conference on Wafer Bonding for Microsystems, 3D and Wafer Level Integration (WaferBond22)*, pp.23-24 (2022).
12. M. P. Maszara, G. Goetz, A. Cavigila, and J. B. McKitterick, *J. Appl. Phys.*, **64**, 4943 (1988).
13. T. Martini, J. Steinkirchner, and U. Gösele, *J. Electrochem. Soc.*, **144**, 354-357 (1997).
14. Y. Bertholet, F. Iker, J.P. Raskin, and T. Pardoen, *Sensors and Actuators*, **A 110**, 157-163 (2004).
15. F. Fournel, L. Continni, C. Morales, J. Da Fonseca, H. Moriceau, F. Rieutord, A. Barthelemy, and I. Radu, *J. Appl. Phys.*, **111**, 104907 (2012).
16. M. Uomoto and T. Shimatsu, *Proceedings of the 34th Spring Meeting of the Japan Institute of Electronic Packaging*, 3C1-02 (2020)
17. K. Takeuchi, and T. Suga, *Proceedings of the Seventh International Workshop on Low Temperature Bonding for 3D Integration (LTB-3D 2021)*, 9 (2021).
18. L. Vitos, A.V. Ruban, H.L. Skriver, and J. Kolla´r, *Surface Science*, **411**, 186 (1998).

ECS Transactions, 112 (3) 207-220 (2023)
10.1149/11203.0207ecst ©The Electrochemical Society

Investigation of Anodic Bond Formation Process and Potential Use of the Results

R. Knechtel, M. Wenig, D. Kley, M. Seyring

Schmalkalden University of Applied Sciences, Chair of the Carl Zeiss Foundation for Autonomous Intelligent Sensors, 98575 Schmalkalden, Germany

Anodic bonding of glass to silicon wafers is an essential step in microsystems manufacturing, combining reliable process setup with robust process control and providing very strong and hermetic wafer bonds. It is general accepted that the bond formation is based on anodic oxidation processes, but it is still under debate where the oxygen originates from and how far the oxidation can be driven. The oxidation mechanism during anodic bonding has been studied using sequential and one-step bonding procedures. It can be concluded that the oxygen for the oxidation originates from the glass. It is therefore possible to completely oxidise sputtered aluminium between two glass wafers during bonding, resulting in a nearly optically transparent bond of both wafers. By understanding the oxidation processes, it is possible to predict which surface layers will bond well (silicon, silicon dioxide, aluminium) and which will be hardly or impossible to bond (silicon nitride, gold). These predictions have been tested and confirmed by experimental results.

Introduction

In microsystems technology, wafer bonding is a crucial process for fully exploiting the 3rd dimension, e.g. by sealing MEMS and microfluidic structures. There are many different technological processes available for such wafer bonding applications [1], e.g. glass frit bonding, bonding with metallic interlayers or surface-activated bonding. However, one of the best controllable wafer bonding process is the anodic bonding of glass wafers. Sufficient control can be achieved during the process by means of the bonding current and its characteristic time dependence which indicates whether the bonding process is proceeding as desired. In addition, it is easy to check for unbonded areas right after the process using light-optical methods, and it is even possible to determine the bond strength non-destructively on special test structures [2]. Many, but not all, coating materials commonly used in microsystems technology allow for anodic bonding. However, since anodic bonding is a very safe bonding process for the reasons mentioned above, the formation of bonds and the bonding of different surface layers was re-investigated, in order to attain a deeper understanding of the anodic bonding process and explore even wider application areas. The andic bonding approach becomes even more attractive due to the fact that the prior limitation of this bonding technology, the limited structuring of glass wafers (so far rather large structures are feasible with a low edge quality), has now been overcome by the availability of laser induced glass etching [3],[4], providing well defined and even small structures in the glass.

Anodic bonding [5] is a relatively simple and safe process for achieving high bond strength and hermetic sealing. For anodic bonding, one of the two wafers to be bond must be made of a sodium-containing glass, whose coefficient of thermal expansion is matched to that of silicon, e.g. SCHOTT Borofloat®33 [6], Corning Pyrex #7740 or Hoya SD2. A bonding stack of a glass and a silicon wafer is heated to a temperature between 300 and 500 °C. At these temperatures, the sodium ions in the glass become mobile. By applying a negative voltage of a few hundred volts to the glass wafers, the sodium ions drift away from the bonding interface, creating a depletion zone in the glass at the interface to the silicon, where most of the bonding voltage is dropping. As a result of the strong electrostatic field, the wafers are pressed together at the atomic level and oxygen bonds are formed between the glass and the silicon by field assisted oxygen diffusion and anodic oxidation. Figure 1 illustrates this process and shows a typical application example.

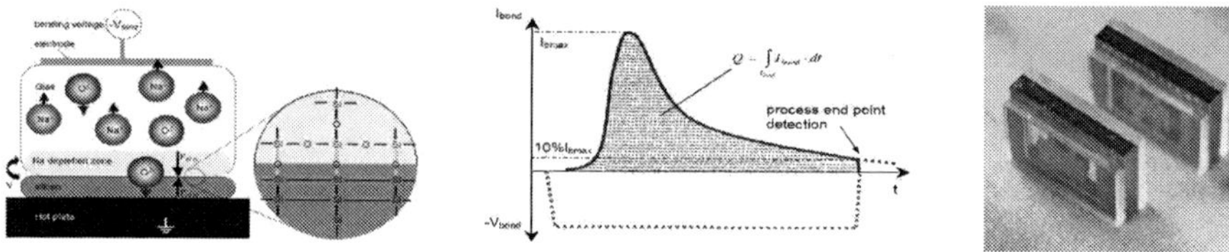

Figure 1: Principle of anodic bonding, voltage and electrical current over time for an ideal anodic bonding process, and a typical application example.

The bond formation in anodic bonding is described by Cozma and Jakobson in [7] as follows:

> *"When Silicon and glass are in intimate contact, chemical reactions take place at the interface, resulting in the oxidation of the Silicon substrate and, hence, in permanent atomic bonds between Silicon and glass."*

Several publications have investigated the sources of oxygen for the oxidation in the bond interface and have concluded that the oxygen is either from the glass (as previously described) or from surface attached hydroxyl groups [8]. The presence of the oxide has been confirmed directly by imaging techniques such as elastic recoil detection analysis [9] and transmission electron microscopy [5], or indirectly by selective etching and subsequent thickness measurement of the bond interface [10].

Based on these descriptions of bond formation during anodic bonding, the following two hypotheses can be derived, which have been investigated and are presented and discussed below:

Hypothesis 1: If the oxygen for oxide formation at the bond interface comes from the glass, then it should be possible to completely oxidise very thin surface layers in extended anodic bonding processes. In this way, two glass wafers could be bonded together via a very thin aluminium interlayer, with the aluminium being completely oxidised and thus becoming transparent. Such an experiment would open promising optical applications and contribute to a deeper understanding of the anodic bonding process.

Hypothesis 2: Materials that are easily to oxidise, such as aluminium and silicon, should be able to be anodically bonded quite well, even if they have a natural oxide layer, whereas this should be difficult or impossible for inert materials such as silicon nitride or gold.

Anodic Bonding of Glass Wafers with Thin Aluminium Interlayer

In order to gain a deeper insight into the formation of the anodic bond and thus open up new applications and an even wider use of anodic bonding, a first basic experiment was carried out as follows: A glass wafer was sputter coated with a thin aluminium layer. A second glass wafer was anodically bonded to this aluminium layer. The sputtered aluminium layer has a higher thickness in the centre of the wafer due to the fact, that the glass wafer was eccentrically rotated under a smaller sputtering target. This thickness gradient should allow the characterisation of different aluminium layer thicknesses in one sample. The sputtering time was set so that the deposited aluminium layer at the centre of the wafer was non-transparent (about 30nm relative to the internal thickness monitor of the coater), while at the edge of the wafer only a few nanometres of aluminium formed a semi-transparent layer. A first bonding was performed using a relatively low bonding voltage of 500 V, resulting in a peak current of less than 2 mA. Bonding was repeated 3 more times with increasing voltages of 1000 V, 1500 V and 2000 V. The typical bonding current characteristics (depletion zone forming and related current drop) were observed for all bonding experiments (Figure 2). For the lower voltages of 500 V and 1000 V the anodic bonding current was below the 10 mA limit of the voltage source, peaking at around 2 mA and just over 9 mA respectively. For the higher voltages, the control behaviour of the voltage source is visible. The voltage is ramped up, until the 10 mA current limit is reached, at which point the depletion zone has already formed at the bond interface and is growing into the glass over time. As the depletion zone expands, the current should decrease, as can be seen at 1000 V. However, for higher voltages, set in the recipe, the target point was not reached before the bonding current saturated, so the voltage was continuously increased by the control electronics until the set point was reached. During this time the bonding current remained constant at the limit of 10 mA. Immediately after the target bond voltage was reached, the bond current decreased according to the depletion zone behaviour. In all four experiments the process continued until 10% of the respective maximum bond current (recipe set point) was reached (end point criteria for the anodic bonding).

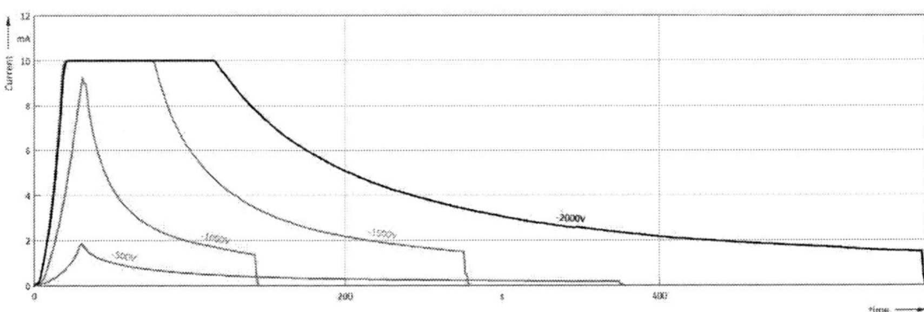

Figure 2: Bond current curves at different bonding voltages for bonding two glass wafers with a 30nm aluminium interlayer (310°C bonding temperature, time normalised to the onset of the bonding current).

Figure 3 shows the initial metallised glass wafer and the bond results of the four bonding conditions mentioned as full wafer images together with details of the blade test. The blade test according to Maszara [11] was performed for a qualitative investigation of the bond strength. A razor blade was inserted at the edge of the bonded glass wafer stack until the interference fringes disappeared at the unbonded wafer edge. This revealed the boundary between the bonded and unbonded areas. From the wedge effect of the balde it can be concluded that sufficient bond strength has been achieved. Due to the boundary conditions (wafer, i.e. no cut-out strips, test in atmosphere, risk of cracking in the glass wafer when the blade is further inserted) no quantitative determination of the bond strength was possible.

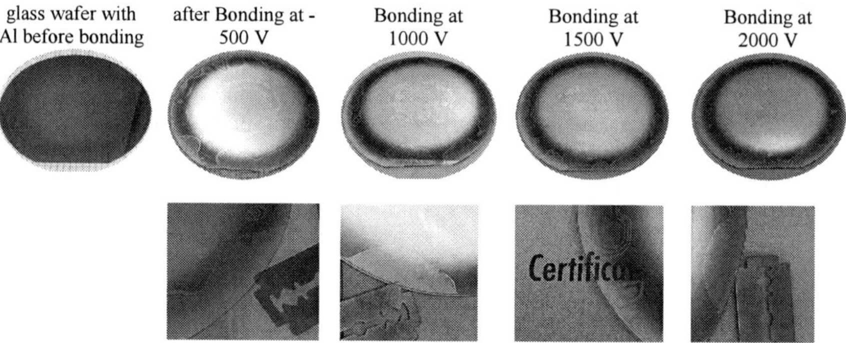

Figure 3: Bond current characteristics at different bonding voltages when bonding two glass wafers with 30nm aluminium interlayer (310 °C bonding temperature).

Bonding has taken place between the 6" wafers for all bonding voltages. Unfortunately, particle contamination could not be completely avoided during processing, resulting in larger unbonded areas, especially at the centre and edges of the wafers. The image series (Figure 3) clearly shows the unbonded areas are in the centre of the wafer. Here with progressing of the bond series, the unbonded areas are reduced in size, since higher bonding voltages, also drives a higher bond pressure at the bond interface. Beside this the areas where the aluminium has a homogeneous silver appearance form a very good bond. These areas have high bond strength as shown by the blade tests. However, large non-bonded areas remain at the edge of the wafer, but these merge directly into neighbouring areas of high bond strength. It can be assumed that the aluminium layer is too thin to form an to form the anodic bond at the wafer edge. Although the transparent area at the wafer edge is slightly wider than the unbonded aluminium sputtered glass, this is the area where no bonding has taken place. As the bonding was carried out under vacuum (<10-3 mbar), it can be assumed that the apparent oxidation that made the aluminium transparent at the wafer edge (see Figure 3, 1500 V) originated from the wafers or the wafer surface. However, as not truly transparent but well bonded areas were obtained, two further experiments were carried out using the same stack of wafers at higher temperatures and the highest possible bond voltage of 2000 V. The results are shown in Figure 4. By using very intensive bonding conditions and accumulating the charge shifts over the sequence of experiments, the 5th bond experiment succeeded in producing at least small well bonded and at the same time almost transparent regions.

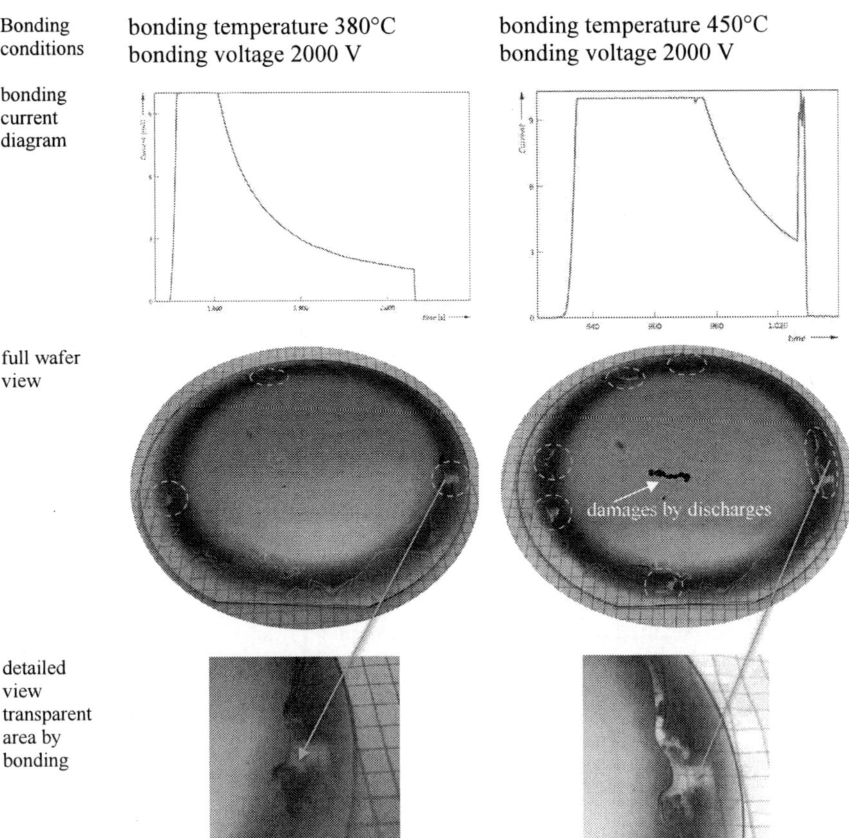

Figure 4: Formation of small transparent bond areas under intensive bonding conditions

These transparent areas were significantly enlarged during a 6th bonding of the same stack during which 4 new transparent areas were created. Unfortunately, it was not possible to continue the experiment to increase the fraction of the transparent areas, because during the last bonding, strong discharges occurred in the centre of the wafer, damaging the surface of the upper glass wafer and preventing further bonding. In the final state of this wafer stack, blade tests were repeated. The blade, inserted from the edge near the largest transparent area, opened a gap between the two wafers at the unbonded wafer edge (Figure 5), but only up to the edge of the transparent area, verifying that the transparent area was bonded with high bonding strength. This blade test is shown in Figure 5, the left part shows the wafer edge close to the transparent area, but without the blade. There are interference fringes visible between the wafer edge and the transparent area, indicating that there is a small gap between the two wafers, i.e. the wafers are not bonded up to the wafer edge. In the right image, the blade is inserted, and the interference fringes are no longer visible because the gap has been opened further by the blade. However, there is no movement of the edge of the transparent area, which means that it is well and strongly bonded. The bonded areas are not perfectly transparent, some opacity is still present, but is expected to disappear as bonding progresses further with higher voltage.

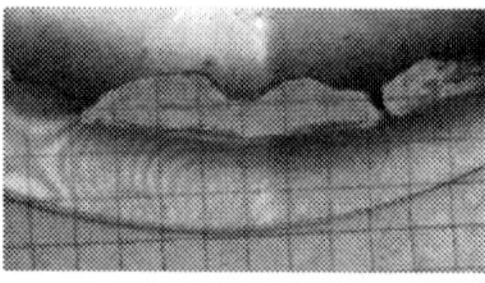 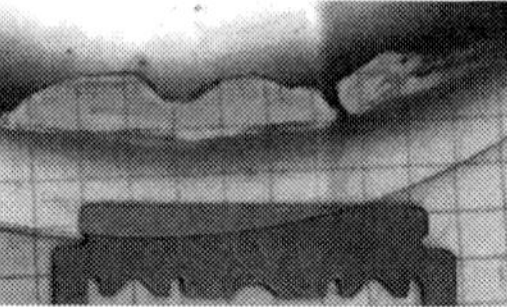

Figure 5: Blade test close to the transparent areas confirming a strong bond there.

Since the first sequential anodic bonding experiments produced only very small bonded transparent areas, and these were in a medium thickness region of the aluminium layer, another glass wafer was sputtered with aluminium (Figure 6) of half the thickness (15 nm according to the layer thickness monitor). This resulted in a wide zone of very thin aluminium at the edge of the wafer, which was expected to be too thin for anodic bonding. However, after a single bond at 2000 V and 430 °C, almost transparent areas appeared, like segments of a circular ring, where the aluminium layer was thick enough for bonding but thin enough to be almost completely oxidised. In this case, the transparency was not quite as perfect as in the first experiment, indicating that the bonding time, and thus the transfer of oxygen ions from the glass, was not yet sufficient for a complete aluminium oxidation. A further bonding sequence was not possible as the wafer brake off at the wafer edge. Discharges also occurred during this bonding experiment when the maximum voltage was reached. To protect the power supply of the bonding tool, the bonding process was stopped. The depletion behaviour up to the start of the discharge was quite perfect, as evidenced by an almost ideal ramping of the voltage in relation to a growing depletion zone (automatic voltage increase by powering at a constant current of 10 mA until the desired voltage is reached). The blade test showed again that the nearly transparent areas were firmly bonded (Figure 6).

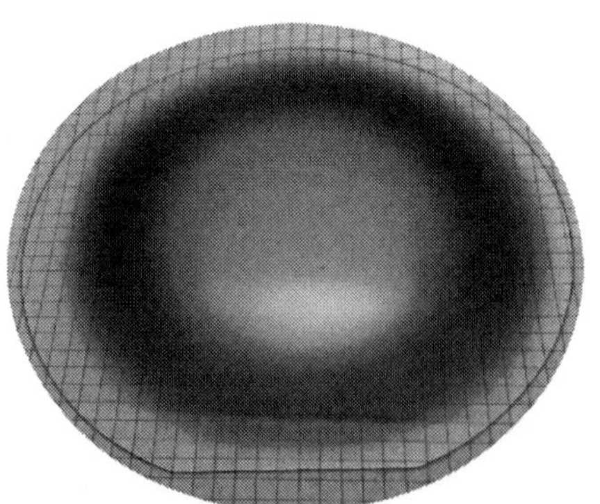

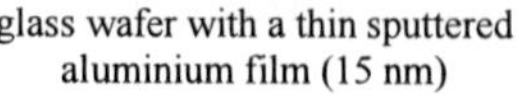

glass wafer with a thin sputtered
aluminium film (15 nm)

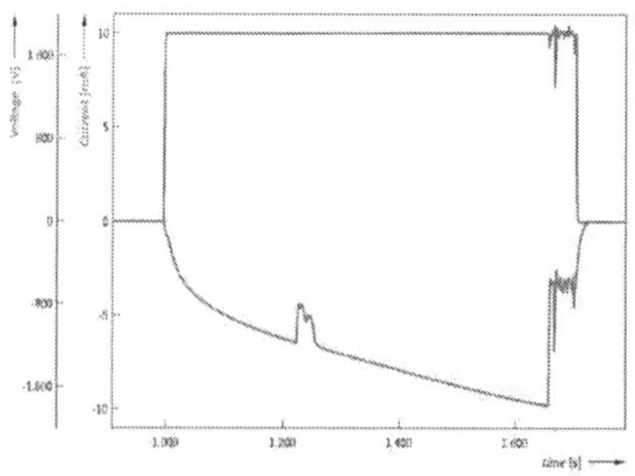

anodic bonding current characteristic of a single
bond glass to glass bonding with a thin aluminium
interlayer

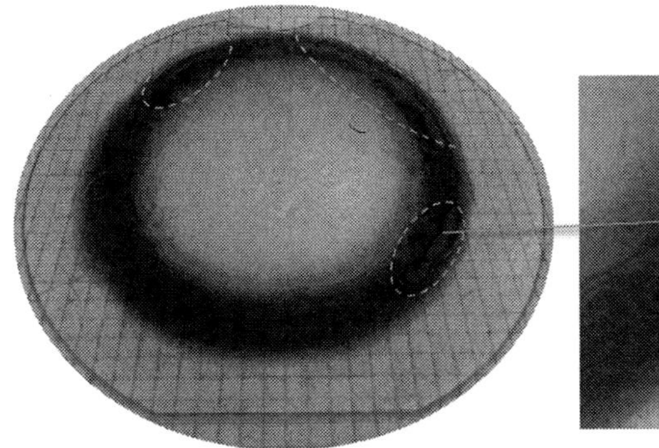
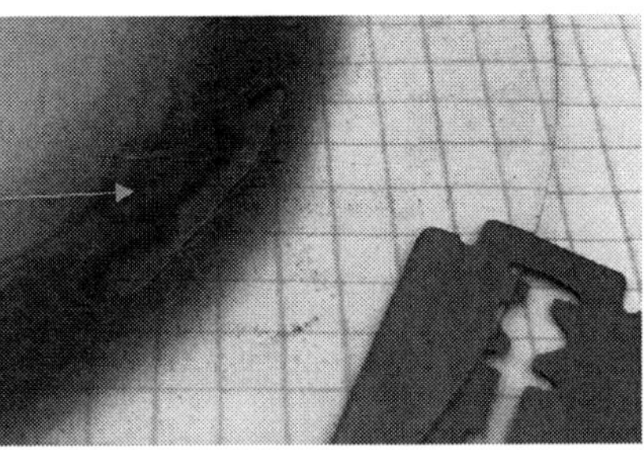

<table>
<tr><td align="center">resulting
glass to glass bonding with thin aluminium
interlayer after a single bond process</td><td align="center">blade test confirming bonding in the transparent
area, crack opening by the blade stopped at the
edge of the bonded and transparent areas</td></tr>
</table>

Figure 6: Results of repeated bonding of glass-glass wafers with a 15 nm thin aluminium interlayer in one bonding step and formation of transparent well-bonded areas.

From these two basic experiments it can be concluded that if aluminium is present in the bonding interface, it can be completely oxidised by the bonding process and a strong bond interface, transparent to visible light, can be formed. The glass wafers are thus bonded together by an aluminium oxide layer. To achieve the desired transparent aluminium oxide bond, the aluminium layer must be thin enough to allow complete oxidation. The optimum bonding time remains to be investigated, but it is likely to be related to the amount of sodium ions displaced, which is also a measure of the oxygen displaced into the bonding interface. Therefore, a bonding process controlled by the moving charges would be ideal (possible control mode in bonding tools). To achieve this, the bond temperature and voltage must be as high as possible (but this is limited by the bond system). As shown, the oxidation of the aluminium progresses over time, the oxygen must diffuse out of the glass, which is like a virtually unlimited reservoir. If the hydroxyl groups attached to the wafer surfaces were the sole source of oxygen, they would be consumed very quickly, and no further oxidation could take place. It has also been shown that the aluminium requires a minimum thickness to act as a bonding layer between two glass wafers. Based on the bonding results, the optimum thickness is estimated to be 10 nm. This needs to be confirmed using glass wafers from sputter tools with better thickness homogeneity. Based on more homogeneous layer thicknesses of the aluminium, larger or full wafer transparent and bonded areas are expected. The so far results confirm hypothesis 1, that strong anodic oxidation occurs in the bond interface, while the required oxygen comes from the glass. Thin aluminium layers can be completely oxidised, resulting in a transparent bond interface suitable for optical applications, if bonding process is long enough and enough oxygen ions are transferred from the glass to the aluminium. To reach this, wafers must be well cleaned to avoid any discharges.

Bonding of Different Surface Layers on Silicon Wafers

Having concluded that oxidation is the mechanism for anodic bond formation, the second hypothesis can be pursued. It is expected that films made of easily oxidisable materials will have a greater ability to form bonds than inert materials. Materials from both groups were selected, deposited on 6" silicon wafers and anodically bonded to glass wafers. The same bonding recipe was used for all these experiments: bonding in vacuum (<10-3 mbar, 310 °C, bonding tool pressure of 500 mbar, bonding voltage of 500 V, end point criterion for the bonding current is 10% of its maximum value). Bond current characteristics, optical inspections of the entire wafer surface and blade test were used to evaluate the bonding process.

Bonding of oxidisable layers

Silicon (with native oxide) and thermally generated silicon oxide (dry oxidation), TEOS based silicon oxide and aluminium were selected as relatively easily oxidisable layers at the bond interface. It should be noted that both silicon and aluminium form natural oxide layers. As is known from the chemical oxidation of silicon, these layers have the ability to grow, i.e. to continue to oxidise the pure material underneath. This requires considerable energy, not so much from the temperature during the bonding process (the 310°C used is too low; thermal oxidation of silicon requires more than 900°C), but rather from the electric field (anodic oxidation). The results of these bonding experiments are listed and briefly described below.

<u>Bonding of Silicon Wafers:</u>   A silicon wafer without any deposited layer was bonded using the above bonding recipe. Silicon means, that the surface of the silicon is covered by its native oxide, which is fast growing, but self-limiting (about 1.5 nm), when silicon is exposed to air. These is the typical configuration of silicon in wafer processing. As expected, a high bonding current with typical depletion was observed during bonding. Apart from a few spots around particles (unavoidable due to wafer handling), the entire wafer area was bonded. The bond is very strong, the blade could not be inserted at the wafer edge. The results are summarised in Figure 7, silicon anodically bonds very well to glass, even at low voltages, which is in line with general experience.

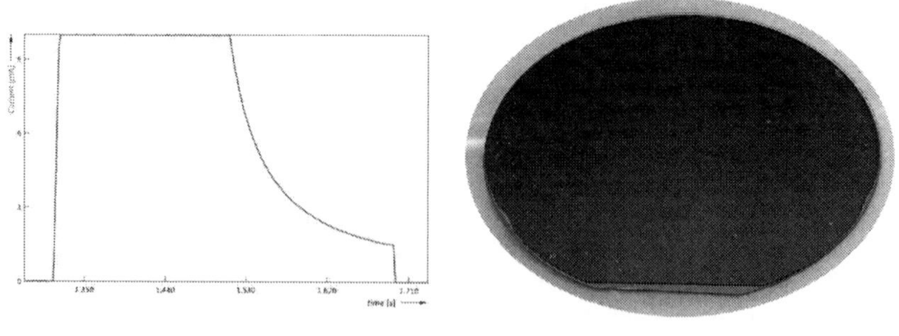

bonding current   picture of bonded stack
blade test – not possible to insert blade from wafer edge very strong bond

Figure 7: Results of anodic bonding test on silicon surface with native oxide.

<u>Thermal oxide bonding:</u> A silicon wafer was thermally oxidised using a wet oxidation process, resulting in 360 nm of silicon oxide on both sides of the wafer. Bonding was carried out using the standard recipe at 500 V, there was a very low bonding current which showed two further maxima after an initial depletion, followed by two more depletions. This is quite atypical for anodic bonding and could just be explained by the effect of more and more wafer area being contacted during the process, providing more charge carriers (sodium ions), which again increases the current. Both the low bonding current and the atypical current behaviour can be explained by the presence of a thermal oxide on both sides of the silicon, which acts as a very good insulator, resulting in a high voltage drop across it. Therefore, less voltage is available to electro-mechanically press the wafers together. Full wafer area contact was thus achieved in 3 steps, moving enough sodium in the glass to form the depletion zone stepwise on the full wafer area. However, the bonding results are very promising in relation to the low bonding current (Figure 8). Only one non-bonded area (opposite flat) was observed, along with some spotty particle related bonding defects (wafer centre). The bond strengths appear to be very high; the blade could not be inserted between the wafers.

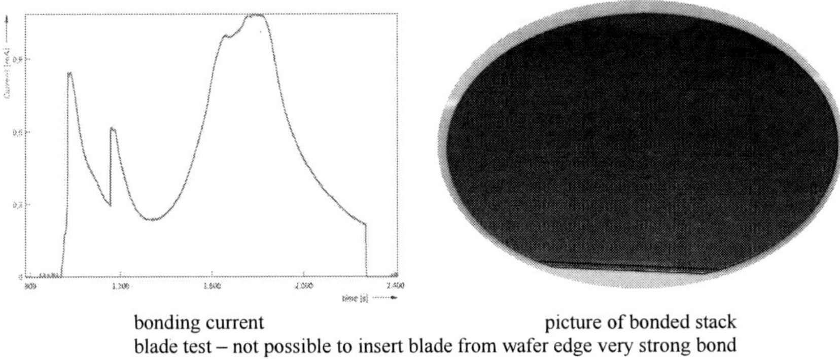

bonding current   picture of bonded stack
blade test – not possible to insert blade from wafer edge very strong bond

Figure 8: Results anodic bonding test thermal silicon oxide.

<u>Bonding of TEOS-based Oxide:</u> Anodic bonding of TEOS based PE CVD silicon oxide is known to be a reliable and stable process. This type of deposited layer is often used as the final bonding layer of stacked films in MEMS applications [13]. In the current study it is shown that a 100 nm thick film can be anodically bonded very well. A high bonding current was observed during the bond process, and optical inspection after bonding revealed only some small unbonded areas attributed to particles collected on the surface of both wafers prior to bonding (Figure 9). The bond is considered to be very strong as also at this wafer pair the blade could not be inserted between the wafers.

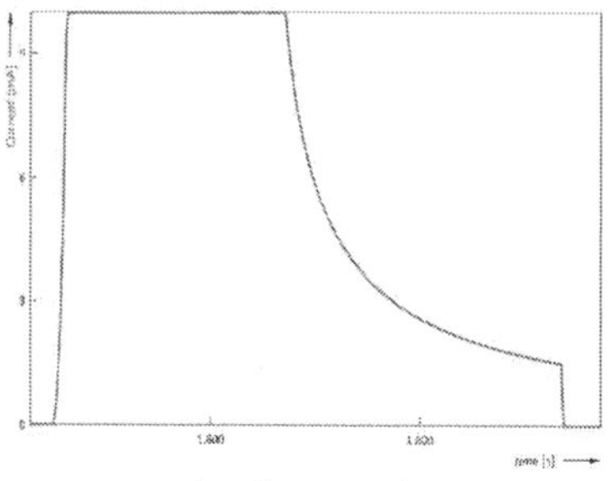

bonding current

picture of bonded stack

blade test – not possible to insert blade from wafer edge with very strong bond

remarks: artefacts at wafer flat are reflections

Figure 9: Results of the TEOS oxide anodic bonding test.

<u>Bonding of Aluminium:</u>   The experiment of anodic bonding of glass to aluminium (100nm thick layer on thin oxide adhesion layer on a 6" silicon wafer) showed excellent results. The expected current behaviour was observed during bonding, i.e. a high bond current, which decreased as expected with the formation of the depletion zone, while reaching the set bond voltage. Surprisingly, no unbonded areas are visible on this pair of wafers (Figure 10). Since it cannot be assumed that these wafers were completely free of particles prior to bonding, it is likely that the particles imprint into the 100 nm thick aluminium layer, reducing their actual topography and allowing bonding almost up to the particles. This bond is also very strong. From all the other results in this study, aluminium is concluded as very best layer for anodic bonding.

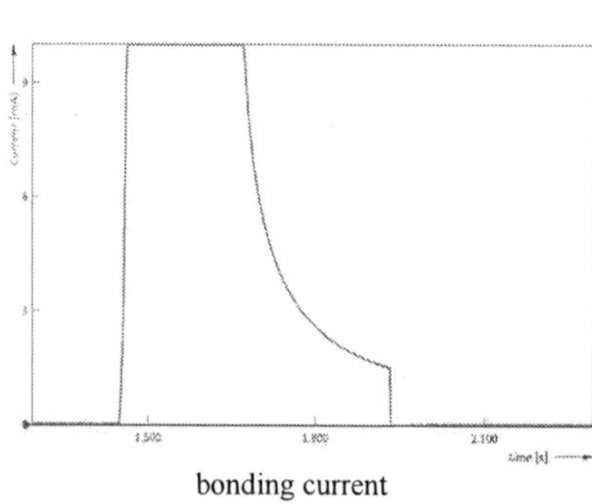

bonding current

picture of bonded stack

blade test – not possible to insert blade from wafer edge very strong bond

Figure 10: Results anodic bonding test aluminium.

For all the well oxidisable surface layers (silicon, silicon oxide in various technological variants, aluminium) it can be concluded that anodic bonding works excellently. In the simple arrangements tested with single layers (only aluminium had a thin silicon oxide adhesion layer), bonding voltages of 500 V at the ideal bonding temperature of 310 °C were sufficient to form strong bonds. Therefore, anodic bonding is a very safe and controllable process for these types of layers.

Anodic bonding test of inert coatings

Based on the previous findings, two materials were selected, silicon nitride and gold, which are hardly oxidisable and for which anodic bonding should be very difficult or even impossible. Bonding tests were carried out using the above recipe, i.e. at 310 °C and 500 V. The results are described below for each material.

<u>Bonding of Silicon Nitride:</u>   The silicon nitride anodic bonding experiment was carried out on a 780 nm thick LP (low pressure) CVD nitride film on a silicon wafer. As expected, the bond current profile shows a high current value associated with the formation of the depletion zone. After removing the wafer from the bonding tool, many large bubble-like unbonded areas are found on the wafer (Figure 11). In addition, a fracture was visible on both wafers opposite the flat, caused by mechanical damage during wafer handling (not a result of the bonding process). When the blade was inserted between the wafers (blade test), it was evident that the wafer bond could be detached (Figure 10). Large parts of the glass wafer could be removed and the remaining glass in the centre of the wafer also has low bond strength. As expected, the silicon nitride is difficult to bond anodically, but at least in the centre of the wafer some bond formation can be observed, which can be improved by applying higher bonding voltages or bonding temperatures. LP CVD layers are usually not perfectly stoichiometric, so oxygen can still form chemical bonds on not fully saturated silicon atoms and bonding can occur. However, process control and monitoring in anodic bonding is very challenging, which is critical for use in industrial technologies.

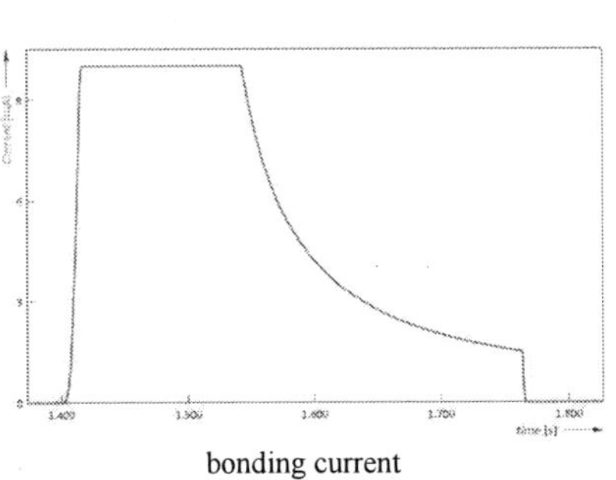

bonding current

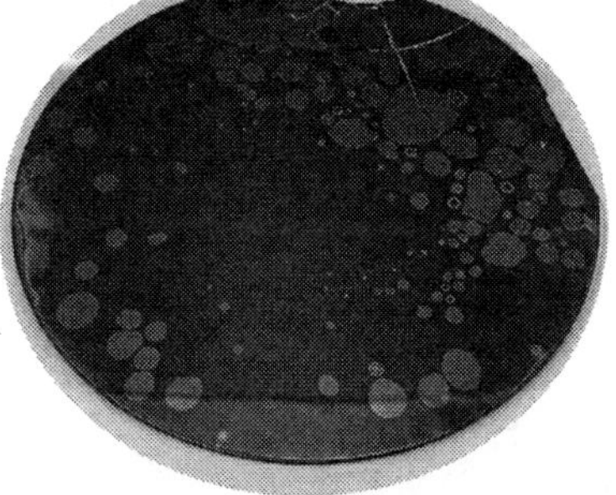

picture of bonded stack, large bubble like
unbonded areas indicate poor bonding quality

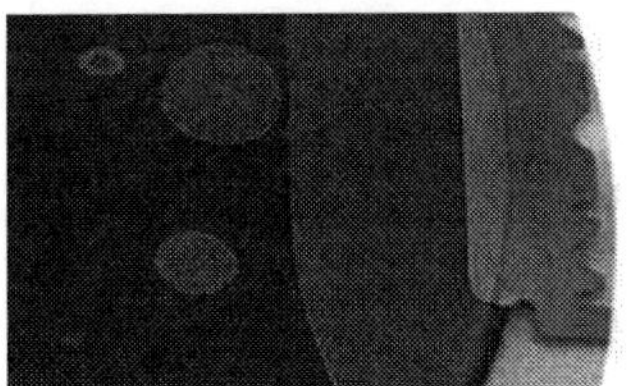

blade test – blade is opening large gaps,
a clear indication for a very weak bonding

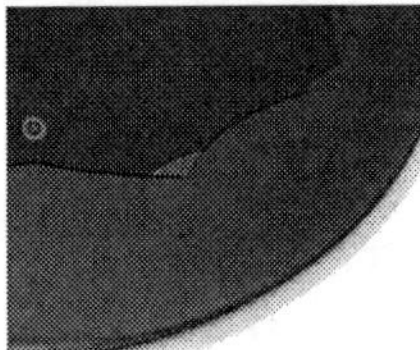

after blade test –spalled glass flakes have been
removed , fringes at remaining glass indicate low
bond strength in the center area, too

Figure 11: Anodic bonding test results silicon nitride.

<u>Gold bonding:</u>   A sputtered gold layer of approximately 200 nm thickness was used to conduct the anodic bonding. In the image of the bonded wafer stack, areas where the gold adhered to the glass wafer are visible as darker appearance of the gold. However, when the blade was inserted, these wafers were easily sheared off as the adhesion of gold to silicon oxide is low. As this is well known, and as intermediate chromium adhesion layers are usually used. In the current experiment, only pure gold was used to investigate whether gold could be transferred to the glass wafer by anodic wafer bonding. In a first approach this appeared to be possible as the glass with the gold could be detached from the silicon wafer during the blade test (Figure 12 blade test). However, in a further test, the gold could also be easily removed from the glass. This suggests that the gold cannot be anodically bonded to the glass, as previously expected.

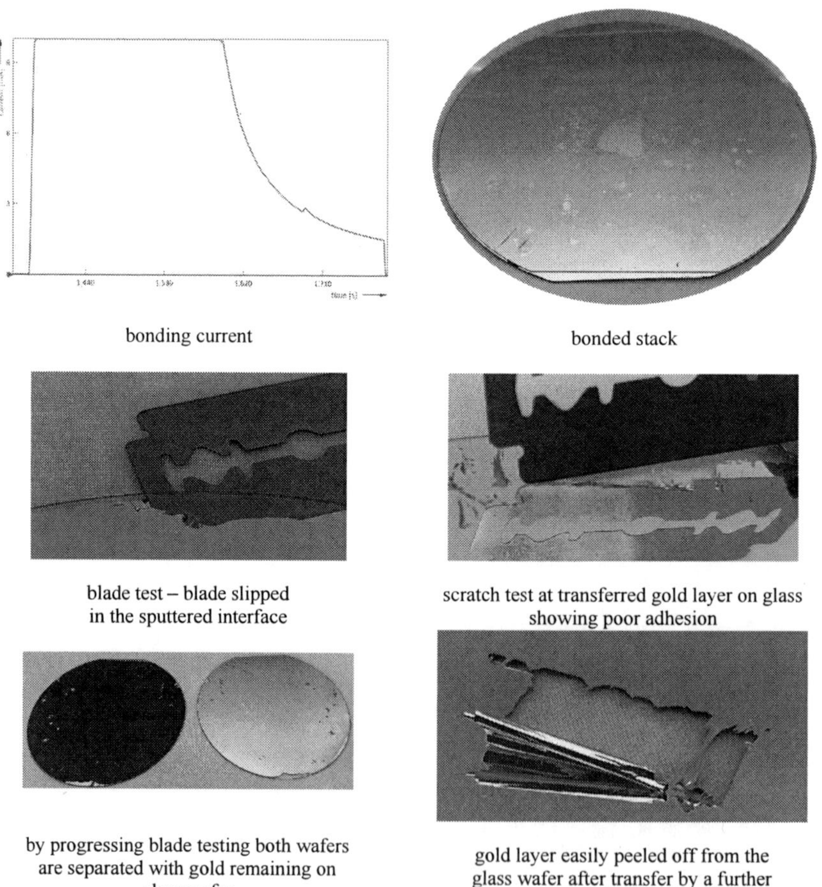

bonding current

bonded stack

blade test – blade slipped
in the sputtered interface

scratch test at transferred gold layer on glass
showing poor adhesion

by progressing blade testing both wafers
are separated with gold remaining on
glass wafer

gold layer easily peeled off from the
glass wafer after transfer by a further
anodic bonding trial

Figure 12: Anodic bonding test results gold layer.

The anodic bonding tests on inert layers clearly show that the decisive effect in anodic bonding is the oxidation of the bonding layer. This creates oxide bonds that hold the wafers together. If oxidation is not possible (as is the case with gold), then no bonds are formed. If only a few bonds are possible (as is the case with silicon nitride), bond formation is difficult to achieve. In this context, hypothesis 2 is also proven. In addition, both experiments with inert materials, showed perfect bond current profiles, so the depletion zone is a necessary but not sufficient condition for the formation of the anodic bond. It ensures that the materials to be bonded come into intimate contact down to the atomic level, but bond formation only occurs if there is a strong oxidising effect on the bond partner surface, starting from the glass. Therefore, the bond current flow is not a reliable indicator of a good bond, and the oxidation processes at the bond interface cannot be directly monitored by the bond tool.

Summary, Conclusions and Outlook

Based on the general understanding of the anodic bond and literature data that oxidation processes trigger the formation of the anodic bond, it was shown that the oxygen for oxidation at the bond interface originates from the glass. This was confirmed by a series of experiments carried out. Several bonding experiments between two glass wafers, one of which had received a thin sputtered aluminium layer, showed oxidation of the aluminium during the bonding process, which held the wafers strongly together. The local formation of transparent aluminium oxide indicates complete oxidation of the aluminium. This process requires high temperatures and high bonding voltages, i.e., long bonding times. The application of high bonding voltages is accompanied by large amounts of displaced sodium ions causing a large amount of more or less unbound oxygen to diffuse from the glass to the bonding partner. This proves that the oxygen for this strong and intense oxidation cannot only originate from hydroxyl groups attached to the surfaces but must be provided by the glass volume. Future experiments using glass wafers with thin (10 nm may be an ideal thickness) homogeneous aluminium layers will probably show the possibility of obtaining larger transparent areas with the potential for optical applications.

In the second part, based on these results, the prediction was made that only well oxidisable layers allow for anodic bonding whereas fully inert layers cannot. This was confirmed by experiments: Silicon, silicon oxide (also in different technological versions) and aluminium can be anodically bonded very well, whereas silicon nitride can only be bonded with limitations and great effort, and gold cannot be anodically bonded at all. Further materials need to be investigated according to this classification and whether higher bonding voltages and temperatures can achieve better bonding results on difficult to bond materials.

Acknowledgments

The authors would like to thank X-FAB MEMS Foundry GmbH Erfurt for providing samples with different surface films used in these investigations. Roy Knechtel would like to thank the Carl-Zeiss-Foundation for funding the research activities of his professorship.

References

1. Knechtel, R., & Schwarz, U. (2021). Wafer Bonding in MEMS Technologies. In Microactuators, Microsensors and Micromechanisms: MAMM 2020 5 (pp. 89-102). Springer International Publishing.

2. Vallin, Ö., Jonsson, K., & Knechtel, R. (2020). Strength of bonded interfaces. In *Handbook of Silicon Based MEMS Materials and Technologies* (pp. 823-832). Elsevier.

3. Gottmann, J., Hermans, M., Repiev, N., & Ortmann, J. (2017). Selective laser-induced etching of 3D precision quartz glass components for microfluidic applications—up-scaling of complexity and speed. *Micromachines, 8*(4), 110.

4. Chen, J., Lu, X., Wen, Q., Jiang, F., Lu, J., Lei, D., & Pan, Y. (2021). Review on laser-induced etching processing technology for transparent hard and brittle materials. The International Journal of Advanced Manufacturing Technology, 117(9-10), 2545-2564.

5. D.I. Pomerantz et al., US Patent 3,417,459, 1968.

6. SCHOTT technical Galss Solutions GmbH, Jena: BOROFLOAT® 33 – Technical Data, https://www.schott.com/de-ch/products/borofloat-p1000314/downloads (June 10th 2023)

7. Cozma, A., & Jakobsen, H. (2020). Anodic bonding. In Handbook of Silicon Based MEMS Materials and Technologies (pp. 581-592). Elsevier.

8. Cozma, A., & Puers, B. (1995). Characterization of the electrostatic bonding of Silicon and Pyrex glass. J. of Micromechanics and Microengineering, 5(2), 98.

9. Nitzsche, P., Lange, K., Schmidt, B., Grigull, S., Kreissig, U., Thomas, B., & Herzog, K. (1998). Ion drift processes in Pyrex-type alkali-borosilicate glass during anodic bonding. Journal of the Electrochemical Society, 145(5), 1755.

10. Baumann, H., Mack, S., & Münzel, H., Bonding of structured wafers, Electrochem. Soc. Proc. PV 95-7 (1995) 471"474.

11. Maszara, W. P., Goetz, G., Caviglia, A., & McKitterick, J. B. (1988). Bonding of Silicon wafers for Silicon-on-insulator. Journal of Applied Physics, 64(10), 4943-4950.

12. Harz, M., & Engelke, H. (1996). Curvature changing or flattening of anodically bonded Silicon and borosilicate glass. Sensors and Actuators A: Physical, 55(2-3), 201-209.

13. Freywald, K., Knechtel, R.: Verfahren und Anordnung zum Passivieren anodischer Bondgebiete, die über elektrisch aktiven Strukturen von mikroelektromechanischen Systemen angeordnet sind (Micromechanical System: MEMS), DE10129 821.8 A1

ECS Transactions, 112 (3) 221-228 (2023)
10.1149/11203.0221ecst ©The Electrochemical Society

Efficient Xe Filling of MEMS Vapor Cells Empowered by Customized Triple Stack Wafer Bond Processing

A. Roshanghias[a], J. Kaczynski[a], G. Grosso[a], A. Rodrigues[a], M. Hübner[b], M. Zauner[a], N. Andrianov[a], M. Khan[a], T. Grömer[c], T. Fuchs[b] and A. Binder[a]

[a] Silicon Austria Labs GmbH, Villach, Austria
[b] Robert Bosch GmbH, Renningen, Germany
[c] EV Group, St. Florian am Inn, Austria

Nuclear-magnetic-resonance (NMR) gyroscopes based on MEMS vapor cell technology are currently being investigated worldwide and show superior advantages over current MEMS gyroscopes. However, there are still challenges in the upscaling and further deployment of NMR gyroscopes, due to the extremely high cost of the required gases (i.e., 129Xe, 131Xe), size, and high power consumption. To tackle these bottlenecks, in this study, a miniaturized, chip-scale, and low-cost NMR gyroscope has been conceptualized and fabricated. Here, a cost-effective and scalable filling of MEMS vapor cells with Xe gas was developed via an innovative microfabrication and wafer stacking process flow. By utilizing ultra-thin glass wafers, Taiko-processed silicon wafers, and an external gas flow system integrated into the wafer bonder, a sequential anodic bonding technique is executed to create a hermetically sealed Xe gas-filled chamber at minimal Xe consumption during the filling process.

Introduction

Nuclear magnetic resonance (NMR) gyroscopes have been proposed as an alternative to mechanical gyroscopes due to their high sensitivity, stability, and accuracy. They have become a key component of navigation systems for modern mobility solutions. NMR gyroscopes are rotation rate sensors that measure a shift in the Larmor precession frequency of the nuclear spins of an atomic gas under an applied magnetic field to detect the angular rate [1-3]. The atomic gas consists of an alkali vapor, such as rubidium (Rb), and a noble gas, such as xenon (Xe), encapsulated in a small vapor cell. The nuclear spins of the noble gas are used to detect rotation, while the alkali vapor is an auxiliary gas used for initialization and readout with pump and probe laser beams. The applied magnetic fields determine the measurement axis of the gyroscope and cause atomic spin precession [1-6].

In recent years, chip-scale wafer-level vapor cells have been developed via micro-electromechanical systems (MEMS) processing not only to enhance the performance of NMR gyroscopes but also to enable further miniaturization of the sensors [5, 7].

Despite their many advancements, there are still some bottlenecks and challenges associated with MEMS vapor cells that limit their widespread implementation and upscaling, i.e., the extremely high cost of the required gasses, complexity, size, and high power consumption. The choice of alkali metal and buffer gas has a remarkable impact on the performance and characteristics of the vapor cells [8, 9]. The Xe isotope gas has found widespread adoption in NMR spectroscopy and imaging [10]. Also, ^{129}Xe and ^{131}Xe gained significant attention for deployment in atomic vapor cells due to their unique material properties. For instance, the spin-exchange optical hyperpolarization of ^{129}Xe-Rb enhances the signal-to-noise ratio of the NMR gyroscopes [12]. However, Xe is a trace gas in the earth's atmosphere, and isotopically pure Xe gas is a very expensive gas, contributing significantly to the total cost of the vapor cells.

In fact, wafer-level packaging of MEMs vapor cells is still challenging in different aspects, including the optimal introduction of Rb and Xe into the cells [13]. Standard wafer bonding procedures to seal the cells involve cycles of evacuation and purging of gas inside a bond chamber with a volume of approximately 6.5 l, necessitating a massive amount of Xe gas to fill the cells. Consequently, in the literature, wafer-level fabrication of MEMS vapor cells employing less expensive gases such as argon (Ar) or neon (Ne) predominates. In a previous study, Overstolz et al. [7] reported on the wafer-scale fabrication of MEMS Rb vapor cells using a standard anodic bonding of Si-glass-Si stack in an Ar atmosphere instead of Xe. Hasegawa et al. also used Ar/Ne for the sealing of the MEMS vapor cells [14]. In another study, Cu-Cu thermocompression bonding under Ar/Ne was conducted to seal the cavities [15].

Correspondingly, in this study, a novel fabrication process for vapor cells is proposed and implemented to improve the filling process of Xe gas during wafer bonding, thereby reducing the required gas consumption and the overall cost of the cells.

Methodology

The proposed process flow to realize a vapor cell with minimized Xe gas filling is schematically shown in Fig. 1. The patent-pending process required modifications to both the wafer bonder and bond chuck to facilitate a channel for external gas flow [16]. A semi-automatic gas-controlling system was developed and incorporated into the wafer bonder (EVG 520 IS, EV Group). Process-dependent parameters could be set by the user via the software or automatically by the software. Two thin glass wafers (Mempax®, Schott) with a diameter of 200 mm and a thickness of 200 μm as well as a silicon wafer with a diameter of 200 mm and a thickness of 1mm, were used to build the vapor cell with a triple-stacked glass/Si/glass structure. As shown in Fig.1, three anodic bonding steps were required to fabricate the customized vapor cells.

A comprehensive simulation study was also conducted to address different aspects of gas filling and stress analysis on the thin glass wafer. Accordingly, two-way-coupled fluid-structure-interaction (FSI) simulations in ANSYS Fluent were performed to optimize the filling of the MEMS cells with Xe gas. Two-way FSI calculations were necessary to determine the real-time required to fill the MEMS cells, as the fluid flow affects the deformation of the structures and vice versa. All structural calculations were performed in Fluent ('intrinsic FSI'). Due to the high deflection of the glass plate, a non-linear elasticity algorithm was used. Since the shape of a domain changes over time due to the movement of domain boundaries (glass plate), a dynamic mesh model in ANSYS Fluent with a smoothing option was used to model the fluid flow. The boundary conditions of the FSI simulations were: at the inlet, a pressure of 30 kPa, a temperature of 25 °C, a gas mixture (Xe, N₂) with a mole fraction of Xenon X_{Xe}= 0.1666 (partial pressure 5 kPa); at the outlet, a pressure of 29.5 kPa. The simulations were transient with an initial condition of pure nitrogen in the fluid domain (X_{N2} =1, P_{t0} = 29.5 kPa).

Additionally, mechanical FEM simulations were performed in ANSYS Mechanical to evaluate the maximum deformation and the maximum stress in the glass subjected to its own weight and processing pressure.

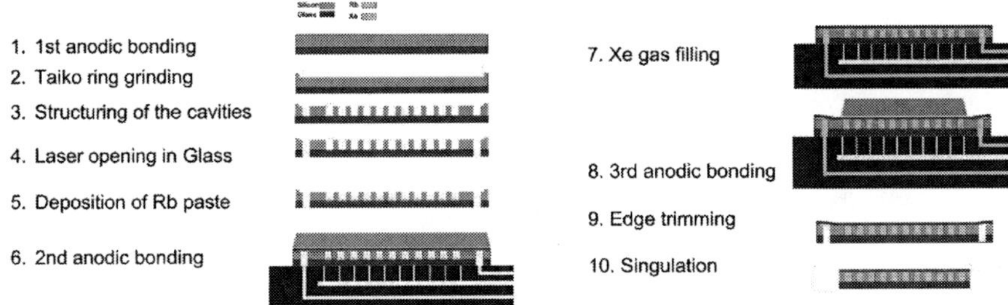

Figure 1. The proposed process flow to fabricate a vapor cell with minimized Xe gas filling.

Results & Discussion

The optimized process flow to fabricate wafer-level vapor cells with minimized Xe gas consumption was developed utilizing both simulation results and empirical verifications. The process comprises 10 steps, as shown in Fig. 1. In step 1, the first anodic bond between blank silicon and the bottom glass wafer is made. Then a Taiko ring is ground on the silicon wafer serving as a hermetic sealing ring for the Xe gas later. Afterwards, the cavities are etched in Si using a standard Bosch procedure, and the corresponding holes are made in glass via picosecond laser drilling. The RbN_3 material is dispensed inside the cavities and dried in the air. The next step is to generate the sealed area via anodic bonding (step 6). The Xe gas thereby can be selectively pumped inside the encapsulated area and decoupled from the bonding chamber. Subsequently, the sealed area is filled with Xe gas, followed by the third anodic bond to enclose the cavities (step 8). To successfully enclose all cavities, the thin glass is pressed down by the pressure disc, while bonding takes place only in the inner area of the wafer. Finally, the edge of the wafers is trimmed out and the vapor cells are singulated via blade dicing (step 10). Fig. 2 schematically shows the customized gas filling system.

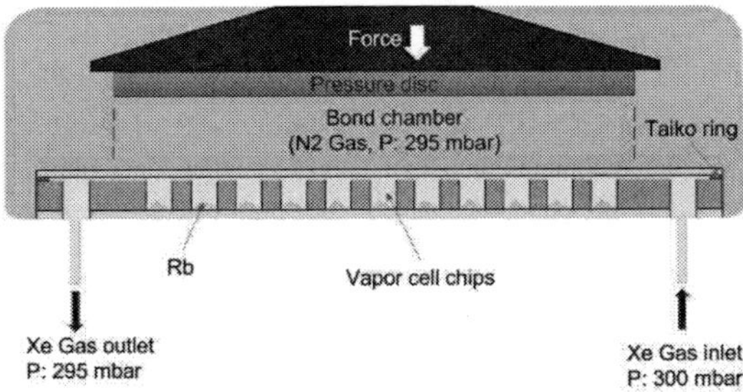

Figure 2. The customized gas filling system: a controlled amount of Xe flows in an enclosed channel, decoupled from the bond chamber.

As inferred from Fig. 1 (step 8), the flexibility of the thin glass wafer is crucial ensuring uniform Xe gas filling, followed by a seamless enclosure. The maximum available area to place the cavities and the optimum size of the Taiko ring were evaluated via mechanical FEM simulations to avoid closing the cell openings during the second bond (step 6).

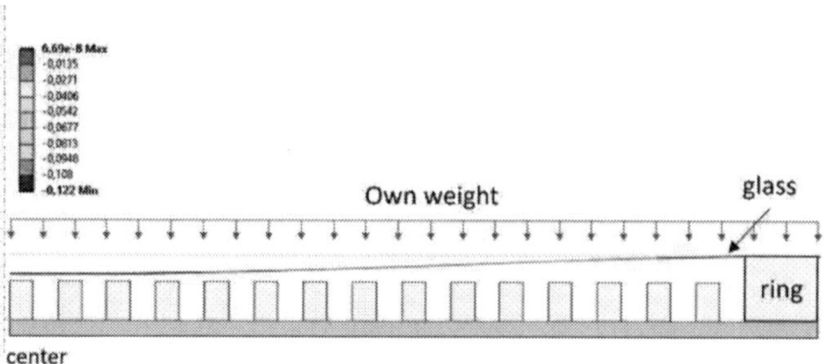

Figure 3. Vertical deformation of the thin glass subject to its own weight.

Accordingly, axisymmetric simulations were performed and different configurations in terms of ring sizes and processing pressures were examined. It was found that, in order to compensate for the own weight of the glass, which tends to vertically deform the glass and close the cell openings (as shown in Fig. 3), a counterpressure from below of about 5 Pa must be applied. As a result, the maximum generated stress in the glass is about 0.2 MPa, which is far away from the bending strength of the glass (25 MPa). This counterpressure (pressure difference between the enclosed area and the bond chamber) ensures that there is no contact between the glass and the silicon in the center of the wafer, preventing unwanted anodic bonding in that area. In fact, for the second bond, the anodic bond should be limited to the ring area, whereas for the third bond, the anodic bond should be conducted over the wafer cavities.

Mechanical simulations were also performed for the third bond to evaluate the maximum stress in the glass during the third anodic bonding and consequently define the maximum size of the pressure disc. The simulation results revealed that by using a pressure disc with a diameter of 150 mm, a maximum stress of ~19 MPa is developed inside the glass (see Fig. 4). According to the simulation results, a minimum force of 6 N is required to deflect the glass wafer and seal the cavities during anodic bonding.

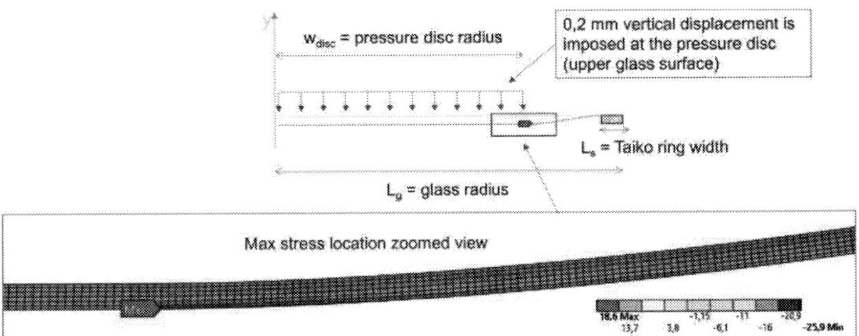

Figure 4. Normal stress in the glass due to the pressure disc load (imposed vertical displacement 0.2 mm). The maximum stress is located close to the pressure disc edge.

Pumping gas into an enclosed area (step 7) can inflate the top hanging glass wafer, forming a slight dome structure over the cells and influencing the gas velocity field in the domain (lower velocity in the wafer's center, as illustrated in Fig. 5). The modified velocity field has a direct effect on the pressure field of the gas, which in turn changes the deformation of the glass structure. The gradual increase of the Xe concentration by increasing the filling time is also consequently affected, as shown in Fig. 6. The two-way coupled FSI simulations were run until convergence to capture the mutual interaction between the gas flow and the glass deformation. Furthermore, Fig. 5 shows that the maximum deformation of the glass plate is 0.76 mm, which consequently leads to the fact that the volume above the vapor cells is more than twice that simulated without FSI.

The mass flow rate of the gas during the efficient filling as given by simulation is 3.2528×10^{-7} kg/s. As shown in Fig. 7, it takes around 100 s to completely fill the cavities.

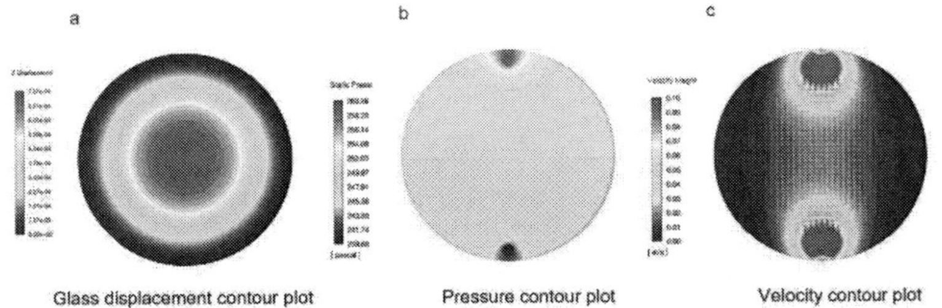

Figure 5. Two-way FSI simulation results: contour plots of the vertical displacement of the thin glass during Xe gas purging (a), gas pressure distribution from inlet to outlet (b), and the gas velocity upon filling (c).

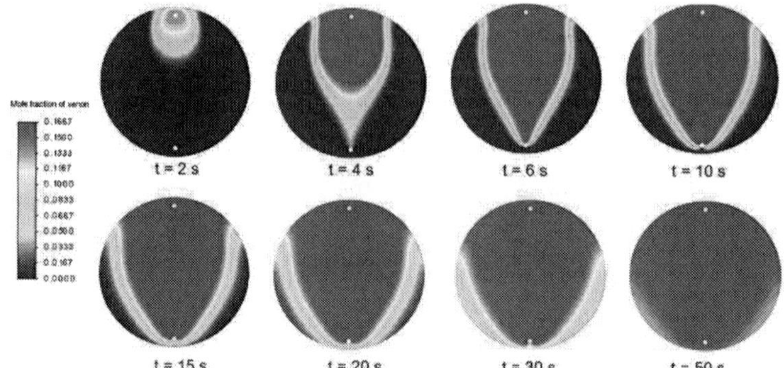

Figure 6. Mole fraction of Xe gas at different simulation times. The dynamics of the filling and the effect of the glass deformation on the flow field and consequently on the Xe concentration can be seen.

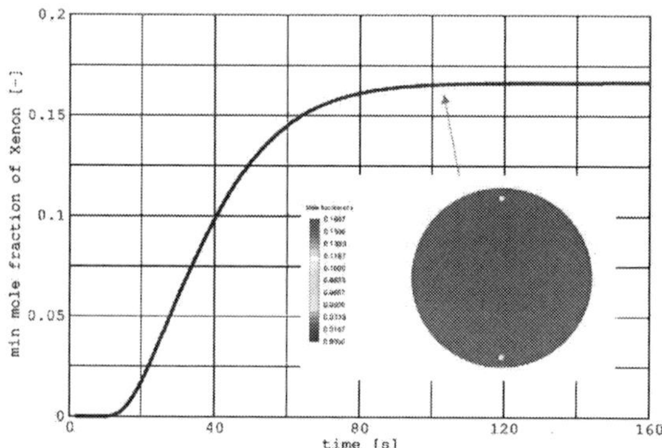

Figure 7. Minimum mole fraction of Xe in the cavities with increasing filling period. Complete filling of the vapor cells is reached $\geq$100 s.

Demonstration

Fig. 8 (a) shows a demonstration of the customized triple-stack bonded wafer after step 8, featuring the vapor cells, sealing ring, gas inlet, and outlet. The final configuration of a vapor cell after trimming and dicing is presented in Fig. 8 (b).

a   b

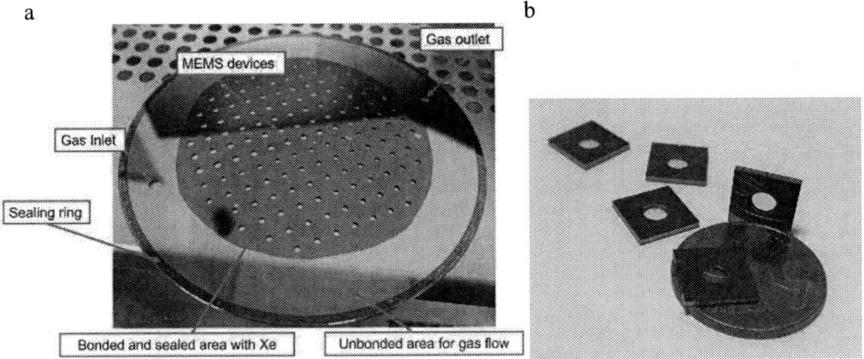

Figure 8. A demonstration of the customized triple-stack bonded, full 8" wafer, featuring vapor cells, sealing ring, gas inlet, and outlet (a) and the final configuration of MEMS vapor cells after singulation (b).

In order to validate the hermeticity of the vapor cells using Raman spectroscopy, N_2-filled vapor cells were separately produced. For these series of experiments, instead of Xe, the cells were selectively filled with 320 mbar N_2 and and evaluated qualitatively and quantitatively [17, 18]. The N_2 content inside the cells was measured over time to confirm the cavities' hermeticity. Fig. 9 shows an example of a Raman spectroscopy result revealing the hermeticity of the cavities in terms of nitrogen content level compared to the environment. The test was successfully passed by every sample.

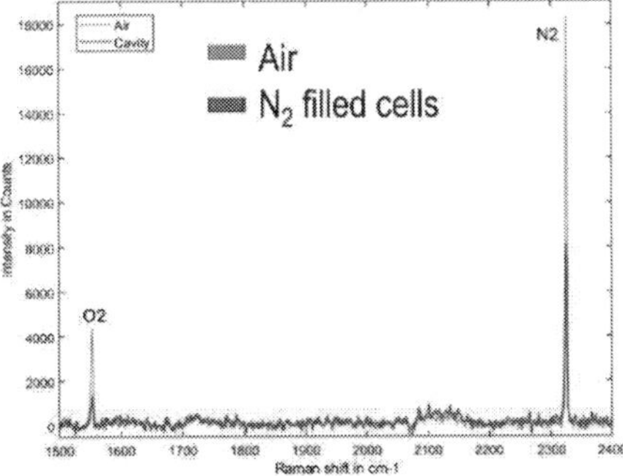

Figure 9. Raman spectroscopy results indicating the hermeticity of the vapor cells in terms of N_2 level (for this evaluation, the vapor cells were filled with 320 mbar N_2)

Conclusion

An innovative process flow for fabricating low-cost, wafer-level NMR gyroscopes based on alkali vapor cells is presented and demonstrated in this study. By utilizing the flexibility of the thin glass wafers, and microfabrication of a fluidic channel, Xe gas flowed inside an enclosed space, drastically reducing its consumption rate. The Xe mass flow rate during the efficient filling process is 3.2528 × 10-7 kg/s with a total filling time of 100 sec, as verified by the two-way FSI simulation data. The proposed process flow can substantially reduce the total cost of the vapor cells by more than a factor of ten. Compared to the conventional fabrication process of vapor cells, where the bond chamber with a volume of 6.5 liters is filled with the costly Xe isotopes, the proposed methodology enables minimized gas flow in a confined area. A demonstration of the fabricated wafer and vapor cells is also shown. The suggested filling method is not limited to the vapor cells and can be advantageous for any wafer bonding technique involving rare or expensive gases.

Acknowledgments

This work was performed within the COMET Centre ASSIC Austrian Smart Systems Integration Research Center, which is funded by BMK, BMDW and the Austrian provinces of Carinthia and Styria, within the framework of COMET—Competence Centres for Excellent Technologies. The COMET programme is run by FFG.

References

1. J. Riedrich-Möller, R. Cipolletti, M. Schmid, T. Buck, R. Rölver, T. Fuchs, *In European Quantum Electronics Conference*, Optica Publishing Group. (2021).
2. S., Knappe, V., Gerginov, P. D. D., Schwindt, V., Shah, H. G., Robinson, L., Hollberg, and , J. Kitching *Optics letters*, **30** 18 (2005)
3. S., P. F. Dyer, A. S. Griffin, , F. Arnold, D. P. Mirando, E. Burt, Riis, and J. P. McGilligan. *J. Appl. Phys.,* **132**, 13 (2022).
4. H. Nishino,Y. Furuya, and T. Ono,. *Optics Express*, **29**, 26 (2021)
5. S. Karlen, J., Gobet, T. Overstolz, J. Haesler, and S., Lecomte, *Optics Express*, **25**, 3 (2017)
6. E.A., Donley, *In SENSORS, IEEE* (2010)
7. T. Overstolz, J. Haesler, G. Bergonzi, A. Pezous, P.-A. Clerc, S. Ischer, J. Kaufmann, and M. Despont, *In 27th Int. Conf. MEMS, IEEE* (2014)
8. Kitching, J., 2018. *Applied Physics Reviews*, **5**, 3 (2018)
9. P. Knapkiewicz, *Micromachine*s **10**, 1 (2018)
10. R., Jiménez-Martínez, D., Kennedy, M. Rosenbluh, E.A Donley,., S., Knappe, , S.J., Seltzer, H.L., Ring, V.S. Bajaj, and J. Kitching, *Nat Commun* **5**, 3908 (2014).
11. M.A. Vlasova, and A.N., Shevchenko, *In IOP Conference Series: Mater. Sci. Eng.,***1215**, 1(2022.)
12. M . Hanni, P. Lantto, M. Repiský, J. Mareš, B. Saam, and J. Vaara, *Phys. Rev. A,* **95**, 3 (2017).
13. P. Knapkiewicz, Micromachines **10, 1** (2018).
14. M., R. K. Hasegawa, C. Chutani, R. Gorecki, P. Boudot, V Dziuban,. S. Giordano, Clatot, and L. Mauri, *Sensors and Actuators A: Physical* **167**, 2 (2011).
15. S. Karlen, J. Haesler, T. Overstolz, G. Bergonzi, *Microelectromech Syst.,* **29,** 1 (2019)
16. A. Binder, DE102020212151A1, (2022).
17. Q Huang, X. Dong,W. Cui, Y. Huang, P. Lai,S. Yang and Y. Wang, *Int. J. Mod. Phys. B,* **34**, 2050107 (2020).
18. S. Costello, M.P. Desmulliez and S. McCracken,. *IEEE Trans. Compon. Packag. Manuf. Technol.,* **2** (2012)

ECS Transactions, 112 (3) 229-246 (2023)
10.1149/11203.0229ecst ©The Electrochemical Society

Investigation of the Processing Behavior and Stability of Different Glass Frit Materials

R. Knechtel[a], M. Wenig[b], S. Svoboda[a], M. Seyring[a], M. Göbelt[b], U. Schwarz[b],
T. Seifert[c,d], F. Roscher[c], and M. Wiemer[c]

[a] Schmalkalden University of Applied Sciences, Chair of the Carl Zeiss Foundation for Autonomous Intelligent Sensors, 98575 Schmalkalden, Germany
[b] X-FAB MEMS Foundry GmbH Erfurt, 99097 Erfurt, Germany
[c] Fraunhofer ENAS, Department System Packaging, 09126 Chemnitz, Germany
[d] Technische Universität Chemnitz, Zentrum für Mikrotechnologien (ZfM), 09126 Chemnitz

Glass frit wafer bonding is a widely used process in the development and production of microsystems, especially for integrating sensors and their signal conditioning circuits. Consequently, glass frit bonded wafers must withstand subsequent process modules, such as silicon (wafer) through vias (TSVs) processing. The properties of glass materials for wafer bonding play a crucial role in ensuring the performance and reliability of such wafers. With new environmental regulations, Lead-free glass frit materials are being developed to replace the current Lead-containing glasses. In this context, four different glass frit materials were investigated and compared in detail, and the bonding behaviors of these materials were analyzed. It was found that the low-melting main components of these glasses determined their properties and performance. The glasses' electrical and chemical properties were also investigated, and their impact on the bonding process was analyzed. The results of this study provide guidance for the process integration of glass frit wafer bonding and open up new possibilities. In addition, the study highlights the need for practical evaluations for specific applications and related details.

Introduction

Although glass frit bonding has been a well-established process in industry, research, and development [1], there are still efforts to continuously improve its application in modern MEMS products. The main advantage of glass frit bonding is its easy integration into even the most complex technologies. Using screen printing, the glass frit paste can be applied in a structured manner to one of the two wafers to be bonded, and no subsequent structuring (e.g., by lithography and etching) is necessary. Subsequently, the paste is transformed into a compact glass in an oven batch process (the organic binder is burned out in a furnace, and the glass particles are melted to a slid glass). This process is called firing. The bonding is performed in conventional wafer bonders. The glass frit, which is located as an intermediate layer between the wafers to be bonded, is melted and joined by surface wetting to form a hermetic seal (at this vacuum or defined gas pressures can be sealed in cavities). During cooling, the glass solidifies and forms a very strong and reliable bond. Virtually all surface layers utilized in microsystems technology can be bonded in that way. The surface roughness of the wafers does not play any role here, and even rather high topographies (e.g., metal lines in the bond interface) can be well covered and sealed [1]. Due to this process flow, glass frit bonding is very cost-effective, compared to Al-Ge eutectic bonding, for example.

In addition to the benefits described so far, glass frit bonding is facing challenges related to modern applications. In recent years, the integration and miniaturization of microsystems have increased. This is accompanied by the need for further wafer processing after glass frit bonding. One example is the processing of through-silicon vias (TSVs) to bring contacts into the bond interface, for example, to avoid big bond pad openings. In this case, the glass frit bond interface has to withstand wet chemical, plasma, and thermal processes. In this context, bond stability needs to be investigated. Figure 1 illustrates glass frit bonding in relation to the TSV process.

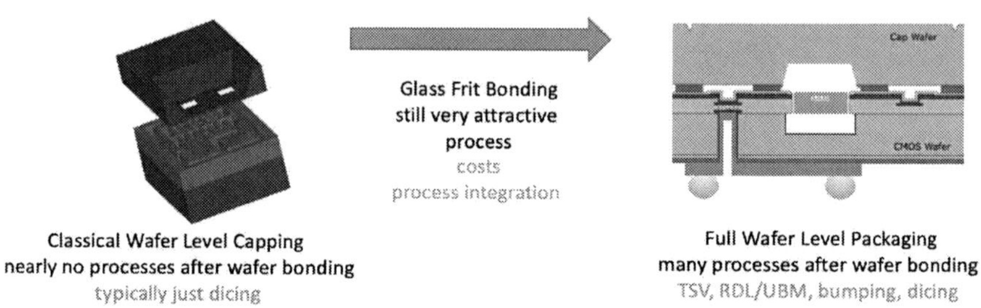

Figure 1. Transition from glass frit bonding as capping to full wafer level packaging.

The transition from a simple capping to a full wafer-level packaging process brings more and higher requirements to the glass frit bonding materials and process. Chips and bond frame structures are becoming smaller, which may increase the coverage degree of the glass frit on the wafers. Both factors make the screen-printing process more demanding. For the production and application of complex microsystems, protection against electrostatic discharges is mandatory. In this context, the residual electrical conductivity of the glass frit material has an impact, as it determines whether and how critical charges occur.

Glass Frit Materials

Glass frit materials are mixtures of powders of low melting point glass, glass ceramic particles with a high melting point, organic binders, and solvents.

- The low melting point glass is the active component for glass frit bonding. At the wafer bonding temperature, this glass needs to reach a viscosity low enough to wet the surface to bond, allowing the interdiffusion of atoms from the surface layers into the glass to form a strong bond while cooling down. Besides being necessary for bond formation, wetting is also vital for hermetic sealing. A low viscosity glass also allows for sealing of structured surfaces. Additionally, the active glass should be non-crystallizing or should at least show a low tendency for crystallization. If an amorphous glass starts crystallizing, the more temperature-stable crystalline fraction shifts the solidification and wetting temperature to higher values, making bonding difficult or even impossible. Partial or complete crystallization may occur in temperature processes like thermal conditioning of the paste (binder burn out and pre-melting) or during the heating stage of the bonding process. In practice, crystallization is avoided by adjusting the glass composition or, if this is not possible, by adapting the temperature profiles.

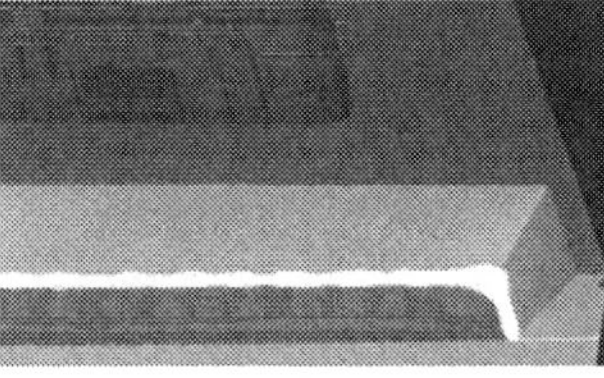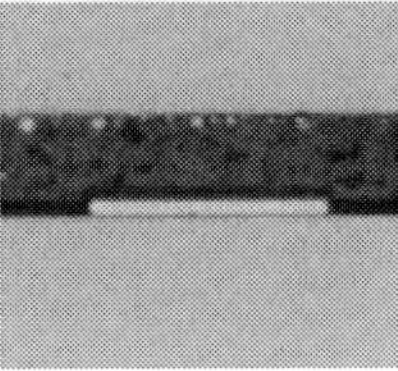

Figure 2. Excellent sealing behavior of a glass frit bond due to sufficient surface wetting by a low glass viscosity at bonding temperature.

- Typical glass frit materials contain filler particles made of glass ceramics with a melting point much higher than the wetting temperature of the low melting point glasses. Accordingly, the glass ceramic particles remain solid throughout the entire glass frit processing. Their coefficient of thermal expansion is lower compared to the low melting point glass. In the final compound, where the filler particles are melted into the glass, the filler significantly reduces the thermal expansion (e.g., from about 10E-6/K to about 8.5 E-6/K at Ferro FX11E-36).

- The organic binder embeds the particles of low melting point glass and of the filler to form a paste with medium viscosity, suitable for screen printing.

- The solvent is added to fine-tune the viscosities of the glass frit paste.

- The production of glass frit material involves an integrated process of grinding and mixing the powders, which provides the best mixing results and a defined viscosity but does not allow for precise control of the particle sizes. For many years, glass frit materials were excluded from the RoHS [2] prohibition of the use of Lead, as the development of Lead-free glass frits turned out to be challenging and required a lot of time and effort. However, Lead-free glass frit materials are now commercially available, and the RoHS exemption for Lead in sealing glasses is expiring on July 21st, 2023. To replace Lead-containing glass frits with Lead-free alternatives, these new materials, their processing behavior, and their performance need to be understood in detail. The presented investigations and results will contribute to this understanding. The materials investigated in this study are suitable for wafer bonding around 430 °C[1] and are listed in Table 1, which also contains the vendor, the general composition of the low melting glass part, and the bonding process temperature regarding specification.

---

[1] about 430 °C is the temperature limit for processing MEMS and CMOS wafers, arising from the metallization systems (alloying in the contact to silicon, thermo-mechanical stress in the blackened stack).

TABLE I. Overview of glass frit materials used in this study.

Vendor	Paste ID	Lead-free	Low Melting Glass	Bond Temp.	Ref.
Ferro Electronics Materials	FX11-036		$PbO_2 - ZnO_2$	430 °C	[3][4][5]
Asahi Glass Company	AP429D1		$PbO_2 - B_2O_2 - SiO_2$	430 °C	[6][7]
	TNS-062	x	$TeO_2 - V2O_5$	380 °C	[8][9]
	AP411AB	x	$Bi_2O_3 - ZnO_2 - B_2O_3$	440 °C	[10]

Table 1 shows that there are two replacements for Lead-containing glass frit materials available. Tellurium-based glasses enable very low bonding temperatures (but for subsequent processes like TSVs, this might often be already too low), while for Bismuth-based glasses, the bonding temperature is 10 °C higher compared to the reference known from the well-established Lead-containing materials. A few degrees Celsius higher bonding process temperature appears to be a rather small increase, but its effects on outgassing into sensor cavities and on the metallization system of MEMS or CMOS wafers should be investigated carefully. The results of the temperature behavior during the bonding of these four glass frit materials are presented below.

Screen Printing

Screen printing is an industry-established, mask-based printing technology that has been proven suitable for accurate deposition of intermediate glass frit paste for wafer-level bonding with high throughput [11], particularly for applications like MEMS Actuators [12]. With smaller chip sizes and reduced widths of glass frit seal rings (<150 μm), screen printing also needs to evolve in order to meet the need for high resolution, and densely packed large array screen printed glass frit seal rings, along with larger wafer sizes. However, the process steps of screen printing remain the same, which involve (i) paste deposition onto the screen, (ii) flooding the screen with paste using a flooding squeegee, and (iii) deposition of paste onto the wafer through the mesh openings of the screen by applying pressure to the screen and paste with the help of a laterally transferred printing squeegee.

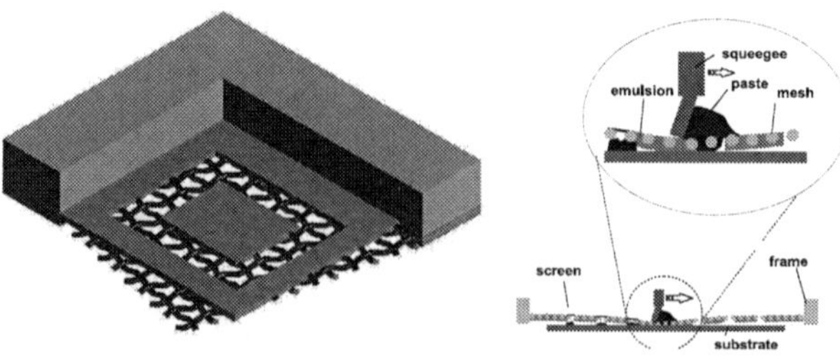

Figure 3. Basic screen design with frame, emulsion, and mesh (left), Working principle of screen printing with printing squeegee transferring paste trough mesh at opened emulsion areas towards substrate (right).

The process of screen printing and schematics of screen design are shown in Figure 3. However, all aspects involved in the process, such as the printing machine (process accuracy), squeegee (paste transfer, screen separation after printing), and screen design defined by mesh-size, emulsion-properties, and cad-based opening area can have a significant influence on the printing results onto relevant wafer sizes.

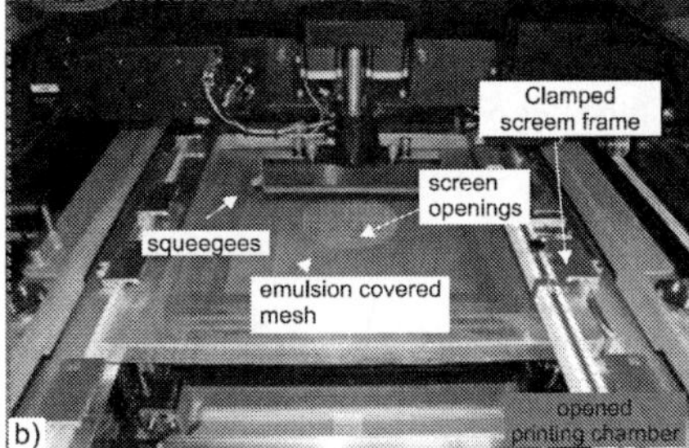

Figure 4. Overview of DEK Horizon System a) complete printing tool, b) view into the printing chamber

Printing different glass frit pastes involves refining the full printing setup, as a developed printing regime for one considered paste cannot be adopted for alternative glass frit pastes without any change. Reasons include, among other things, differences in paste viscosity, thixotropic behavior, surface tension, particle size distribution, vapor pressure of involved binder-solvent regimes, solids content, and chemical interaction with screen build and squeegee material. Results of developed paste-related printing setups and printed sealing rings are shown in Table II. All printing tests were performed with a DEK Horizon 03iX system equipped with a special, wafer-optimized platen carrier as shown in Figure 4.

TABLE II. Overview of screen-printed sealing rings of different glass frit pastes on Si-Wafers.

Paste ID	FX11-036	AP4290D1	TNS-062	AP4115AB
Lead-free			x	x
Sealing ring width (CAD)	200 μm	200 μm	200 μm	200 μm
Sealing ring width (Print)	201 ± 2 μm	239 ± 12 μm	200 ± 3 μm	207 ± 10 μm

It is clear that while having an identical CAD-designed sealing ring width, printing results differ based on the chosen paste material, screen design, and paste-adjusted printing setup. Changes in the CAD-design itself, whether in sealing ring dimensions or sealing ring density related to the printed area, also have an impact on material deposition due to paste transfer and screen separation during printing. The wetting properties and drying behavior of the paste also represent a significant impact on the final occurring sealing ring topography. The drying process of the paste influences the cross-sectional profile, while wetting properties related to the paste's surface tension and the substrate's free surface energy could lead to different spreading of the paste and occurring sealing ring width. Consequently, comparable CAD designs for sealing ring width, would have to be designed in order to anticipate paste-related wetting properties and realize the considered frame width after printing and drying.

Thermal conditioning of Glass Frit Materials

After the screen printing, the glass paste structures need to be converted into solid glass. This is achieved by burning out the organic binder and solvents at about 360 °C, followed by pre-melting at a temperature of about 10 °C higher than the later bonding temperature. The essential step in this process is to completely burn out the organics. The temperature needs to be high enough and the time long enough to ensure full burning of the organics. However, selecting and optimizing this temperature is much more complex, as an open porous structure for degassing of the burned organics must be maintained, while the glass particles should melt slightly to join themselves and the filler particles with the wafer surface. The full thermal conditioning process and the mentioned binder burn out conditions are shown in Figure 5

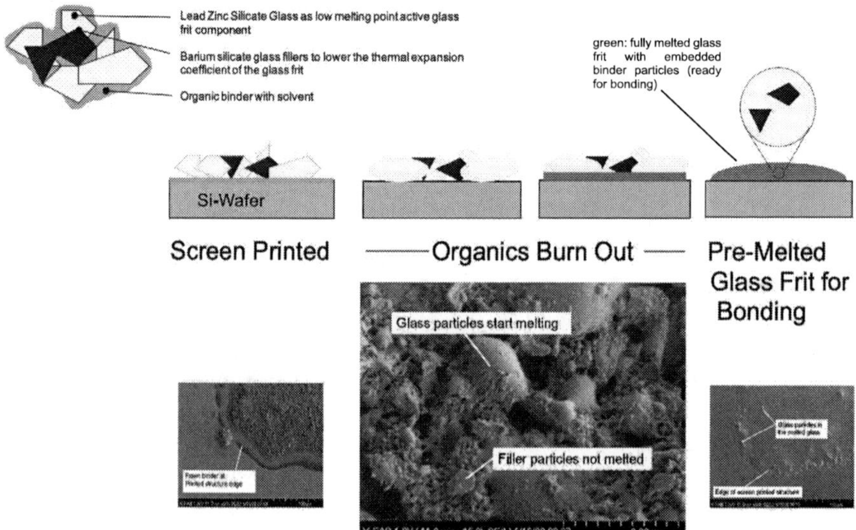

Figure 5. Thermal conditioning and structure of the glass frit material during binder burnout by example of FX11-036 (Lead-based glass frit).

The complete burnout of the organics is rather difficult to evaluate. Bubbles and voids in the glass frit, as well as increased cavity pressure in sealed MEMS devices, are indications of remaining organics in the glass frit, which might be released during the bonding step. However, following the recommendations of the materials vendors usually provides a sufficient and nearly complete binder burn out. More decisive are the heating rates in the thermal condition profile. Small deviations can easily cause partial crystallization, especially in new Lead-free materials, which may deteriorate the following wafer bonding step. So far, suitable, and stable thermal conditioning processes for Lead-free glass frit materials are available in just one particular furnace, which are deeply investigated to obtain the required knowledge to transfer it to other equipment. These investigations include detailed SEM investigations for all materials, as shown in Figure 5.

Bonding Process of Glass Frit Materials

The glass frit bonding process involves the reflow of the conditioned low melting point glass between two wafers to be bonded. The first wafer, equipped with the glass frit, comes into contact with the second wafer to be bonded by a mechanical force. This setup is heated up to the bonding temperature, and the glass frit wets the surface to be bonded, allowing diffusion between the glass and the wafer surface to take place, forming a very strong and hermetic bond during cool down. Glass substrates were chosen as bonding partners to investigate the bonding, especially the flowing behavior of different glass frit materials, by optical microscopy. Table III shows the macroscopic results of the bonding tests at a constant bonding force.

TABLE III. macroscopic results of initial bonding test of different glass frit materials

Paste ID	Lead-free	Bonding Temp.	Bonding Results	Remarks
FX11-036		430 °C		very good wetting at 430°C – bonding force too high – glass frit structures lost shape due to glass flow
AP429D1		430 °C	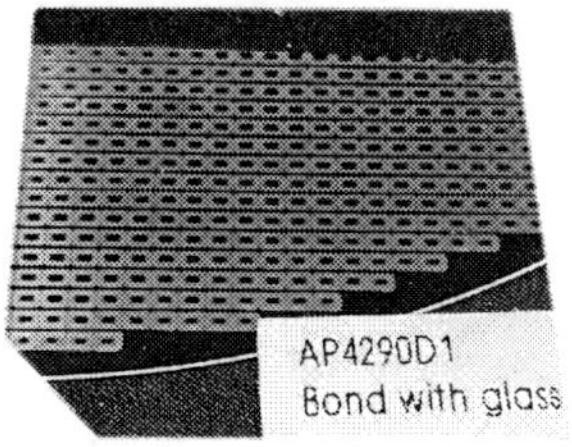	very good wetting at 430°C – bonding force slightly too high – glass frit structures with some shape loss due to glass flow - nearly perfect bonding process

| TNS-062 | x | 340 °C | | good wetting, low viscosity already at 340 ° is with strong shape loss on left side – force to high at this position, whereas seems to be perfect on right side – process (temperature and force) difficult to control |
| AP411AB | x | 430 °C | | good bonding process with good wetting – all structures in shape temperature and/or pressure a little too low |

From these basic investigations it can be concluded that the bonding temperature is the most important parameter – the glass needs to be soft enough to wet the surface and solve surface atoms and to flow for hermetic sealing. When the optimal bonding temperature is reached, the flow of the material can be well controlled by the force of pressing the wafers. The established Lead-containing materials display the best control of wetting and flowing behavior. The tellurium-based TNS-062 has the lowest bonding temperature of 340 °C, enabling good bonding quality even at lower temperatures. However, flowing of this glass is difficult to control since its viscosity is very sensitive to small temperature changes. For the Bismuth-based AP411AB, the best bonding temperature is 440 °C, and the 430 °C used in the first approach is a little low. Further investigations show that even at 440 °C, bond forces are required to support wetting for sufficient bonding. This is in contrast to the Lead-containing glass frits, where pressure is applied rather to bring the wafers and glass frit in contact, and wetting is driven by the low glass viscosity.

TABLE IV. Detailed bond temperature investigations of different glass frit materials

Paste ID	Lead-free	360 °C	400 °C	420 °C	440 °C
FX11-036					

AP429D1

TNS-062   x

AP411AB   x

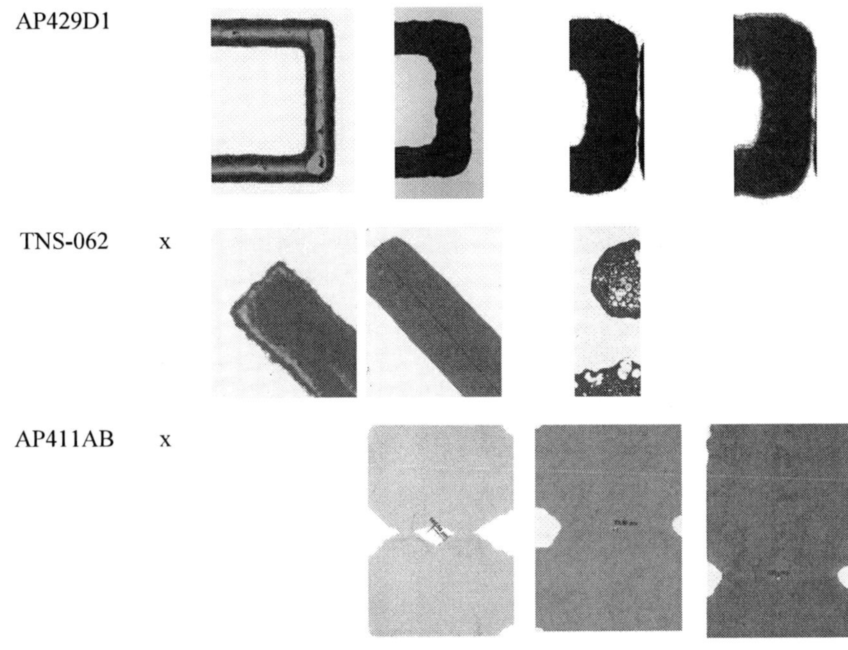

The temperature is the key parameter in the glass frit bonding process. Therefore, a more detailed characterization of the bonding temperatures was conducted, as documented in Table IV. The viscosity of the Lead-containing glass frits is increasing with temperature, resulting in a more pronounced flowing of the glass under constant pressure, as demonstrated by an increased bond frame width up to a factor of 4. Comparing the two Lead-containing glasses investigated, AP429D1 exhibits a higher flowing than FX11-036.

The rather low bonding temperatures of the Tellurium-based glass frit (TNS-062) are confirmed in this test. Between 360 °C and 400 °C, good bonding is possible, but at 420 °C, strong outgassing effects Lead to bubble generation resulting in decreased bond strength. This glass frit is well-suited for materials and applications with bonding temperature limitations - bonds below 400 °C are possible, but only if the later processing temperatures are not higher than 320 °C. Material AP411AB shows less change in viscosity in the range between 400 °C and 440 °C. The wetting behavior is well-suited but seems to be temperature-independent in this range. As confirmed by further testing, this glass frit displays a higher dependence of the glass flowing during bonding on the applied bond force than the other materials analyzed.

At a bond temperature of 360 °C, the Lead-containing material AP429D1 displays a slightly deformed glass frit bond frame, which is melted only at its thickest sections (highest points of glass frit). From that, it can be concluded that the material AP429D1 is rather solid up to 380 °C. For wafers bonded with this material, a maximum temperature of 360 °C (considering a 20 °C safety margin) can be defined for further processing without any risk of debonding or shift in the bonded wafer stack. This is enough to process, for example, TSVs on such glass-frit-bonded wafers. For the Lead-free materials, this maximum process temperature after glass frit bonding still needs to be determined.

Chemical Stability of Glass Frit Materials

For further processing of glass-frit-bonded wafers, not only thermal stability but also chemical resistance is essential. It is important that the glass frit withstands process chemicals and is not influenced by water rinsing. To ensure that no liquids enter the gap (which is defined by the glass frit thickness) between the wafers, multiple glass frit sealing rings are designed into the wafer layout. During thermal processing, entered liquids would evaporate rapidly, causing the explosion of wafers. Besides well-printed and bonded glass frit seal rings, it is important that the glass frit is not attacked by chemicals. In this context, the interaction of the bonded glass frit with acids, bases, solvents, and water as cleaning media was investigated at room temperature (about 24°C).

Glass frits, especially the Lead-containing types, are considered hygroscopic, attracting and storing water and humidity, which is released during the wafer bonding process. This can lead to increased pressure in the MEMS cavities. Therefore, usually printed and fired glass frit structures are kept as dry as possible, and water cleaning is avoided. Table V summarizes the results on the interaction of water and different glass frit materials.

TABLE V. Glass Frit Interactions with water

Paste ID	Lead-free	Reference GF after thermal conditioning	Water Low Magnification	High Magnification
FX11-036		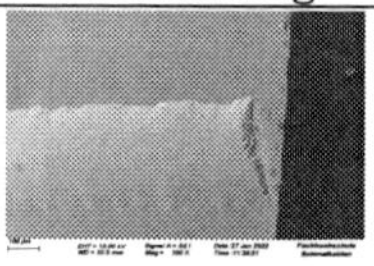	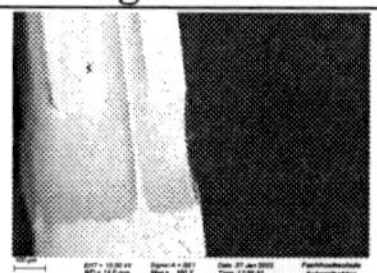	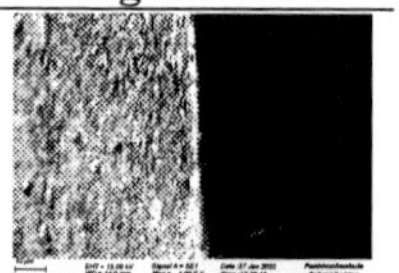
AP429D1				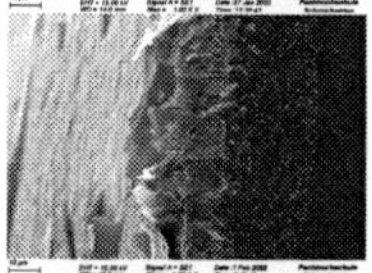
TNS-062	x	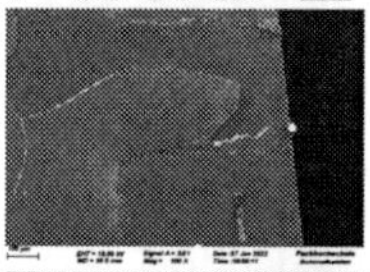		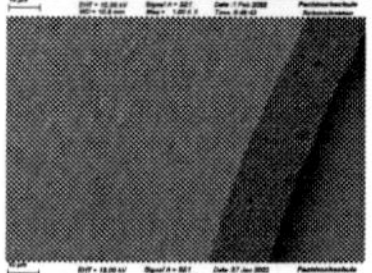
AP411AB	x	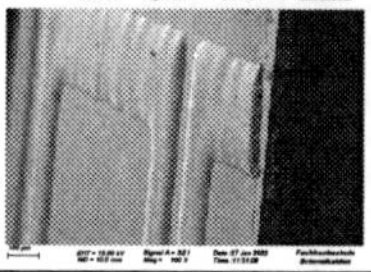	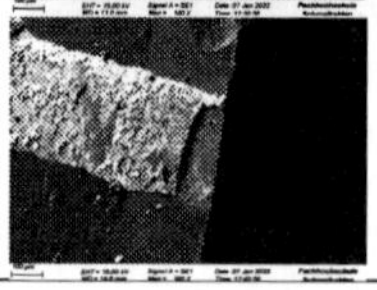	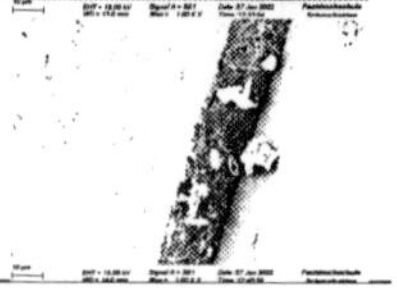

Glass frits, especially Lead- and Bismuth-based glass frits, show the tendency to absorb water at the surface. This is not regarded as a chemical attack of the glass network, but the bonding properties can be altered, causing spalling after bonding. Therefore, the bonding behavior of a Lead-containing glass frit (AP429D1) was investigated after 20 minutes of water rinsing and drying in clean room air. The bonding was conducted at 400 °C, the lowest temperature with suitable results (see Table IV). This experiment provided very good results, with good bonding strength and no bubble generation. This outcome was not expected because of the surface modification of the glass frit by the water (see Table V). The optical images after rinsing and bonding are shown in Figure 6. Since there is no visible influence of water rinsing on the bonding results in this experiment, rinsing of printed and fired glass frit, can be considered in technological flows if needed, but application-related aspects need to be considered, e.g., outgassing in MEMS cavities.

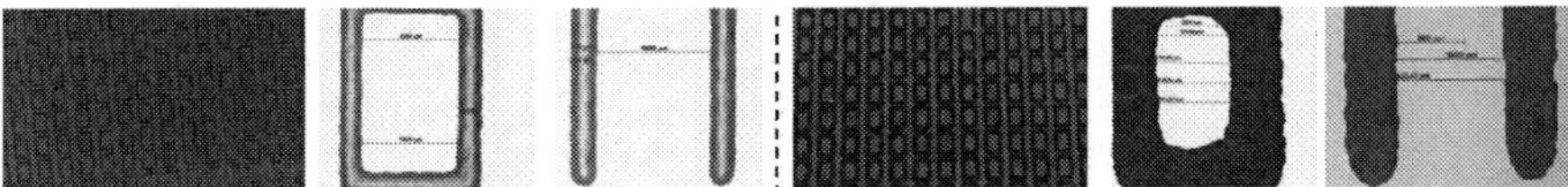

Figure 6. Bonding experiment water rinsed glass frit AP429D1 (left after 20min water rinsing and drying, right bonding results at 400 °C).

The first group of chemicals that have been studied in their effect on glass frit are acidic ones. Acids are used in microsystems technology for surface cleaning and as etching solutions. Thus, the resistance of glass frit against this type of chemicals must be considered. The corresponding results are summarized in Table VI.

TABLE VI. Chemical stability of glass frit materials in acids

Paste ID	Lead-free	HCl 10%	HF 10%	H₂SO₄ 10%
FX11-036				
AP429D1				
TNS-062	x			
AP411AB	x			

The behavior in acids is very different depending on both the acid and the glass frit material. The two Lead containing materials are very resistant against sulfuric acid, but can be removed nearly completely with hydrofluoric acid, whereas the Lead-free AP411AB is chemically resistant against HF. In all the other combinations the glass frit is attacked, but not removed. The application of acids to glass frit materials should be considered carefully, the influence of each acid needs to be evaluated individually. In some cases, acids can be used to rework printed and fired glass frits – remove the glass frit by HF etching and repeat the printing and firing process. Besides this it is possible to use acids to remove caps (Figure 7) form glass frit bonded chips without mechanical force, to allow for failure analysis close to the original bond interface.

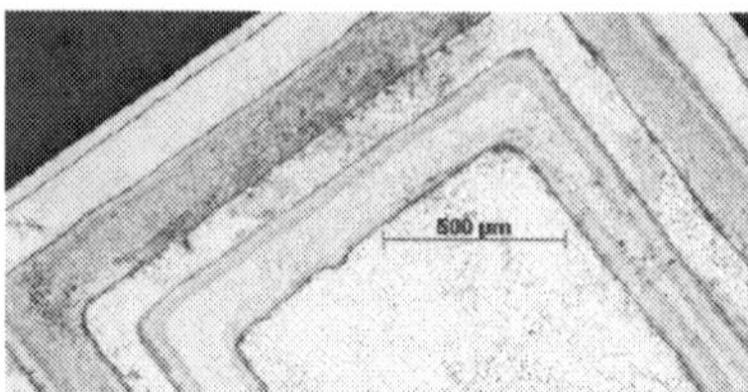

Figure 7. Cap of a chip with glass frit (AP429D1) residues after using HCl for chemical cap removal without mechanical force.

In addition to acids, alkaline solutions are also interesting in terms of their effect on glass frit materials. Such chemicals are also used for etching processes and are the components of photoresist developers. Therefore, in line with the experiments on acids, alkaline chemicals were also investigated. The results in the form of SEM images are shown in Table 7.

TABLE VII. Chemical stability of glass frit materials in alkaline chemicals

Paste ID	Lead-free	KOH 10%	NaOH 10%	NH$_4$OH 10%
FX11-036				
AP429D1				
TNS-062	x			
AP411AB	x			

Regarding the effect of alkaline media, it is surprising that the two Lead-free glass frit materials are not attacked by sodium hydroxide and also show no surface changes, while potassium hydroxide, which usually has a similar effect in terms of chemical action, causes surface changes (washout). Modifications of the glass surface can also be observed when Lead-containing glass frit FX11-036 is exposed to NaOH and KOH. Similar effects on all investigated materials can be seen for ammonium hydroxide (NH_4OH), with slight changes visible at the surface. The effect of ammonium hydroxide on the Lead-containing material AP4290D1 is quite special; here, the formation of crystalline structures occurs, similar to the behavior of this material in water, but much more pronounced. The effect of KOH and NaOH on the Lead-containing material FX11-036 is different. Parts of the glass have been lifted off, weakening the interface between the glass frit and the substrate. In summary, it can be stated that also with alkaline solutions, there are different effects for each glass frit material. All the materials are less affected by alkaline solutions than by acids, and it has been found that the new Lead-free materials are more resistant to alkaline solutions.

Organic solvents are also frequently used in semiconductor and microsystem manufacturing. These are utilized to remove photoresists and polymers (by-products of plasma etching) and for cleaning wafers (compatibility of metal structures). Therefore, the effect of solvents on the completely conditioned glass frit was investigated as well. These results are summarized in Table VII using SEM images. After treating the samples with solvents, no water rinsing was done in order to investigate the actual influence of the solvents and to exclude effects caused by water, which have already been investigated (Table V).

TABLE VII. Chemical stability of glass frit materials in solvents

Paste ID	Lead-free	Ethanol		Acteon	
		Low Magnification	High Magnification	Low Magnification	High Magnification
FX11-036					
AP429D1					
TNS-062	x				
AP411AB	x				

All the glass frit materials studied show the same behavior regarding treatment with solvents independent of the type of solvent. The glass frit materials are not attacked by solvents. The SEM images show only minor debris, which are presumably due to sample handling. Since the glasses are resistant to solvents, there are many possibilities for cleaning and other treatment before and after wafer bonding, which simplify integration into overall technological processes.

Electrical Characterization Glass Frit Materials

The electrical properties of glass frit materials are also of particular interest. On the one hand, unpassivated metals are often melted directly into the glass to electrically connect the structures in MEMS components (Figure 2). Here, the glass frit should provide strong electrical insulation. On the other hand, from an electrical point of view, the glass frit separates the two wafers and thus, after sawing, also the lid and the functional chip that was provided with it. In this case, low residual conductivity is advantageous to avoid electrostatic charging of the lid and subsequent uncontrolled discharge via the glass solder (ESD issues). It is known that Lead glasses, in particular, are not perfect insulators, and conductive paths form in the glass matrix at high temperatures, which can persist even during cooling.

To investigate the electrical conductivity, the experimental setup described in Figure 8 was implemented: silicon was bonded onto a wafer provided with a metal layer (aluminum) and broken out part of a wafer provided with glass frit. In this arrangement, the total electrical resistance of the parallel-connected glass structures can be measured (ohmmeter), and the insulation resistance per chip bond frame determined.

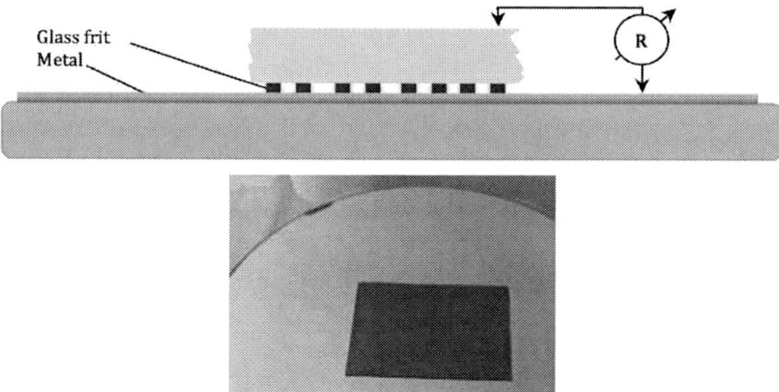

Figure 8. Configuration for electrical conductivity measurement glass frit (schematics left and realization right).

This setup was varied so that optional metal layers (titanium and aluminum) were placed on the upper wafer before glass frit printing. The thermal conditioning of the glass frit material and the bonding conditions were the same for all samples. Bonding was done at 430 °C in each case. Both, Lead-free and Lead-containing glass materials were investigated. The design of these investigations was based on the technological possibilities in real sensor technologies, in which the ESD behavior should be improved. The results are shown as a diagram in Fig. 9.

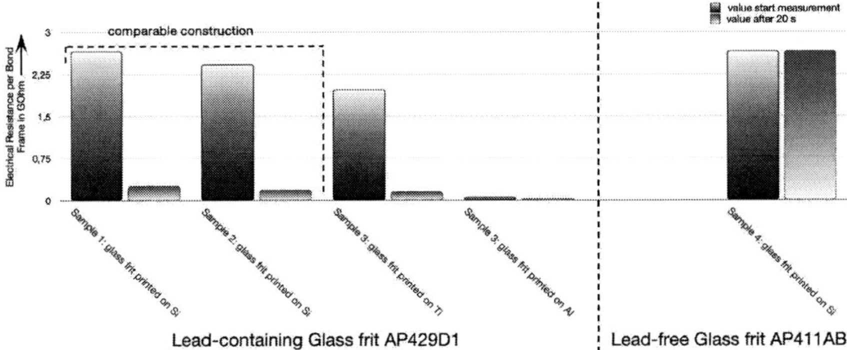

Figure 9. Results of the electrical investigations of different glass frit materials in different electrical configurations.

The results of the electrical characterization of different glass frit materials require detailed considerations. Samples 1 and 2 have the same configuration. The upper wafer is without an additional metal layer, i.e., the upper contact is between silicon and glass, the lower one is glass to aluminum. The only difference is that the aluminum was sputtered on different equipment (sample lab, sample 2 and all other samples industrial equipment). Considering this and the fact that contacting silicon with the measuring tip is not perfect, a reproducible measurement can be asumed. Thus, the results of the further measurements can be considered representative.

For the Lead-containing material, it should be noted that the resistance values at the start of the measurement and after 20 seconds differ considerably. In all configurations, there was a significant reduction in the resistance of the Lead-containing glass (factor 2...10, depending on the contact conditions in the glass-to-top-wafer interface). Subsequent measurements have shown that the low resistance values are then stable. The reason is likely the permanent formation of conductive paths in the Lead-containing glass, as already mentioned above. In the case of the Lead glasses, it is also shown that the electrical transition from the substrate to the glass is very crucial for the electrical resistance of the bond. The electrical contact between silicon and glass is the worst, while it improves with an additional titanium layer on the upper wafer, and when aluminum is used, the contact is quite low resistant. These statements are valid for the initial measurement and the measurement after 20 seconds. The time response is, therefore, determined by the glass, while the contact material determines the actual value. The second contact was chosen advantageously with aluminum, so there was always a good electrical contact to the lower wafer, which made the measurement of the contact to the upper wafer possible. It can be concluded that Lead-containing glass frit materials are not perfect insulators, and caution is required for insulating applications. Other investigations have shown that with the application of lower bonding temperatures, the formation of conductive paths could be prevented. If limited conductivity (even with the two-sided contact surfaces made of aluminum still in the Mega Ohm range) of Lead-containing glass frit materials should be used, e.g., to prevent ESD events, then rather high bonding temperatures (to stimulate the formation of conductive paths) and the use of aluminum as contact material are necessary. Based on the results and glass chemical experience, it can be assumed that part of the aluminum surface is dissolved in the glass, which then leads to the lower contact resistances (influence both interface and glass material). For Lead-free materials, only one investigation was carried out at first, using a sample without additional metal on the upper wafer. Here, the resistance was almost identical to that of the Lead-based material (sample 1), but this value was very stable over the measurement time, which indicates a generally better electrical insulation behavior for the Lead-free material AP411AB.

Summary and Conclusions

Glass frit wafer bonding is an attractive process for the development and production of microsystems, particularly for sensor integration and signal conditioning circuits. However, additional requirements must be met for glass frit bonded wafers, especially if they need to survive subsequent process modules such as wafer through vias (TSVs) processing. To ensure this, a deep understanding of the properties of the glass materials is necessary. This is particularly true for new Lead-free glass frit materials, which will replace the currently established Lead-containing glasses by mid-2024 to comply with environmental regulations (RoHS). In this paper, four different glass frit materials (two established Lead-containing and two new Lead-free) were investigated and compared in detail. It should be noted that the low-melting main components, i.e., the actual glasses, determine the properties and performance. Since completely different glass systems (PbO2, TeO2, Bi2O3 based) are investigated, their properties differ significantly. Although these differences are initially hardly visible in screen printing, firing, and bonding processes, slight differences in screen printing behavior (bond frame width) become relevant for modern applications with very narrow bond frames (100µm and narrower) as well as high coverage ratios of the screen-printing layer. These differences can be compensated with design measures and optimization in screen printing. However, differences in the glasses' properties are more critical in the actual bonding process. The Lead-free material AP4115AB has a 10 °C higher optimum bonding temperature but still flows less at this temperature than the Lead-containing reference materials, so higher bonding forces must be applied. However, higher temperature and higher bonding force may have negative effects on secondary bonding results such as wafer bow and internal pressure of sealed MEMS cavities (outgassing). Detailed investigations are necessary for specific applications to find optimal bonding process conditions. This paper also presents investigations on the chemical resistance of glass frit materials. The study shows that different glass compositions react differently to acids, bases, and water, but behave almost identically towards organic solvents, i.e., they are not affected. These chemical resistance investigations are helpful in guiding the process integration of glass frit wafer bonding and open up new possibilities. Lead-containing and Lead-free glasses also differ in terms of electrical properties. In Lead based glasses, conductive paths are formed in the electric field, resulting in a permanent reduction of electrical resistance, which did not occur in the Lead-free glass studied. The differences in the electrical behavior of the glasses need to be considered for the application, which determines whether lower resistance is good (ESD protection) or bad (electrical insulation of metal lines sealed in the glass frit). In general, it can be stated that glass frit materials for wafer bonding are very different in some aspects due to differences in their glass composition. Based on the investigations published here, initial classifications of the glasses for their application are possible, but practical evaluations for specific applications and related details are necessary.

Acknowledgments

The authors would like to thank all colleagues of the partners Fraunhofer ENAS Chemnitz, X-FAB MEMS Foundry GmbH Erfurt and Itzehoe as well at the University of Applied Sciences Schmalkalden, who participated in this extensive work on the different glass frit materials during the last two years, who made the sample preparations and investigations possible and were available for discussion. Prof. Roy Knechtel is indebted to the Carl Zeiss Foundation for the financial support of his professorship, which makes research like this possible.

References

1. Knechtel, R., Glass frit bonding: an universal technology for wafer level encapsulation and packaging.; Microsystem technologies 12.1-2 (2005): 63-68.

2. Directive 2011/65/Eu of The European Parliament and of The Council, http://data.europa.eu/eli/dir/2011/65/oj

3. Ferro Electronic Materials: 11-036, 11-155, 11-201, 1180A Pb-Based Sealing Glass Pastes, Product Information rev. 10/08

4. Ferro Electronic Materials: Technical Data Sheet Electronic Glass Materials DL11-210 Pb-Free, Alkali-free Sealing Glass Paste, Ferro Corporation I 6060 Parkland Blvd, Suite 250 I Mayfield Heights, OH 44124 I USA, October 2018

5. Ferro Electronic Materials: Material Safety Data Sheet DL11-210 Sealing Glass, September 9th 2022

6. Asahi Glass Company (AGC): Technical Datasheet AP4290D1 Lead Base Glass Paste

7. Asahi Glass Company (AGC): Safety Data Sheet of AP4290D1, Version 2, December 12th 2018

8. Asahi Glass Company (AGC): Technical Datasheet of AP4115AB No Lead Glass Paste

9. Asahi Glass Company (AGC): Safety Data Sheet AP4115AB, July 2nd 2018

10. Asahi Glass Company (AGC): Technical Datasheet of TNS062-Z26 Glass Paste

11. Wiemer, M.; Roscher, F.; Seifert, T.; Gessner, T.: Low Temperature Thermo Compression Bonding with Printed Intermediate Bonding Layers. Pacific RIM Meeting on electrochemical and solid state science 2016, Honolulu, Hawaii (USA), 2016 Oct 2-7; ECS Transactions (ECST), 75, 9 (2016) pp 299-310, (DOI 10.1149/07509.0299ecst)

12. Sandner, T.; Gaumont, E.; Graßhoff, T.; Rieck, A.; Seifert, T.; Auböck, G.; Grahmann, J. (2020): Wafer-Level Vacuum-Packaged Translatory MEMS Actuator with Large Stroke for NIR-FT Spectrometers. In: *Micromachines* 11 (10). DOI: 10.3390/mi11100883.

13. Knechtel, R., Dempwolf, S., & Hering, S. (2021). Heat Conductivity Based Inner Cavity Pressure Monitoring and Hermeticity Monitoring for Glass Frit Wafer Bonded MEMS Devices. ECS Journal of Solid State Science and Technology, 10(8), 084006.

14. El-Damrawi, G., & Mansour, E. (2005). Electrical properties of Lead borosilicate glasses. Physica B: Condensed Matter, 364(1-4), 190-198.

ECS Transactions, 112 (3) 247-263 (2023)
10.1149/11203.0247ecst ©The Electrochemical Society

Recent Developments in Low Temperature Wafer Level Metal Bonding for Heterogenous Integration

T. Wernicke[a], B. Rebhan[a], V. Vuorinen[b], M. Paulasto-Krockel[b], V. Dubey[c], K. Diex[c], D. Wünsch[c], M. Baum[c], M. Wiemer[c], S. Tanaka[d], J. Froemel[d], K. E. Aasmundtveit[e], H.-V. Nguyen[e], and V. Dragoi[a]

[a] EV Group, DI Erich-Thallner Strasse 1, St. Florian am Inn, 4782, Austria
[b] Aalto University, Otakaari 1B, 02150 Espoo, Finland
[c] Fraunhofer ENAS, Technologie-Campus Chemnitz, 09126, Germany
[d] Tohoku University, Sendai, Miyagi, 980-8577, Japan
[e] University of South-Eastern Norway, Raveien 205, 3184 Borre, Norway

Abstract

An overview of various low temperature (<200°C) wafer bonding processes using metal interlayers is presented. Such processes are very attractive for novel applications in 3D heterogenous packaging as the allow for simultaneous formation of electrical interconnects, as well as hermetic encapsulation of various sensors and microelectromechanical systems-based devices.
Metal wafer bonding is a generic category of processes consisting of various sub-categories, each one defined by the different principles governing the process. One can differentiate between eutectic wafer bonding (a eutectic alloy is formed as bonding layer during the process by liquid-solid interdiffusion), intermetallic wafer bonding (an intermetallic alloy is formed as bonding layer during the process by solid-liquid interdiffusion, process known also as Solid Liquid Intermetallic Diffusion – SLID or Transient Liquid Phase – TLP), and metal thermo-compression (TC) wafer bonding. Different critical/gating parameters were investigated and their impact for generally reducing processing temperatures for the different metal bonding systems was studied.

Introduction

The interest in adopting various wafer bonding techniques in volume manufacturing processes increased significantly over the past two decades as wafer bonding provides interesting cost effective and technical solutions for industrial applications. The applications based on heterogeneous devices and materials integration primarily require connecting mechanically and electrically two substrates via wafer bonding.

Among the wafer bonding processes currently in use, wafer bonding based on metal interlayers is very attractive as besides fulfilling the mechanical stability and the specific electrical conductivity requirements, the bonding interfaces additionally might provide hermetic or vacuum sealing for microelectromechanical systems (MEMS) or, for example, might act as a mirror for light emitting diodes (LEDs). Furthermore, the good heat conductivity of metals makes this bond very attractive for devices, where heat dissipation is relevant. In order to expand the applications range for metal wafer bonding, researchers were looking into decreasing the thermal budget below 200°C. Thus, parasitic effects due to the thermal mismatch of the bonded materials or negative thermally-induced effects on materials compositions are significantly decreased or fully eliminated. The main features of the metal wafer bonding processes considered in this work are summarized in **TABLE 1**.

TABLE 1 High Level comparison of the different metal bonding processes

	Eutectic Bonding	SLID Bonding	Metal TC Bonding
Bonding principle	Liquid-solid diffusion	Solid-liquid diffusion	Diffusion and grain growth
Liquid phase during bonding	Yes	Yes	No
Surface roughness tolerance	High	High	Low
Typical bonding temperature	T_{eut} +10°C (depends on the metal system of choice)	T_{int} +10°C (depends on the metal system of choice)	>300°C (in combination with contact pressure)
Remelting temperature	$T = T_{eut}$	$T>T_{int}$	NA

It can be observed that two of the categories exhibit a fluid interface during the bonding process, requiring the contact pressure to be in the medium-low range, to avoid metal squish and inducing a misalignment budget. By contrast, metal thermo-compression requires high contact pressure in the first stage, combined with heating. An important difference in terms of thermal budget between the two types of metal bonding (with and without liquid phase) is that for eutectic and SLID wafer bonding the temperature range is relatively narrow (typically ~10°C higher than T_{eut} or T_{int}) and the bonding time relatively short, while for metal TC bonding the temperature range can be quite big in conjunction with the adjustment of the contact force values and the bonding time. Due to this particular aspect, the development work for SLID is mostly focusing on finding new metal systems suitable for low temperature applications, while for metal TC bonding the focus is mostly on metal layers preparation (deposition, native oxide management) and process conditions optimization.

In this work we report results on two types of processes: SLID bonding using Au-In, In-Bi and Cu-In-Sn, and low temperature metal TC bonding using Cu-Cu and Al-Al bonding.

SLID Bonding

Solid-Liquid Interdiffusion (SLID) bonding is a bonding technique using a layered metal system: a metal with low melting temperature (M_L) is sandwiched between layers of a metal with high melting temperature (M_H). M_L and M_H may be two pure metals or alloys, typical examples are Cu or Au for M_H, and Sn, In (or various alloys where Sn or In is a constituent) for M_L. M_L and M_H are chosen such that they can react to intermetallic compounds (IMCs) with higher melting temperature than M_L. This allows bonding at a temperature higher than the melting temperature of M_L, and by designing the layer thicknesses with surplus of M_H, M_L can be completely consumed, leaving only high-temperature stable species in the bond line. Thus, the final bond line can withstand higher temperatures than the bonding temperature. This feature can be exploited either for manufacturing of high-temperature devices, or for bonding at low temperatures while still obtaining acceptable temperature stability. Furthermore, the limited amount of liquid phase involved in the bonding allows for fabrication of fine-pitch interconnects, and the resulting bond line with well-defined, thin metal/ intermetallic layers makes the technique suitable for lamination and sealing.

<u>AuIn Bonding</u>

In has a melting temperature of 156 °C, making In-based SLID bonding an attractive alternative for bonding at lower temperatures than the Sn-based SLID bonding. The Au–In SLID was the system of choice, as various Au–In IMCs all have melting temperatures > 450 °C. Au–In interdiffusion and reaction is significant already at room temperature, implying that a typical SLID design with thick Au and thin In would lead to rapid conversion of In to $AuIn_2$, on a timescale shorter than the typical time between metal deposition and bonding. Thus, no liquid phase would be available during bonding. To ease the logistics of the fabrication process, the Au–In SLID system was designed asymmetrically and with thin Au layers: one bonding partner had 0.16 µm Au / 1.25 µm In and the other bonding partner had 0.8 µm Au. Au was deposited by sputtering, In by thermal evaporation. The test vehicles were 100 mm diameter Si wafers. Bonding was performed at wafer level, at a temperature of 180 °C.

The resulting bonds had shear strength in the range of 30 MPa. Cross-section microscopy with SEM and EDX (**Figure 1**) reveals that both Au and In are completely consumed, the resulting bond line consisting of two Au–In IMCs.

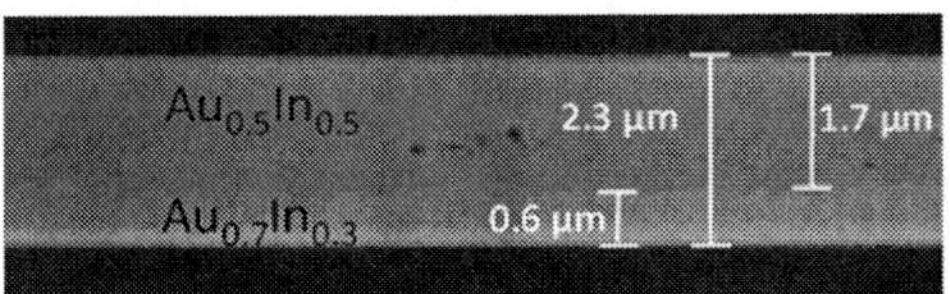

Figure 1: Cross-section of a Au–In bonded sample. Two Au–In IMCs are present in the final bond-line. Reprinted with permission from Springer Nature (1)

To verify the predicted high-temperature stability of the Au–In SLID bond, die shear tests at elevated temperatures, up to 300 °C, was performed. As shown in **Figure 2**, the bond is indeed solid at temperatures well above the melting temperature of In, and even shows increased strength at 300 °C. This increase in strength was explained to be related to the actual composition and geometry of our investigated bond (1,2). A solid-state phase transition occurring in the Au–In system above 224 °C leads to interdiffusion of Au and In across the original bond interface, giving an annealing effect at this interface. Inspection of the fracture surfaces of room temperature sheared samples showed that this original interface was indeed the weakest part of the bond line (as can be the case if oxide or impurities at the surface limits the wetting of the bonding partners). Inspection of the fracture surfaces of 300 °C sheared samples showed that the fracture mode has changed to a cohesive, ductile fracture, not following a particular plane in the sample.

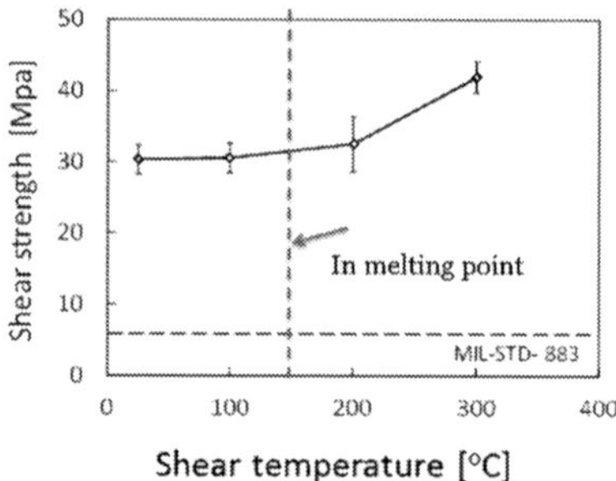

Figure 2: Au–In strength versus temperature. Reprinted with permission from Springer Nature (1)

CuInSn Bonding

Since already for several decades the In-Sn system has been the basis for numerous low-temperature solders, In is logical ternary alloying element for Cu-Sn based SLID bonding metallurgy when lower processing temperatures are required. Materials like In-Sn pre-mix, as well as the related manufacturing processes are commercially available. Moreover, In is metallurgically very similar to Sn and, therefore, as can be seen from **Figure 3**, alloying with the Cu-Sn system In should not drastically change the interconnection microstructure (3). Both phases Cu_6Sn_5 and Cu_3Sn have high In solubility and, therefore, the diffusion path can almost directly follow the contact line (dashed line in **Figure 3** a). Hence, similar IMC formation sequence $Cu|Cu_3(Sn,In)|Cu_6(Sn,In)_5|$ $Cu_3(Sn,In)|Cu$, as with binary Cu-Sn SLID, is expected. The stabilizing effect of In on the liquid phase can be seen when comparing the **Figure 3** c) to **Figure 3** d). The areas of the liquid phase, corresponding to the size of the process window for the bonding, are highlighted with light-blue color in **Figure 3** c and d, where magnified image from the eutectic point in binary Cu-Sn system is compared to that of ternary Cu-In-Sn system. It is obvious that In alloying allows the usage of considerably lower bonding temperatures. Additionally, as shown with the green dotted lines, the solubility of Cu into liquid phase is almost twice as high when In is added to the system in comparison to binary Cu-Sn system. Since the solubility of Cu to the liquid phase is an essential parameter affecting the reaction kinetics, as it defines the dissolution rate, the In alloying can either decrease the bonding time or allow the usage of lower bonding temperatures with same processing time. On the other hand, In has similar effect on the Cu-Sn intermetallics than to the liquid phase i.e. dissolved In increases the stability (Gibbs free energy of formation) of both Cu_3Sn and Cu_6Sn_5 phases (3). Therefore, the remelting temperature, estimated from the thermodynamic assessment, of $Cu_6(Sn,In)_5$ is significantly higher than that of binary Cu_6Sn_5. This can be seen from **Figure 3** b), where the dashed line shows that the melting temperature increases rapidly up to ~600°C when the Cu nominal content exceeds 60 at-%. To conclude, by incorporating In as a ternary alloying element to Cu-Sn binary system both lower bonding as well as higher re-melting temperatures can be obtained.

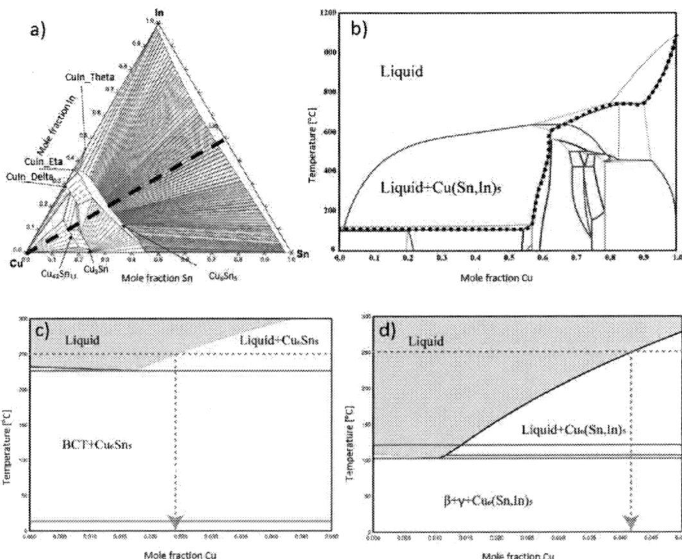

Figure 3 a) Cu-In-Sn 250°C isothermal section with superimposed dashed contact-line, b) vertical section from 50Sn50In (at-%) to pure Cu, c) enlarged area from eutectic point in binary Cu-Sn phase diagram, and d) corresponding area from ternary Cu-In-Sn system. (3)

Due to the fact that the dissolved In has different stabilizing effect on Cu_6Sn_5 and Cu_3Sn, the SLID interconnection microstructure is primarily defined by bonding temperature, and bonding time has significantly smaller effect. As demonstrated before when the bonding temperature is ≥250°C the bond is mainly composed of $Cu_3(Sn,In)$ phase, while depending on the bonding time some residual $Cu_6(Sn,In)_5$ can be detected at the center of the bond line (4). However, when the bonding temperature is ≤200°C the bond is composed of single phase $Cu_6(Sn,In)_5$, which doesn't transform to $Cu_3(Sn,In)$ even after extensive solid state annealing (>500h at 150°C) (3). In order to demonstrate that small µ-bonds can be manufactured at temperatures as low as 150°C Si wafers containing 10 µm-sized microbumps based on the Cu-Sn-In ternary system were fabricated with wafer-level bonding (5,6). The test wafers had symmetrical metallization structure of 4 µm Cu| 1,5 µm Sn|1,5 µm In. **Figure 4** shows the SEM cross-sectional images from the 10 µm bumps after the successful bonding process at 150°C for 1h. Higher magnification micrograph in **Figure 4** b) shows that significant fraction of the Cu is still remaining after the bonding process. Furthermore, some Sn-In squeeze-out can be observed at the edges of the bond indicating that the metals form eutectic liquid phase below melting temperature of pure In (157 °C). EDS analysis taken from the points marked 1-3 (Cu, Sn, and In as 55.5±1.5 at.%, 29.1±1.1 at.%, and 15.4±0.4 at.%, respectively) indicates single intermetallic Cu_6Sn_5 phase, with In substituting Sn in the sublattice. In order to verify adequate bond formation, mechanical tensile tests were executed. The results show that the bonds have on average a mechanical tensile strength of 32.7±4 MPa. Moreover, the fracture surface analyses see **Figure 4** c) and d) verify that the fractures mainly propagate through the homogenously formed $Cu_6(Sn,In)_5$ phase. EDS analysis taken from points 4-6 in **Figure 4** d) shows the Cu, Sn, In elemental composition of 59.5±0.8 at.%, 25.1±0.7 at.%, and 15.4±0.4 at.%, respectively.

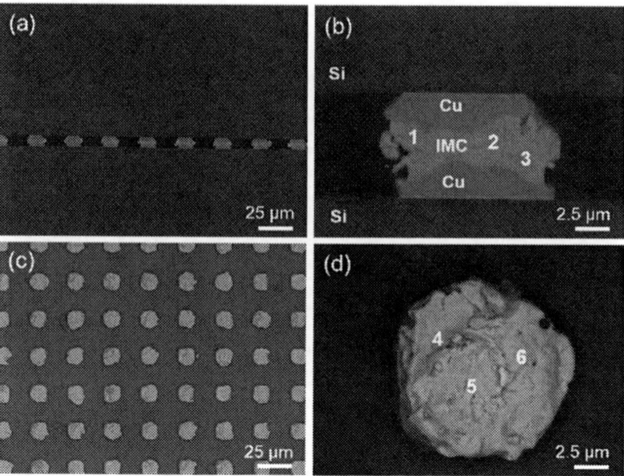

Figure 4 SEM images of as bonded microbump cross-section and the top view of fracture surface after mechanical pull test at (a,c)500x, and (b,d) 5000x magnification. The numbers marked the location used for EDS point analysis. (5)

To conclude, wafer-level bonding has been successfully demonstrated with 10 µm sized square bumps at 150 °C based on the Cu-Sn-In ternary system. The obtained results from the bonded µ-bumps show that the In alloying to Cu-Sn system reduces the temperature to form a liquid phase and, therefore, allows bonding at temperatures even below the melting point of In. This is turn enables to significantly decrease the bonding process related residual stresses especially at the reliability critical locations like Si to metal bond interface as well as around defects in the actual interconnection.

<u>In–Bi Bonding</u>

In–Bi is a metal system with particularly low melting points, with the eutectic composition (79 at% In) having as low melting temperature as 73 °C (7). As such, it is a good candidate for low-temperature SLID bonding, in combination with a suitable metal with high melting temperature.

In this case Au was chosen as being a high-temperature stable metal. Au and Bi are immiscible and have no IMCs that are stable at ambient temperatures. The resulting bond line is therefore expected to consist of Au–In IMCs, together with elemental Bi, if all Bi–In IMCs are consumed. The expected remelt temperature of such a bond will then be the Bi melting temperature, 271 °C. Bonding was performed by sandwiching an eutectic In–Bi foil (thickness around 140 µm) between Au-coated dies and substrates. Most of this thick foil was squeezed out during bonding, resulting in bond lines of a few µm thickness, comparable with typical SLID bonds obtained when using electroplated layers. Successful bonding was achieved at bonding temperature as low as 90 °C. However, these bonds comprised low-temperature melting Bi–In IMCs such as $BiIn_2$, so this particular bond is not expected to withstand temperatures higher than 90 °C. To achieve SLID-like high-temperature stability, a bonding temperature of 110 °C (highest melting temperature of Bi–In IMCs) or higher should be used.

Bonding at 110 °C, for 4.5 hours, gave SLID bonds as shown in **Figure 5**. The expected bond line consisting of Au–In IMCs and elemental Bi. Cross-sections at different locations reveal a very non-uniform Bi distribution: Some parts of the sample show a continuous layer of Bi, whereas other parts of the sample show no Bi at all. At locations where no Bi is present, the expected temperature stability of the bond line is in the order of 450 °C, similar to the Au–In SLID bond.

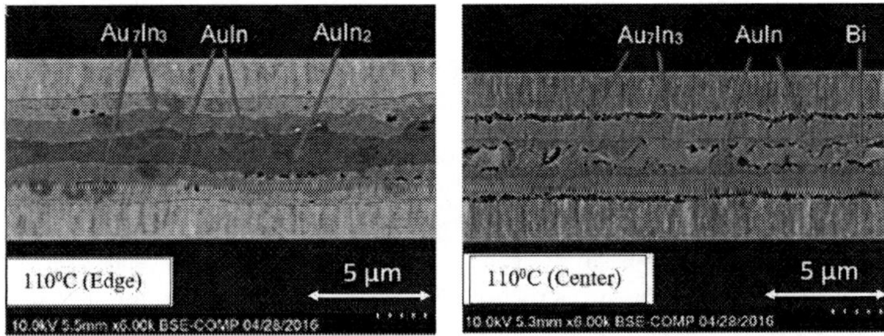

Figure 5: Cross-section micrograph of In–Bi SLID bond on Au pads, bonding temperature 110 °C, bonding time 4.5 hours. The phases are identified by EDX (8). © 2016 IEEE

Since the required bonding time for Au–In–Bi SLID bonding at 110 °C is several hours, thin films (2.5–3 µm) of eutectic In–Bi was deposited on Au layers by thermal evaporation. Bonding can then be achieved at 115 °C, with a bonding time of 30 minutes.

These Au–In–Bi SLID bonds are strong, with a die shear strength up to 50 MPa. The technique is particularly suitable for bonding of piezoelectric materials, since the bonding temperature is below the Curie temperature of PZT (~150 °C), the most commonly used piezoelectric material for ultrasound transducers. Acoustically active materials were bonded/laminated using Au–In–Bi SLID, and the resulting bonds were confirmed by electrical impedance spectroscopy that voiding is limited and compatible with ultrasonic applications (9).

Ag–In–Bi SLID bonding has also been investigated in recent work, showing quite comparable results to the Au–In–Bi SLID bonding (10, 11). It is because Au, Ag are not miscible with Bi, and the Ag–In system has several high-temperature stable IMCs, similar with the Au–In system. The main difference to the Au–In system is that the most In-rich Ag–In IMC ($AgIn_2$) has a moderate temperature stability, melting at 166 °C. Ag–In–Bi has recently been demonstrated for solid-state bonding at temperatures as low as 65 °C, when allowing for long bonding times (~days) (12). Solid bonds are obtained and the bond line consists of Ag / $AgIn_2$ / Bi–In IMCs / $AgIn_2$ / Ag. At some locations, the $AgIn_2$ phase can be observed across the bond line, thus indicating a local temperature stability of 166 °C.

TC Bonding

Metal thermo-compression bonding (TCB) is a highly efficient direct bonding method that eliminates the need for additional intermediate layers, like a soldering component. Apart from having to deposit less different metals, not having a liquid phase during the bonding process can severely increase the resulting wafer to wafer alignment accuracy to values <1 µm. Generally there are less materials of interest in semiconductor industry used for TCB compared to SLID bonding, which leads to rather optimizing the material itself instead of combining multiple material properties for overall process temperature reduction. This process relies on the crucial role played by the metallic material at the bond interface (13). The formation of any thermo-compression bond is based on diffusion, which is well defined by the Arrhenius equation:

$$D = D_0 \left(-\frac{Q_D}{RT} \right) \qquad [1]$$

Where D is the diffusion coefficient, $\mathbf{D_0}$ the temperature independent pre-exponential factor, $\mathbf{Q_D}$ the diffusion activation energy, R the universal gas constant and T the temperature. Since the diffusion activation energy is depending on the actual diffusion mechanism it can be considered as optimization parameter for reducing the actual bond-process temperature. The mechanisms which are typically considered for wafer bonding are the surface Diffusion D_S, the grain boundary diffusion D_{GB}, the dislocation diffusion D_D and the lattice diffusion D_L. The respective kinetics can be qualitatively described as

$$D_S > D_{GB} > D_D > D_L \qquad [2]$$

<u>Physical and Chemical Impact factors on CuCu Bonding</u>

We have reviewed and investigated the key influencing Cu layer characteristics that reduce $\mathbf{Q_D}$ for $\mathbf{D_S}$, $\mathbf{D_{GB}}$ and $\mathbf{D_D}$ to accelerate diffusion at lower temperatures for a Cu-Cu TCB. The dislocation diffusion $\mathbf{D_D}$ was not considered within this work, since the impact for reducing the bonding temperature is negligible.

The first parameter to consider is the surface roughness as it has direct impact on $\mathbf{D_S}$. It has been well described in numerous articles how the surface roughness impacts the mechanical contact of two surfaces, which can trigger surface diffusion (14, 15, 16)
The surface roughness after deposition can be decreased by chemical-mechanical polishing towards R_q values of <1 nm. Such samples have been analyzed and the AFM results are shown in **Figure 6**:

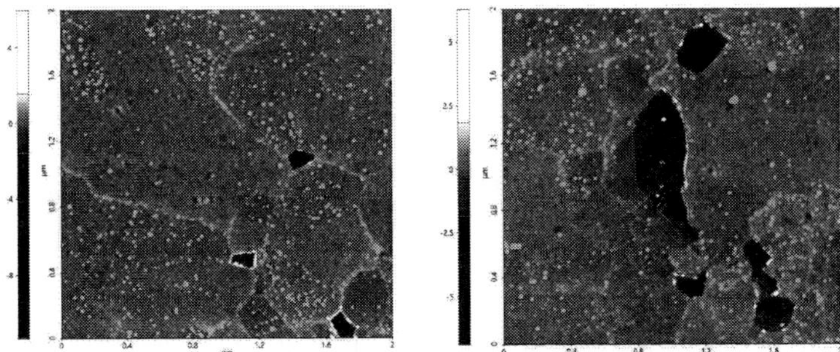

Figure 6 surface microroughness measured by AFM at the wafer center (left Rq~0,63nm) and near the wafer edge (right Rq ~0,68nm) on 200mm Si wafer with 1μm deposited and CMP polished Cu layer.

It was shown, that wafers with such low roughness could actually be direct bonded at room temperature due to Van-der-Waals surface interaction. However, it was also shown that such direct bonded wafers result in low bond qualities due to the native Cu-Oxide. This layer is typically in the range of 3-5 nm and acts as diffusion inhibitor, if not reduced or completely removed. (15,17, 18)

There are two major procedures that can be used for oxide reduction. One is an ex-situ treatment that involves the using 2% citric acid and a second based on an in-situ treatment, either involving formic acid vapors or forming gas (typically 4% H_2 in an inert carrier gas). Both procedures can also be combined when dealing with thick oxide layers. The formic acid and citric acid treatments were performed on CMP polished Cu surfaces and the change in surface roughness was measured (**Figure 7**)

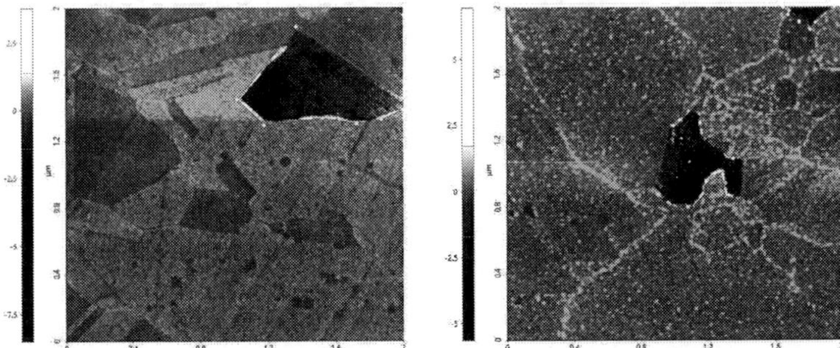

Figure 7 surface microroughness measured by AFM after a surface treatment with citric acid (left) and formic acid vapors using an acid bubbler (right).

The R_q value of the citric acid treated wafer stayed relatively same at ~0,64nm while the R_q value of the formic acid vapor treated wafer has increased to ~0,74nm. Even though the absolute change value seems small, the relative increase ~10%. This potential change needs to be considered when choosing the appropriate pre-treatment. Experimental work, done by various groups show the influence of the Cu deposition method (e.g. PVD vs.

ECD) on the resulting bondability. This is related to the respective different Cu grain sizes and the related grain size distribution. **Figure 8** shows a direct comparison between the different resulting grain sizes of a PVD vs. an ECD deposited Cu layer and their respective grain size distributions. The EBSD analysis shows mean grain sizes of $\langle d_{PVD}\rangle = 380nm$ and $\langle d_{ECD}\rangle = 978nm$ respectively. The different entropy of different grain sizes has significant influence on the diffusion kinetics. This has also been thoroughly investigated (14) and can also be described by the change of the Gibbs Free Energy ΔG during nucleation. Equation (4) describes the simplified ΔG for a spherical nucleus.

$$\Delta G = \frac{4}{3}\pi r^3 \Delta G_v + 4\pi r^2 \gamma \qquad [3]$$

Where ΔGv describes the difference of volume free energy (equation (5)), r the nucleus radius and γ the surface tension of the nucleus

$$\Delta G_v = \frac{\Delta H_f(T_m - T)}{T_m} \qquad [4]$$

When considering equations [3] & [4] it becomes obvious that smaller grains tend to nucleate faster than larger ones. This can be a driving force for migration of grain boundaries which subsequently can lead to bond interface diffusion. Thus, the deposition method has a direct kinetical impact factor for reducing the processing temperature.

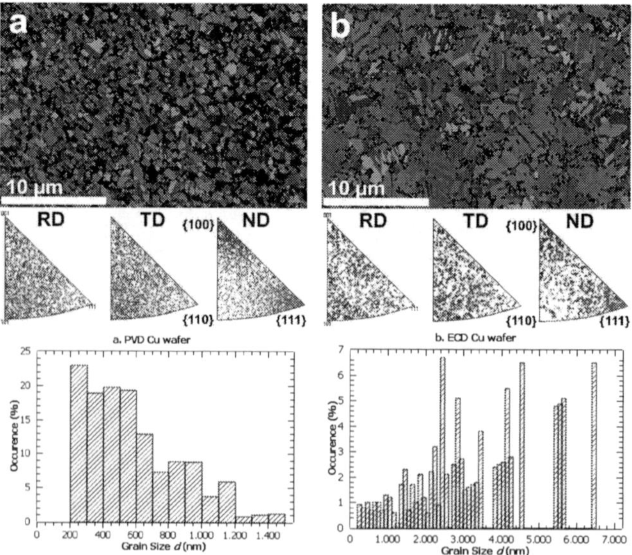

Figure 8 EBSD analysis of (a) PVD Cu an (b) ECD Cu and the related grain size distribution (19)

When considering all above-mentioned parameters, their relation and impact on the diffusion behavior, the process temperature for a covalently bonded Cu-Cu interface can be optimized to temperatures well below 200°C. By optimizing the surface roughness to values close or below 1 nm R_q, not only D_S can be decreased but it also enable room-temperature direct bonding of 2 Cu surfaces after being treated with citric acid (**Figure 9**).

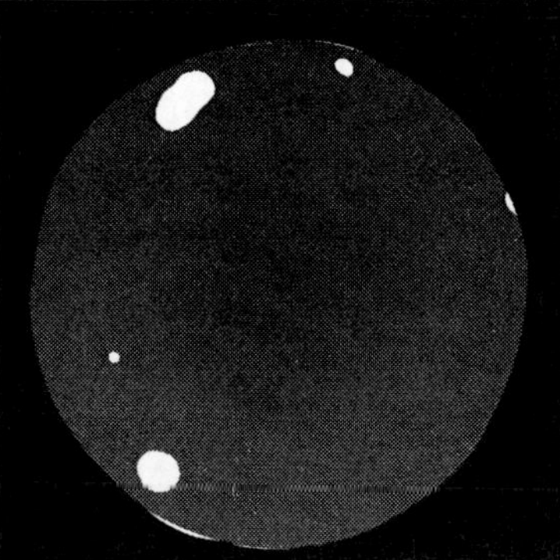

Figure 9 C-SAM image of two Cu-Cu direct bonded 200mm wafers

Figure 10 shows two wafers which were bonded at 175°C and subsequently analyzed by C-SAM and SEM cross sectioning

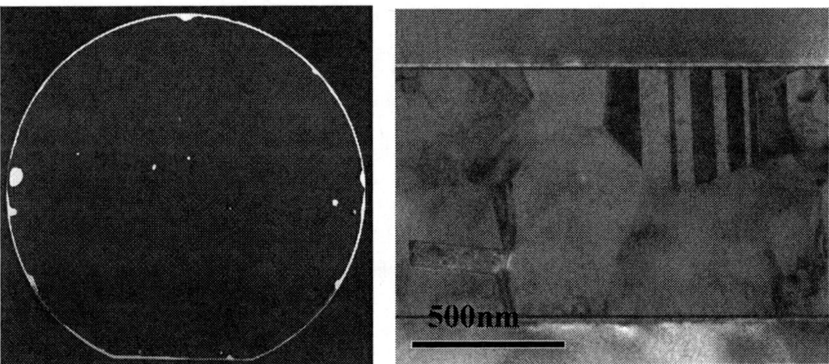

Figure 10 C-SAM image (left) and related SEM cross section (right) of two Cu-Cu wafers bonded at 175°C (15)

It can be seen, that the bond interface looks uniformly bonded, but that the Cu grains have decently inter-diffused and re-crystallized. There is no detectable bond line visible.

<u>Plasma Enhanced Passivation for Cu-Cu Bonding</u>

In order to avoid or minimize the well understood ambient Cu oxidation (20, 21), a passivation of the surfaces with self-assembled monolayers (SAM) is being investigated. It is widely acknowledged that organic acids, like citric acid, possess effective oxide removal capabilities (22, 23, 24). In addition, citric acid serves as a complexing agent in the Copper Chemical Mechanical Polishing (Cu CMP) process (25).

The goal of the SAM is to prevent the native oxide build and rather control it with a well known uniform carbon chain polymeric layer. For this, after removing the native oxide with 1% citric acid, two different types of SAM were used, hexanethiol and decanethiol. The SAM deposition was carried out for 2 hours after cleaning at room temperature.

In a seminal investigation conducted by Kang et al.(26), significant findings were obtained regarding the post-treatment of copper (Cu) surfaces using H_2 plasma. The study demonstrated the remarkable ability of H_2 plasma treatment to achieve a clean Cu surface. The absence of a passivation layer on the pristine Cu surface was identified as a critical factor contributing to the heightened susceptibility of Cu to oxidation and carbon contamination from the ambient environment. These insightful findings shed light on the intricacies of Cu surface modifications and have profound implications for high-impact research in various disciplines.

As already shown in this review and other work (27), the surface roughness is not impacted significantly post cleaning by these techniques. However, SAM deposition may lead to slight increase in the surface roughness of the bonding site due to the presence of self-assembled monolayer and the roughness may also depend upon the type of precursor used, that is, short-chain or long-chain (28).

After cleaning and passivation, the Cu surfaces are bonded with a force of 30 kN at 300 °C for 60 min. Subsequently the bond is characterized using the tensile test by TIRA test 2805. The sample was fixed to the jigs with a help of a glue (ethyl cyanoacrylate) and the pull test is performed in the vertical direction. The tensile test of the bonded interface is shown in **Figure 11**. For each pre-treatment nine samples are tested (29).

The tensile test results show a very good bond strength of 300 MPa for formic acid and H_2/Ar plasma pre-treated samples. The bond strength of the samples pre-treated with citric acid, ammonia plasma and passivated with SAM coating are in the range of 200 MPa and 250 MPa. The reduced bond strength is evident due to the presence of the Cu nitride and SAM at the bonding interface due pre-treatment.

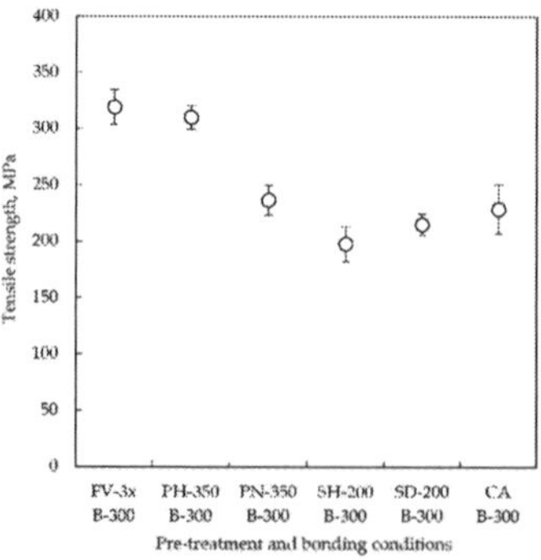

Figure 11 Tensile test vs various pre-treatment method of the direct bonded Cu interface. The Cu direct bond was realized at 300°C for the pre-treated samples (29)

To understand the strong bond strength using H_2/Ar plasma treated Cu surface, thermal desorption spectroscopy (TDS) measurements were performed on the Cu surface. The H_2/Ar plasma pre-treated Cu surface is compared with the citric acid treated Cu surface.

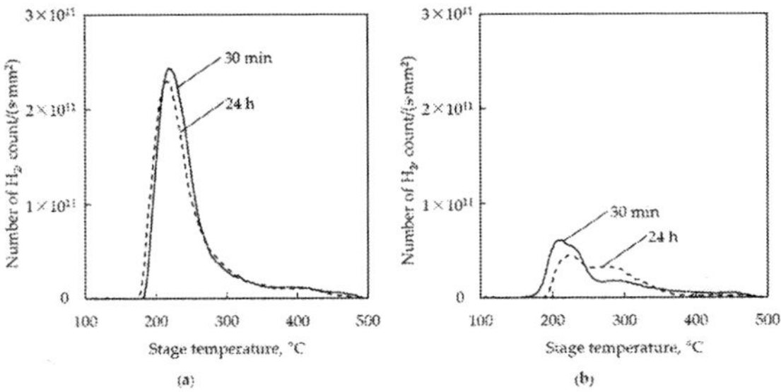

Figure 12 The TDS spectra of the pre-treated surface after 30 min and 24 Hr of the treatment. The graphs depict the hydrogen desorption rate with temperature for (a) H2/Ar plasma pre-treated surface and (b) citric acid pre-treated Cu surface (29)

The comprehensive analysis of Thermal Desorption Spectroscopy (TDS) spectra show that the H_2/Ar plasma treatment of Cu film results in an impressive 3.1-fold increase in desorption of H_2 molecules compared to the citric acid treatment. This heightened desorption can be attributed to the chemisorbed hydrogen atoms on the Cu film, since physical adsorption of H_2 on Cu exhibits a shallow potential energy well of only 20 meV (30). Notably, the catalytic effect commonly observed with metal surfaces, where hydrogen molecules are readily dissociated, does not occur with Cu. Dissociation and chemisorption of molecular hydrogen on Cu necessitate additional energy. In contrast, atomic hydrogen immediately chemisorbs on the Cu surface without activation energy barriers (31). Hence, the desorbed hydrogen molecules observed in the H_2/Ar plasma-treated Cu film are presumed to originate from hydrogen radicals generated during the H_2/Ar plasma treatment. It is postulated that a Cu hydride-like layer, previously discussed by Baklanov (32), forms due to the chemisorption of hydrogen atoms on the Cu layer. This Cu hydride-like layer is believed to hinder the oxidation of the treated Cu surface by terminating some of the dangling bonds on the pure Cu surface with hydrogen atoms. **Figure 12**(a) shows that the H_2 desorption rate of the H_2/Ar plasma-treated Cu film remains relatively stable even after a 24-hour exposure. The slight decrease in H_2 desorption is attributed to desorption caused by the growth of more stable Cu oxide. Consequently, the chemisorption state of atomic hydrogen proves to be remarkably stable and can persist for at least 24 hours, even when subjected to atmospheric conditions. This stability can be attributed to the substantial depth of the potential energy well for a hydrogen atom on Cu, calculated through first-principle calculations to be approximately 2.5 eV on the hollow site of the Cu(111) surface (33, 34). Thus, these findings suggest that high-strength Cu-Cu bonding can be achieved even after prolonged exposure of up to 24 hours.

Low temperature Al-Al Bonding

Al thermocompression bonding, despite its many advantages like the CMOS compatibility, also presents certain challenges that need to be addressed and managed for successful implementation in various applications. Some of the key challenges associated with Al thermocompression bonding are:

- Surface contamination: Al surfaces are highly susceptible to contamination. Surface oxides and other contaminants like organic residues, or moisture can hinder the formation of a reliable bond. Therefore, thorough surface cleaning, preparation and passivation are critical to achieving strong and defect-free bonds (14, 35).
- Surface Roughness and Flatness: The surface roughness and flatness of Al substrates can significantly affect the bonding process. Thick Al is often deposited using electrochemical deposition (36) which may lead to uneven surfaces or high roughness. As discussed before, this limits the interdiffusion potential.
- Bonding Temperature and time optimization: The selection of an appropriate bonding temperature and time is crucial for achieving a high bond quality while not exceeding the thermal budget of the bonded components. Finding the right balance between temperature, time, and pressure is a complex task that requires careful experimentation and optimization (37, 38).

Apart from these general aspects, another critical process parameter, similar to Cu-TCB, is the Al native Oxide. A possibility to manage metal surface oxides is the passivation with thin Pd layers (39). This approach has been evaluated for Al TCB by doing an in-situ sputtering of 5 nm and 10 nm Pd respectively on 800 nm Al layers. These were subsequently bonded using an EVG wafer bonding system under nitrogen atmosphere, a temperature of 350°C and a force of 55 kN for 2 hours. To evaluate the performance of the bonds, they were diced into chips measuring 10 mm x 2 mm. The qualitatively high yield, nearly reaching 100%, is illustrated in **Figure 13** and demonstrates the successful bonding without any in-situ oxide management during the bonding process.

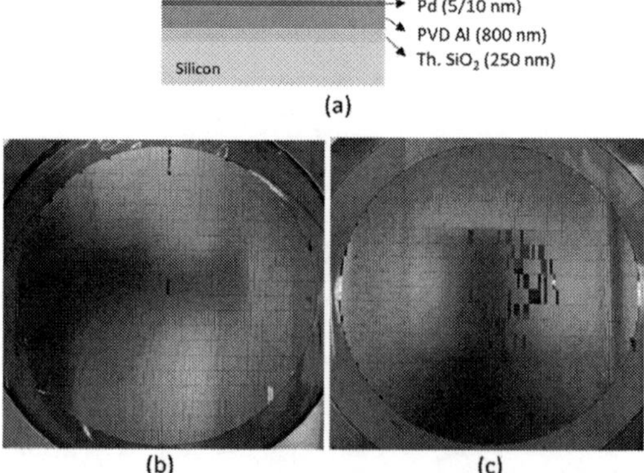

Figure 13 (a) Showing the metal stack on the thermal silicon dioxide. Dicing yield after bonding with (b) 5 nm Pd and (c) 10 nm Pd as the capping layer on Al

The diced chips were analyzed by SEM cross section analysis, optical microscopy and mechanical strength testing.
The bond strength is measured using TIRA test 2805 and the average strength of the bond strength is measured as 27 MPa, suggesting mechanically strong bond at the interface. The subsequent SEM inspection suggests grain growth at the bond interface as shown in **Figure** *14*.

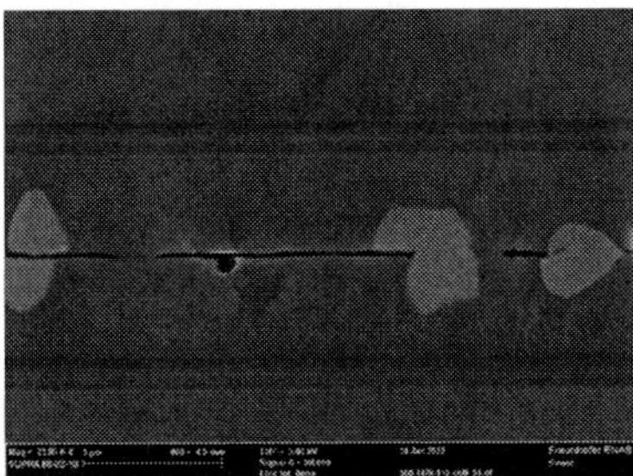

Figure 14 SEM image of the Al bonded interface using the palladium capping showing the grain growth at the interface

The residual bond gaps in the interface are most likely related to other gating process parameters that can still be optimized, for example the surface roughness and planarity. Similar results could be achieved with patterned wafers with bond frames of 60 μm and 80 μm width respectively.

Summary and Outlook

A variety of different approaches, ideas and principles have been reviewed in order to reduce the bonding temperature of metal bonds. Having all the advantages of being hermetic, electrically conducting and having highest mechanical strengths, these types of bonds cannot be replaces in semiconductor industry. In order to support new architectures with heterogenous material combinations, power devices or piezo-electric materials, the related thermal budgets must be considered. It was seen that by understanding and combining multiple material properties and their respective advantages can be combined, for example for SLID bonding. The reviewed TCB data clearly showed by how much a processing temperature can be optimized by identifying and subsequently optimizing critical-to-function parameters. The work presented in this paper clearly shows a path forward for next generation metal-bond applications.

References

1. K. E. Aasmundtveit, T.-T. Luu, H.-V. Nguyen, A. Larsson, and T. A. Tollefsen, in Intermetallic Compounds - Formation and Applications, M. Aliofkhazraei Ed.: IntechOpen, ch. 3, pp. 43 (2018)
2. T.-T. Luu, N. Hoivik, K. Wang, K. E. Aasmundtveit, and A.-S. B. Vardøy, *Metall. and Mat. Trans. A*, 46A (6), pp. 2637 (2015)

3.   V. Vuorinen, H. Dong, G. Ross, J. Hotchkiss, J. Kaaos and M. Paulasto-Kröckel, *J. Electron. Mater.* **50**, 818 (2021)

4.   V. Vuorinen, G. Ross, A. Klami, H. Dong, M. Paulasto-Kröckel, T. Wernicke, A. Pönninger, IEEE Components, Packaging and Manufacturing Technology, pp. 1-8, 2021

5.   O. Golim, V. Vuorinen, G. Ross, T. Wernicke, M. Pawlak, N. Tiwary, M. Paulasto-Kröckel, *Scripta Materialia* **222**, 114998 (2023)

6.   O. Golim, V. Vuorinen, N. Tiwary, R. Glenn and M. Paulasto-Kröckel, in 23rd European Microelectronics and Packaging Conference & Exhibition (EMPC), pp. 1-4 (2021)

7.   H. Okamoto, in Binary Alloy Phase Diagrams, vol. 1, T. B. Massalski Ed.: ASM International, pp. 748 (1990)

8.   K. E. Aasmundtveit, T. A. V. Nguyen, and H.-V. Nguyen, in the 6th Electronic System-Integration Technology Conference (ESTC), Grenoble, France, 2016: IEEE, pp. 1-5

9.   K. E. Aasmundtveit, T. Eggen, T. Manh, and H.-V. Nguyen, Soldering & Surface Mount Technology, pp. 1-6, 2018

10.   S. L. Kuziora, H. V. Nguyen, and K. E. Aasmundtveit, *J. of Electron. Mat.* **52**, pp. 1284 (2023)

11.   H.-V. Nguyen, S. L. Kuziora, and K. E. Aasmundtveit, in the 9th Electronics System-Integration Technology Conference (ESTC), Sibiu, Romania, 2022: IEEE, pp. 373-378

12.   S. L. Kuziora, H.-V. Nguyen, and K. E. Aasmundtveit, *J. of Mat. Sci.: Mat. in Electron.* **34**, 2023

13.   M. Baum, L. Hofmann, M. Wiemer, S. Schulz and T. Gessner, in Int. Semicond. Conf. Dresden - Grenoble (ISCDG), Dresden, Germany, pp. 1 (2013)

14.   Kai-Cheng Shie, A.M. Gusak, K.N. Tu, Chih Chen, *J. of Mat. Res. and Techn.* **15**, 2332 (2021)

15.   B. Rebhan, G. Hesser, J. Duchoslav, V. Dragoi, M. Wimplinger, and K. Hingerl, *ECS Trans,* **50**(7)

16.   P. Gondcharton, F. Baudin, L. Benaissa, and B. Imbert, in MRS Online Proceedings Library (OPL), 1559 (2013)

17.   P.-F. Lin, D.-P. Tran, H.-C. Liu, Y.-Y. Li, and C. Chen, *Materials* **15**, 937 (2022).

18.   B. Rebhan, T. Plach, S. Tollabimazraehno, V. Dragoi and M. Kawano, in Int. Conf. on Electron. Pack. (ICEP), Toyama, Japan, pp. 475-479 (2014)

19.   B. Rebhan, S. Tollabimazraehno, G. Hesser, and V. Dragoi, *Microsys. Techn.* **21**, 1003 (2015)

20.   H. G. Tompkins and D. L. Allara, *J. of Coll. & Interf. Sci.* **49**(3), December 1974

21.   K. L. Chavez and D. W. Hess, *J. of Electrochem. Soc.* **148**(11), pp. G640 (2001)

22.   E. J. Jang, S. Hyun, H. J. Lee and Y. B. Park, *J. of Electron. Mat.* **38**(12), pp.2449 (2009)

23.   O. J. Kwon, J. H. Bae, B. K Cho, Y. J. Kim and J. J. Kim, *Kor. J. Chem. Eng.* **28**(7), 1619 (2011)

24.   M. Lambert, P. R. Khani, J. T. Veen, L. V. Nimwegen and F. Frederix, *ECS Trans.* **25**(5) 55 (2009)

25. V. R. K. Gorantla, K. A. Assiongbon, S. V. Babu and D. Roy, *J. of Electrochem. Soc.* **152**(5), pp.G404 (2005)

26. T. K. Kang and W. Y. Chou, *J. of Electrochem. Soc.* **151**(6), pp.G391 (2004).

27. V. Dubey, J. Derakhshandeh, E. Beyne, C. Gerets, E. Coper, P. Laermans, K.D. Leersnijder, K. Baumans, K.J. Rebibis, A. Miller and I. De Wolf, IEEE 66th Electronic Components and Technology Conference (ECTC), Las Vegas, NV, USA, pp. 2435 (2016)

28. M. Lykova, I. Panchenko, M. Schneider-Ramelow, T. Suga, F. Mu, and R. Buschbeck, *Micromachines* **14**, 1365 (2023)

29. K. Tanaka, W.S. Wang, M. Baum, J. Froemel, H. Hirano, S. Tanaka, M. Wiemer, and T. Otto, *Micromachines* **7**(12), 234 (2016)

30. G. Vidali, G. Ihm, H.-Y. Kim, M.W. Cole, *Surf. Sci. Rep.* **12**, pp. 135 (1991).

31. K. Christmann, *Surf. Sci. Rep.* **9**, 1 (1988)

32. M.R. Baklanov, D.G. Shamiryan, Z. Tokei, G.P. Beyer, T. Conard, S. Vanhaelemeersch, K. Maex, *J. Vac. Sci. Technol.* **B** *Microelectron. Nanomater. Struct.* **19**, 1201 (2001)

33. K. Nobuhara, H. Nakanishi, H. Kasai, A. Okiji, *Surf. Sci.* **493**, 271 (2001)

34. A.D. Jewell, G. Peng, M.F.G. Mattera, E.A. Lewis, C.J. Murphy, G. Kyriakou, M. Mavrikakis, E,C.H. Sykes, *ACS Nano* **6**, 10115 (2012)

35. W.-D. Zabka, M. Mosberger, Z. Novotny, D. Leuenberger, G. Mette, T. Kälin, B. Probst and J. Osterwalder *J. Phys.: Condens. Matter* **30** 424002, (2018)

36. M. S. Al Farisi, S. Hertel, M. Weimer and T. Otto, *Micromachines* **9**(11), 589 (2018)

37. N. Malik, K. Schjølberg-Henriksen, E. Poppe and T. G. Finstad, in Transducers & Eurosensors XXVII: The 17th International Conference on Solid-State Sensors, Actuators and Microsystems (TRANSDUCERS & EUROSENSORS XXVII), Barcelona, Spain, pp. 1067 (2013)

38. A.P. Hinterreiter, B. Rebhan, C, Flötgen, V. Dragoi, and K. Hingerl, *Microsys. Techn.* **24**, 773 (2018)

39. Y. -C. Tsai, H. -W. Hu and K. -N. Chen, in *IEEE Electron Dev. Lett.* **41**(8), pp. 1229, (2020)

ECS Transactions, 112 (3) 265-268 (2023)
10.1149/11203.0265ecst ©The Electrochemical Society

Hydrophilic Bonding of GaN and Diamond Substrates

T. Matsumae[a], S. Okita[b], S. Fukumoto[b], M. Hayase[b], Y. Kurashima[a], and H. Takagi[a]

[a] National Institute of Advanced Industrial Science and Technology, Ibaraki 305-8564, Japan
[b] Tokyo University of Science, Chiba 278-8510, Japan

We have developed a hydrophilic bonding technique for GaN and diamond substrates. Before the bonding step, the GaN substrate was dipped into HCl acid, and the diamond substrate was dipped into NH_4OH/H_2O_2 solution to generate hydrophilic surfaces. The treated GaN and diamond substrates were contacted with each other under atmospheric conditions. They are annealed at 300 °C in 2 h for bonding formation. We expect that this bonding technique would contribute to the fabrication of the GaN-on-diamond structure.

Introduction

GaN-on-diamond devices have attracted worldwide attention because it is suitable for high-power and high-frequency amplifiers[1]. In this structure, GaN high electron mobility transistor (HEMT) is bonded with the diamond heat spreader. One typical approach for the GaN/diamond integration is hetero-epitaxial growth, which develops a polycrystalline diamond layer on the GaN device substrate[2]. However, the poly-crystalline diamond has lower thermal conductivity compared with a single-crystaline diamond[3], which has the highest value in sold materials. The integration of the GaN device on the single-crystalline diamond heat spreader requires the development of a bonding technique between GaN and diamond substrates for overcoming lattice mismatch.

Between GaN and diamond, there is a large difference in the coefficient of thermal expansion (CTE, GaN: ~5.6 ppm/K, diamond: ~1.1 ppm/K). Thus, a high-temperature bonding process is undesirable for the bonding of GaN and diamond substrates. For the GaN/diamond integration, J. Liang et al. realized the room-temperature bonding using surface activated bonding (SAB)[4]. In this process, the GaN and diamond surfaces were sputter-etched under ultra-high vacuum conditions and then contacted with each other. In addition, Z. Cheng et al. demonstrated the GaN/diamond interface using high thermal boundary conductance by the modified SAB method with a Si nano-adhesion layer[5]. Meanwhile, this bonding process requires a special ultra-high-vacuum bonding machine, which hinders widespread applications.

Hydrophilic bonding is another candidate because it allows a vacuum-free bonding process. In this bonding method, the substrates functionalized with -OH and/or -NH₂ groups were contacted with each other and annealed at low temperatures (~200 °C)[6]. This process can form atomic bonds by a dehydration reaction across the surfaces. We have developed the hydrophilic bonding of the diamond substrate by a wet chemical treatment using NH_3/H_2O_2 mixture[7]. In addition, we demonstrated that the SiC surface dipped into

HF acis can be bonded by the hydrophilic bonding method[8]. The pre-bonding treatment with HF acid removes the surface oxide layer and simultaneously generates -OH groups on the SiC surface. Thus, the oxide layer at the bonding interface is extremely thin while the SiC substrate was bonded under atmospheric conditions. In the case of GaN, a HCl-dipped surface is more hydrophilic than an HF-dipped surface[9]. For the GaN/diamond bonding under atmospheric conditions, the present study demonstrates the hydrophilic bonding of HCl-dipped GaN and NH_3/H_2O_2-dipped diamond surfaces.

Experimental

A 3-mm-square diamond (111) substrate (from EDP Corp.) was bonded with a self-standing 10 mm × 10.5 mm GaN (0001) substrate (from MTK Corp.) in this study.

The diamond substrate was dipped into a mixture of NH_4OH/H_2O_2, which is so called standard clean 1 (SC1), for 10 min. The ratio of $NH_4OH:H_2O_2:H_2O$ was 1:1:5, and the temperature was 70 °C for 10 min. Our previous studies demonstrated that the diamond surface was cleaned and functionalized with OH groups by this process[8,10]. On the other hand, the GaN substrate was dipped into a 5% HCl solution at room temperature (~20°C) for 10 min. This process expectedly removes the native oxide layer and forms -OH, -NH₂, and -Cl groups on the GaN surface[9].

The treated GaN and diamond substrates were rinsed with purified water for ~5 min and dried using a N_2 gas blow. Subsequently, the GaN and diamond surfaces were contacted under atmospheric conditions in our clean room (temperature: 23 °C, relative humidity: 40%). The contacted specimens were annealed at 300 °C for 2 h. We believe that the proposed bonding process generated chemical bonds between GaN and diamond surfaces as illustrated in Fig. 1.

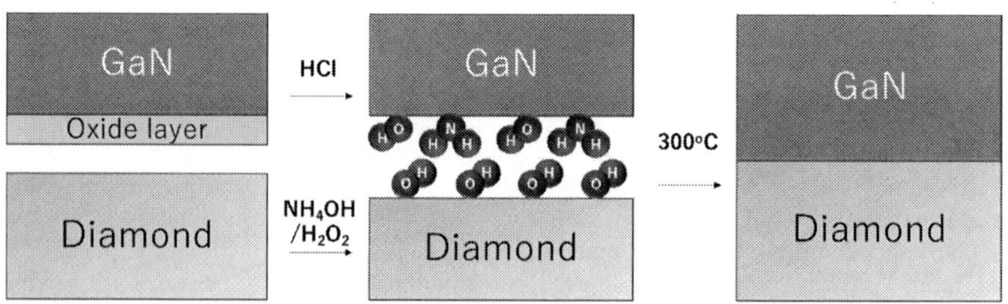

Figure 1. GaN and diamond surfaces are bonded after dipping into
HCl and NH_4OH/H_2O_2 solutions, respectively.

Results

For low-temperature bonding, the pre-bonding treatment should not largely increase the surface roughness. The polished diamond (111) surface is atomically smooth even after the treatment with NH_4OH/H_2O_2 mixture in our previous study[5]. On the other hand, Fig. 2 compares the surface roughness of the GaN substrates before and after dipping into HCl acid. They were investigated using an atomic force microscope (AFM). The root-mean-square (RMS) roughness is initially 0.212 nm. It slightly increased to 0.237 nm by treating with diluted (5%) HCl acid. However, the concentrated (35%) HCl acid significantly increased the RMS roughness to 0.334 nm. This indicates that the pre-bonding step with the diluted (5%) HCl acid is more suitable for hydrophilic bonding.

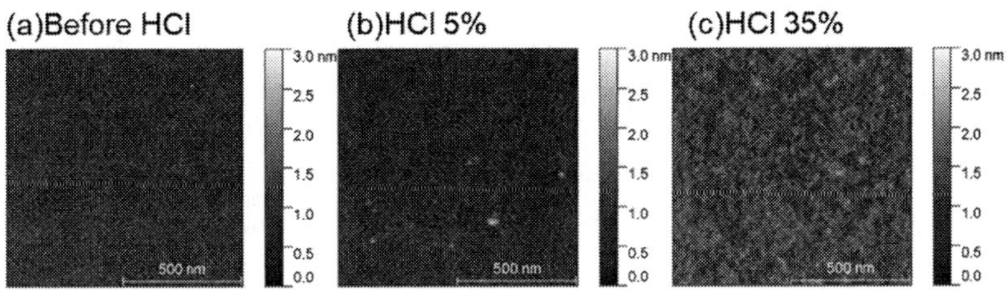

Figure 2. Nanoscale surface roughness of GaN substrate (a) before and after processes dipping into (b) diluted and (c) concentrated HCl.

Figure 3 shows the GaN and diamond substrates during the bonding process. They were fully adhered to each other when contacted under atmospheric conditions. However, Newton's ring appeared after the annealing step. It indicates that the left half of the diamond substrate was exfoliated by annealing. The possible reason for the exfoliation is the thermal stress because of the CTE mismatch. The annealed specimen was not debonded by handling; however, it was fractured during a grinding process for the GaN substrate. Note that this diamond substrate was a convex surface. For wafer-scale GaN/diamond bonding, it is necessary to improve the bonding process and utilize a flat diamond substrate.

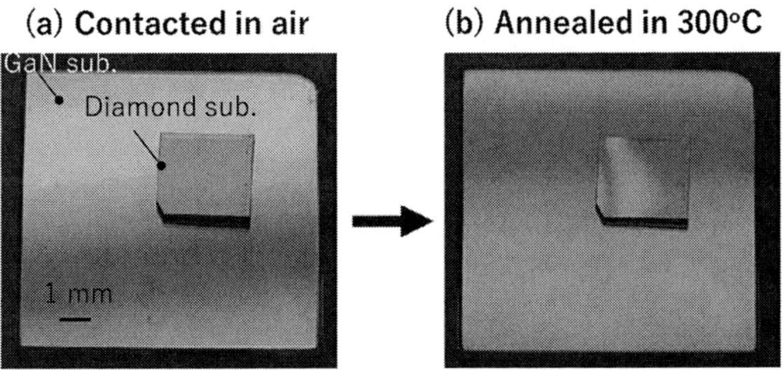

Figure 3. Diamond substrate (a) contacted with GaN substrate under atmospheric conditions and (b) annealed at 300 °C for 2 h.

Conclusions

This study demonstrates the vacuum-free bonding process of GaN and diamond substrates. It is known that the diamond (111) substrate cleaned with NH_4OH/H_2O_2 solution is hydrophilic and can have atomic bonds with plasma-activated semiconductor substrates. In this study, we created the hydrophilic GaN surface by dipping it into diluted HCl acid. As this GaN surface was smooth, it can form atomic bonds with the diamond surface by the hydrophilic bonding method at 300 °C. We believe that the simple bonding process would contribute to the future fabrication of the GaN-on-diamond structures.

Acknowledgment

This paper is based on results obtained from a project, JPNP14004, commissioned by the New Energy and Industrial Technology Development Organization (NEDO).

Reference

1. F. Ejeckam et al., *Lester Eastman Conf. 2014 - High Perform. Devices, LEC 2014* (2014).
2. P. W. May, H. Y. Tsai, W. N. Wang, and J. A. Smith, *Diam. Relat. Mater.*, **15**, 526–530 (2006).
3. J. Anaya et al., *Acta Mater.*, **103**, 141–152 (2016).
4. J. Liang et al., *Adv. Mater.*, **33**, 2104564 (2021) https://onlinelibrary.wiley.com/doi/full/10.1002/adma.202104564.
5. Z. Cheng, F. Mu, L. Yates, T. Suga, and S. Graham, *ACS Appl. Mater. Interfaces*, **12**, 8376–8384 (2020) https://pubs.acs.org/doi/abs/10.1021/acsami.9b16959.
6. C. Ventosa et al., *J. Appl. Phys.*, **104**, 123524 (2008) http://aip.scitation.org/doi/10.1063/1.3040701.
7. S. Fukumoto et al., *Appl. Phys. Lett.*, **117**, 201601 (2020) http://aip.scitation.org/doi/10.1063/5.0026348.
8. T. Matsumae, Y. Kurashima, H. Takagi, H. Umezawa, and E. Higurashi, *J. Appl. Phys.*, **130**, 085303 (2021) https://aip.scitation.org/doi/abs/10.1063/5.0057960.
9. M. D. Losego et al., *J. Mater. Res.*, **31**, 36–45 (2016) https://link.springer.com/article/10.1557/jmr.2015.332.
10. T. Matsumae, Y. Kurashima, H. Umezawa, and H. Takagi, *Jpn. J. Appl. Phys.*, **59** (2020) http://iopscience.iop.org/article/10.7567/1347-4065/ab4c87.

ECS Transactions, 112 (3) 269-278 (2023)
10.1149/11203.0269ecst ©The Electrochemical Society

Towards Controlled Transfer of (001) β-Ga₂O₃ to (0001) 4H-SiC Substrates

M. E. Liao[a], K. Huynh[b], B. Carson[b], L. Matto[b], K. Pan[b], J. S. Lundh[a],
M. J. Tadjer[c], K. D. Hobart[c], and M. S. Goorsky[b]

[a] National Research Council Postdoctoral Fellow at the U.S. Naval Research Laboratory
[b] Department of Materials Science and Engineering, University of California,
Los Angeles, CA, 90095, USA
[c] U.S. Naval Research Laboratory, Washington, D.C., 20375, USA

We demonstrate successful surface blistering of He-implanted (001) β-Ga₂O₃ substrates, bonding to (0001) 4H-SiC, and initial results towards large-area transfer of (001) β-Ga₂O₃ to 4H-SiC. Surface blistering of unbonded, implanted substrates is an important indication of successful exfoliation and transfer of films, which is achieved by initiating He bubble nucleation during a low temperature anneal followed by bubble growth at a high temperature anneal. Prior to annealing, implanted substrates were bonded to (0001) 4H-SiC at room temperature using a thin ~5 nm Ti interlayer. However, the β-Ga₂O₃ substrate did not wafer split from the bonded structure after annealing. Instead, small area transfers up to ~200 μm were achieved (~7% of the total bonded area transferred while the entire structure remained bonded). Further optimization of implant parameters is underway. These are promising results towards achieving large wafer-scale (001) β-Ga₂O₃ composite wafers suitable for β-Ga₂O₃ devices with efficient thermal management characteristics.

Introduction

Exfoliation and transfer of films is an important component for the heterogenous integration of semiconductor materials. Part of the ultrawide-bandgap family with materials such as AlN and diamond, β-Ga₂O₃ has a bandgap of ~4.85 eV and is an appealing candidate for next generation high-power (> 20 kV) device applications (1,2). Despite successful reports of β-Ga₂O₃ device fabrication towards realizing its potential for electronic devices (3,4,5), the most pressing hindrance to β-Ga₂O₃ power applications is efficient thermal management. The thermal conductivity of β-Ga₂O₃ is very low ranging from 11 to 27 W/(m·K), which is one to two orders magnitude lower than Si, GaN, 4H-SiC, and diamond (1). The variation in materials properties of β-Ga₂O₃ along different crystallographic directions is due to its low-symmetry monoclinic crystal structure (6,7,8,9). Poor heat dissipation in either the lateral or vertical β-Ga₂O₃ device structure degrades device performance (10) and can even cause permanent device failure (11,12). It is evident that efficient heat management during β-Ga₂O₃ device performance requires integration with other materials with higher thermal conductivities. Thin film β-Ga₂O₃ growth on various substrates have been demonstrated on sapphire (13), SiC (14), and diamond (15) with high thermal boundary conductance values (thermal conductivity across the interface), but all suffer from reduction in thermal conductivity of the β-Ga₂O₃ film due to a high density of defects. Growing β-Ga$_2$O$_3$ on SiC or sapphire results in films with a high density of stacking faults or twin boundaries, respectively. For the case of diamond, the resulting film is polycrystalline, and grain boundaries greatly reduce the film's thermal conductivity.

Employing wafer bonding techniques, on the other hand, to integrate high-quality single crystal β-Ga$_2$O$_3$ to a high thermal conductivity material would avoid growth-related defects and enable the integration of any β-Ga$_2$O$_3$ orientation. Growth of β-Ga$_2$O$_3$ is done from a melt source, which is appealing for several reasons including rapid growth rates and low production costs especially when comparing to growing other wide bandgap materials that are not melt-growth compatible. The edge-defined film-fed growth (16) and Czochralski (17,18) growth of β-Ga$_2$O$_3$ are the two main melt growth methods used to produce some of the highest quality β-Ga$_2$O$_3$ to date. Furthermore, utilizing light atom ion implantation, for example, to induce exfoliation and transfer of β-Ga$_2$O$_3$ films would achieve β-Ga$_2$O$_3$ thin films of any orientation on a substrate without suffering from defect-induced film thermal conductivity reduction. By engineering the properties of the bonded interface, wafer bonding of β-Ga$_2$O$_3$ could be a pathway to fabricate a heterostructure that exhibits a high interfacial thermal boundary conductance and high thermal conductivity of the film simultaneously. Fundamentally understanding and engineering interfaces via the wafer bonding approach extends beyond thermal management applications and can produce interfaces with emergent properties (e.g., electrical transport) that would not be realizable with only growth techniques.

Light-atom ion implantation of either hydrogen (19) or helium (20) and subsequent annealing was first demonstrated to exfoliate silicon layers to fabricate silicon-on-insulator structures. Annealing an implanted substrate will surface blister due to H$_2$ or He gas bubble growth near the implanted species projected range beneath the substrate surface. To controllably and reproducibly induce large surface blisters, the anneal involves a low temperature followed by a high temperature step (21). The low temperature anneal serves to initiate the nucleation of either the H$_2$ or He bubbles while the subsequent high temperature step induces bubble growth. It has been shown that a strong indication of successful exfoliation is the occurrence of surface blistering of an unbonded, implanted substrate. If an implanted substrate were bonded to a handle substrate prior to the high-temperature anneal step, uniform wafer splitting can be achieved after the high-temperature anneal. Large, wafer-scale area thin films are then transferred to a handle substrate after the splitting. The current literature and our previous work have further extended the efficacy and fundamental understanding of hydrogen and/or helium implantation not only for silicon (22,23,24), but also for a diverse roster of materials including germanium (25), SiC (26), III-V's (21,27,28,29,30), II-VI's (31), and various ferroelectric materials (32). Thin films of each of these materials were successfully exfoliated and transferred. For β-Ga$_2$O$_3$, implantation of either hydrogen or helium has been successfully demonstrated to exfoliate and transfer the (010) and ($\underline{2}$01) orientations (33,34). The focus of this current work is to present initial results towards the exfoliation of another technologically relevant orientation – (001) β-Ga$_2$O$_3$. Currently, 4-inch (001) β-Ga$_2$O$_3$ substrates are commercially available with thick drift layers grown using the hydride vapor phase epitaxy method.

Experiment

Epi-ready two-inch (001) β-Ga_2O_3 substrates were implanted with He^+ at an energy of 160 keV with a dose of 5×10^{16} cm^{-2} at room temperature, which are the same ion implantation parameters used in our previous work to successfully exfoliate (010) β-Ga_2O_3 (33). Some of the implanted substrates were then bonded to (0001) 4H-SiC at room temperature under ultrahigh vacuum using a ~5 nm thin Ti interlayer to assist with the bond. Ti was deposited on both the β-Ga_2O_3 and 4H-SiC prior to bonding. The primary flats of each substrate were aligned prior to bonding such that the in-plane alignment was [100] β-Ga_2O_3 $\|$ [10$\underline{1}$0] 4H-SiC. High-resolution symmetric ω:2θ X-ray diffraction (XRD) scans were performed using a Bruker-JV D1 diffractometer whose incident X-ray beam is conditioned by a Göbel mirror and a (220) channel-cut silicon crystal to produce a highly collimated monochromatic Cu Kα_1 beam. The as-implanted XRD was fitted using software that utilizes a genetic algorithm called Differential Evolution (35). An FEI Nova 600 DualBeam focused ion beam system was used to prepare transmission electron microscopy (TEM) samples. An FEI TITAN S/TEM operating at 300 keV was used to measure cross-sectional TEM images of the bonded structure.

Results and Discussion

XRD scans were measured for the as-implanted, unbonded substrates using the (004) β-Ga_2O_3 symmetric reflection. Implantation induces strain by causing the lattice to expand due to the intercalation of He and point defects. The underlying substrate material beyond the implanted region imposes in-plane compressive biaxial stress on the implanted region, preventing the lattice within the implanted region to expand in-plane. The typical response to in-plane biaxial compressive stress is out-of-plane expansion – which corresponds to tensile strain. Tensile strain causes peaks to shift towards lower angles in an XRD ω:2θ scan. As shown in Figure 1(a), the as-implanted (004) symmetric ω:2θ scan shows strain fringes left of the main substrate peak towards lower angles. The strain fringes were then fitted using a model to determine the thickness and strain induced by the He implantation. The peak strain value is ~1.9%, which is nearly a factor of 2 higher than the peak strain value found when implanting (010) substrates under the same conditions (33). This is likely attributed to the higher Poisson's ratio for (001) compared to (010) β-Ga_2O_3 (36); the theoretical difference in strain due to biaxial stress between (001) and (010) is expected to be ~2× as well.

The He concentration and displacements-per-atom (DPA) profiles were simulated in SRIM (37) and compared to the simulated strain profile used to model the XRD data as shown in Figure 1(b). The strain profile approximately matches the overlap between the He concentration and DPA profiles, which is what was observed in our previous work when implanting hydrogen in Si using the same dose (5×10^{16} cm^{-2}) at either 30 keV or 140 keV (24). This suggests that the predominate cause of strain in these He-implanted substrates are from He-vacancy complexes (i.e., involving both He atoms and the displaced Ga and O atoms in the β-Ga_2O_3 lattice).

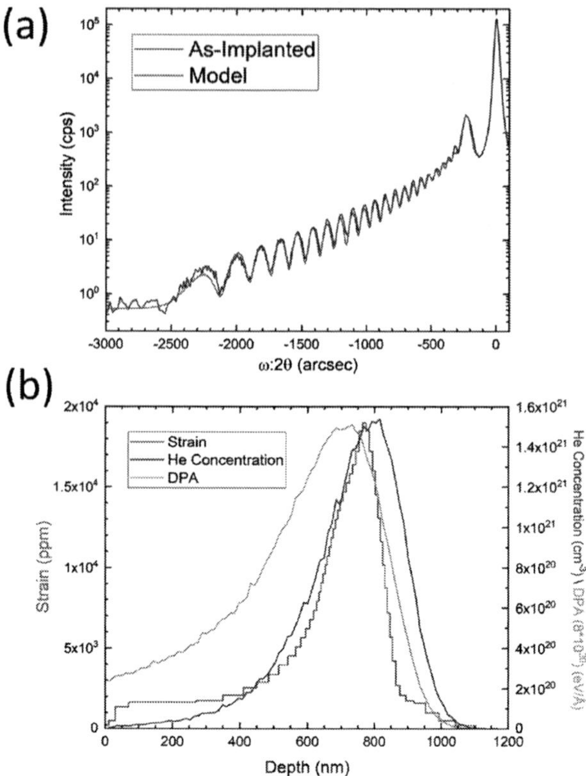

Figure 1. (a) Symmetric (004) ω:2θ β-Ga$_2$O$_3$ XRD scan corresponding to the blue curve, where ω:2θ = 0" corresponds to the main substrate away from the implanted region. The Bragg angle for the (004) reflection is ~33.18°. The red curve corresponds to a simulated curve from a model used to fit the strain profile due to the implant. (b) The red curve is the fitted strain profile while the blue and green curves are the He concentration and displacements-per-atom (DPA) profiles simulated with SRIM, respectively.

Following a similar annealing procedure from our previous work on exfoliating He-implanted (010) substrates (33), performing a low-temperature followed by high-temperature anneal on the unbonded implanted substrates reduced the strain induced by the implant. As shown in Figure 2, the strain fringes are removed and only a shoulder remains, which corresponds to leftover strain (on the order of ~0.2%) that could be removed upon further annealing. Performing the two-step annealing procedure resulted in surface blisters, as shown in the plan-view optical Nomarski image in Figure 3. The ~10 μm light contrast surface features correspond to surface blisters due to He bubble growth that have not broken the surface. Dark contrast features with straight vertical edges are blisters that broke the surface – the vertical edge corresponds to the (100) primary cleavage plane. It has been shown with other materials that demonstrating surface blistering is a strong indication that successful exfoliation and transfer can be achieved.

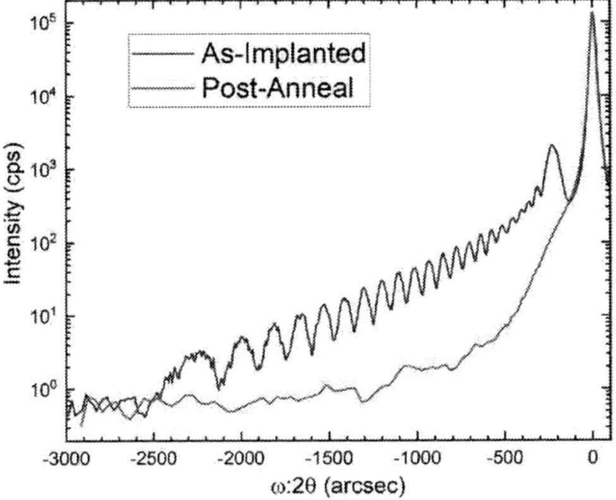

Figure 2. Symmetric (004) β-Ga$_2$O$_3$ ω:2θ XRD scan for the as-implanted (blue curve) versus post-anneal (red curve). ω:2θ = 0" corresponds to the main substrate peak. The Bragg angle for the (004) reflection is ~33.18°. After annealing, the strain fringes are removed and only a shoulder is observed, which corresponds to a lower strain of ~0.2%.

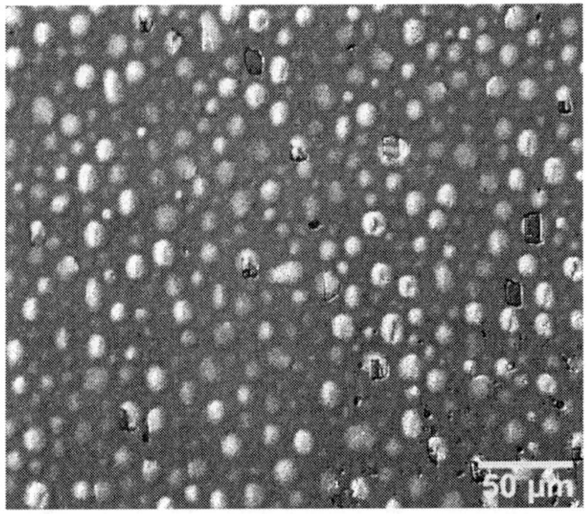

Figure 3. Planview optical Nomarski image of the unbonded (001) β-Ga$_2$O$_3$ surface after the low-temperature followed by high-temperature annealing. The round ~10 μm light contrast features are He surface blisters. The dark rectangular features are exfoliated regions, with the vertical edges corresponding to the (100) primary cleavage plane.

A set of implanted (001) β-Ga$_2$O$_3$ substrates were bonded prior to annealing. The bonding was performed under ultrahigh vacuum with (0001) 4H-SiC using a thin ~5 nm

Ti interlayer to assist with the bond. Ti has been used in the literature to bond Si|Si (38) and SiC|diamond (39) due to the chemical reactivity between Ti with Si and C and especially because of its high adhesion to SiO_2. However, utilizing Ti for bonding has not yet been explored in depth for β-Ga_2O_3. The cross-sectional high-resolution TEM image of the bonded structure is shown in Figure 4(a). Contrast can be seen within the implanted region, with a darkest contrast band occurring at the projected range of the implant (~750 nm). The thickness of the modelled strain profile from Figure 1(b) is consistent with this experimentally measured projected range. The dark contrast is due to Z-contrast from the relatively high He content of ~11%. In addition to the contrast, lattice distortion can be seen on smaller length scales as shown in Figure 4(b) and 4(c). Figure 4(b) shows the pristine lattice planes beyond the implanted region that shows low overall contrast. Figure 4(c), on the other hand, shows fluctuations in contrast that correspond to lattice distortion induced by the implantation. Figure 5 shows a magnified cross-sectional TEM image focused on the bonded interface, which clearly shows the Ti interlayer. Within the TEM sampling region, the Ti is single crystalline. The $(10\underline{1}0)$ Ti surface plane is parallel to the (001) β-Ga_2O_3 surface plane and the $[0001]$ Ti in-plane direction is parallel to the $[\underline{1}10]$ β-Ga_2O_3 in-plane direction. Studies on the impact of interfaces prepared with Ti on thermal boundary conductance are underway as well as the chemical and structural evolution with post-bonding annealing.

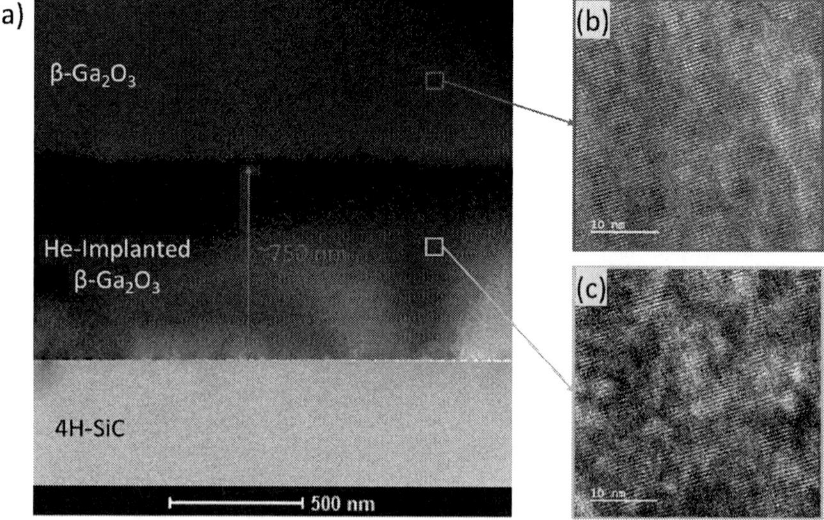

Figure 4. (a) Cross-sectional high resolution TEM image of the bonded structure. The implanted region projected range is ~750 nm which can be seen by the dark contrast band. (b) Magnified image within the bulk of the β-Ga_2O_3 beyond the implant projected range showing pristine, undistorted lattice planes. (c) Magnified image within the implanted β-Ga_2O_3 region that shows contrast fluctuations due to lattice distortion from the implant.

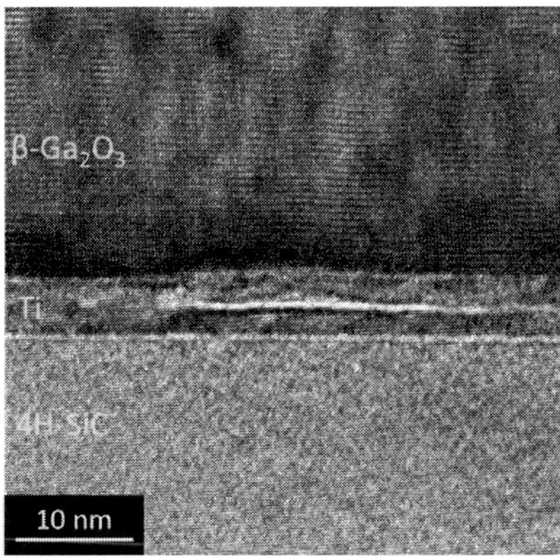

Figure 5. Cross-sectional high resolution TEM image of the bonded structure magnified at the bonded interface. ~5 nm of Ti was used to assist with bonding between β-Ga$_2$O$_3$ and 4H-SiC. The zone axis used here is aligned along the [$\underline{1}$10] β-Ga$_2$O$_3$. The [0001] Ti zone axis is found to be parallel to this β-Ga$_2$O$_3$ zone axis.

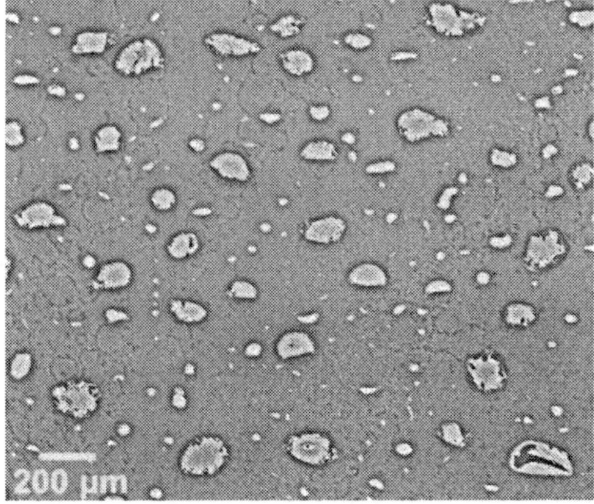

Figure 6. Planview optical Nomarski image of the bonded structure viewed through the β-Ga$_2$O$_3$ wafer after annealing. ~7% of the total bonded area transferred to the (0001) 4H-SiC (round light contrast features). The structure remained bonded and the β-Ga$_2$O$_3$ did not wafer split.

The plan-view optical Nomarski image after annealing the bonded structure using the same anneal conditions that induced surface blistering is shown in Figure 6. While localized regions up to ~200 μm wide exfoliated and transferred, the β-Ga₂O₃ surprisingly did not wafer split. Solutions to achieve wafer splitting and complete β-Ga₂O₃ film transfer are underway. The reduction in strain shown by the XRD after annealing in Figure 2 and surface blistering in Figure 3 is evidence of He diffusion and bubble growth. The formation of He bubbles at the implant projected range provides mechanical weak points in the β-Ga₂O₃ at this range beneath its surface. Thus, provided the bond strength with the 4H-SiC is sufficiently strong enough, the bonded structure after annealing as shown in Figure 6 may be able to transfer but subjecting the structure in a pull-test setup. Alternatively, a higher He dose may also be effective in producing a more continuous layer transfer to induce complete wafer splitting.

Conclusion

The first report of surface blistering He implanted (001) oriented β-Ga₂O₃ is demonstrated. The strain induced by the implant was modelled with a strain profile that matched neither the He concentration profile nor the DPA profile, but rather the overlap between the concentration and DPA profiles. We speculate the correlation between this overlap and the strain profile suggests the main contributor to the implant-induced strain is from He-defect (e.g., He-vacancy) complexes. This implant-induced distortion is elastic and removed upon annealing. Successful wafer bonding of (001) β-Ga₂O₃ to (0001) 4H-SiC using a thin ~5 nm Ti interlayer is also demonstrated. While Ti has been used to bond Si, SiC, and diamond, bonding β-Ga₂O₃ using Ti has not yet been utilized. Initial results transferred up to ~200 μm wide β-Ga₂O₃ to 4H-SiC. Further optimization of implant and anneal conditions are expected to increase transfer yield towards full-wafer-scale areas, as has been done with other orientations of β-Ga₂O₃.

Acknowledgments

The authors would like to acknowledge the support from the Office of Naval Research through a MURI program, grant No. N00014-18-1-2429. This research was performed while M.E.L. and J.S.L. held an NRC Research Associateship award at the U.S. Naval Research Laboratory.

References

1. S. J. Pearton, J. Yang, P. H. Cary IV, F. Ren, J. Kim, M. J. Tadjer, and M. A. Mastro, *Appl. Phys. Rev.* **5**, 011301 (2018).
2. M. J. Tadjer, *Science* **378**, 6621, 724 (2022).
3. A. Bhattacharyya, S. Sharma, F. Alema, P. Ranga, S. Roy, C. Peterson, G. Seryogin, A. Osinsky, U. Singisetti, and S. Krishnamoorthy, *Appl. Phys. Express* **15**, 061001 (2022).
4. J. K. Mun, K. Cho, W. Chang, H.-W. Jung, and J. Do, *ECS J. Solid State Sci. and Technol.* **8**(7), Q3079 (2019).
5. K. Zeng, A. Vaidya, and U. Singisetti, *Appl. Phys. Express* **12**, 081003 (2019).
6. Z. Guo, A. Verma, X. Wu, F. Sun, A. Hickman, T. Masui, A. Kuramata, M. Higashiwaki, D. Jena, and T. Luo, *Appl. Phys. Lett.* **106**, 111909 (2015).

7. M. E. Liao, C. Li, H. Yu, E. Rosker, M. J. Tadjer, K. D. Hobart, and M. S. Goorsky, *APL Mater.* **7**, 022517 (2019).

8. K. Huynh, M. E. Liao, A. Mauze, T. Itoh, X. Yan, J. S. Speck, X. Pan, and M. S. Goorsky, *APL Mater.* **10**, 011110 (2022).

9. J. B. Varley, J. R. Weber, A. Janotti, and C. G. Van de Walle, *Appl. Phys. Lett.* **97**, 142106 (2018).

10. M. Singh, M. A. Casbon, M. J. Uren, J. W. Pomeroy, S. Dalcanale, S. Karboyan, P. J. Tasker, M. H. Wong, K. Sasaki, A. Kuramata, S. Yamakoshi, M. Higashiwaki, and M. Kuball, *IEEE Electron Device Lett.* **39**(10), 1572 (2018).

11. A. J. Green, K. D. Chabak, M. Baldini, N. Moser, R. Gilbert, R. C. Fitch, Jr., G. Wagner, Z. Galazka, J. McCandless, A. Crespo, K. Leedy, and G. H. Jessen, *IEEE Electron Device Lett.* **38**(6), 790 (2017).

12. M. Xian, R. Elhassani, C. Fares, F. Ren, M. Tadjer, and S. J. Pearton, *J. Vac. Sci. Technol. B* **37**, 061205 (2019).

13. Y. Song, P. Ranga, Y. Zhang, Z. Feng, H.-L. Huang, M. D. Santia, S. C. Badescu, C. U. Gonzalez-Valle, C. Perez, K. Ferri, R. M. Lavelle, D. W. Snyder, B. A. Klein, J. Deitz, A. G. Baca, J.-P. Maria, B. Ramos-Alvarado, J. Hwang, H. Zhao, X. Wang, S. Krishnamoorthy, B. M. Foley, and S. Choi, *ACS Appl. Mater. Interfaces* **13**, 38477 (2021).

14. N. Nepal, D. S. Katzer, B. P. Downey, V. D. Wheeler, L. O. Nyakiti, D. F. Storm, M. T. Hardy, J. A. Freitas, E. N. Jin, D. Vaca, L. Yates, S. Graham, S. Kumar, and D. J. Meyer, *J. Vac. Sci. Technol. A* **38**, 063406 (2020).

15. Z. Cheng, V. D. Wheeler, T. Bai, J. Shi, M. J. Tadjer, T. Feygelson, K. D. Hobart, M. S. Goorsky, and S. Graham, *Appl. Phys. Lett.* **116**, 062105 (2020).

16. A. Kuramata, K. Koshi, S. Watanabe, Y. Yamaoka, T. Masui, and S. Yamakoshi, *Jpn. J. Appl. Phys.* **55**, 1202A2 (2016).

17. Z. Galazka, S. Ganshow, P. Seyidov, K. Irmscher, M. Pietsch, T.-S. Chou, S. B. Anooz, R. Grueneberg, A. Popp, A. Dittmar, A. Kwasniewski, M. Suendermann, D. Klimm, T. Straubinger, T. Schroeder, and M. Bickermann, *Appl. Phys. Lett.* **120**, 152101 (2022).

18. J. Blevins, A. Brady, G. Foundos, C. Scott, D. Snyder, W. Everson, R. Lavelle, and V. Gambin, *CS ManTech Conf.* **2022**, 291 (2022).

19. M. Bruel, B. Aspar, and A.-J. Auberton-Hervé, *Jpn. J. Appl. Phys.* **36**, 1636 (1997).

20. C. Qian and B. Terreault, *J. Appl. Phys.* **90**, 5152 (2001).

21. S. Hayashi, M. Goorsky, A. Noori, and D. Bruno, *J. Electrochem. Soc.* **153**(12), G1011 (2006).

22. C. M. Varma, *Appl. Phys. Lett.* **71**, 3519 (1997).

23. X. Lu, S. S. K. Iyer, J. Min, Z. Fan, J. B. Liu, P. K. Chu, C. Hu, and N. W. Chueng, *Proc. 1996 IEEE Int. SOI Conf. 96CH35937* **48** (1996).

24. C. Miclaus and M. S. Goorsky, *J. Phys. D: Appl. Phys.* **36**, A177 (2003).

25. I. P. Ferain, K. Y. Byun, C. A. Colinge , S. Brightup, M. S. Goorsky, *J. Appl. Phys.* **107**, 054315 (2010).

26. V. P. Amarasinghe, L. Wielunski, A. Barcz, L. C. Feldman, and G. K. Celler, *ECS J. Solid State Sci. Technol.* **3**, P37 (2014)

27. S. Hayashi, D. Bruno, and M. S. Goorsky, *Appl. Phys. Lett.* **85**, 236 (2004).

28. S. Hayashi, R. Sandhu, and M. S. Goorsky, *J. Electrochem. Soc.* **154**(4), H293 (2007).

29. E. Padilla, M. Jackson, and M. S. Goorsky, *ECS Trans.* **33**(4), 263 (2010).

30. K. D. Hobart and F. J. Kub, *Electron. Lett.* **35**(8), 675 (1999).

31. C. Miclaus, G. Malouf, S. M. Johnson, and M. S. Goorsky, *J. Electron. Mat.* **34**(6), 859 (2005).
32. I. Szafraniak, I. Radu, R. Scholz, M. Alexe, and U. Gösele, *Integrated Ferroelectrics* **55**, 983 (2003).
33. M. E. Liao, Y. Wang, T. Bai, and M. S. Goorsky, *ECS J. Solid State Sci. Technol.* **8**, P673 (2019).
34. Z. Cheng, F. Mu, T. You, W. Xu, J. Shi, M. E. Liao, Y. Wang, K. Huynh, T. Suga, M. S. Goorsky, X. Ou, and S. Graham, *ACS Appl. Mater. Interfaces* **12**, 40 (2020).
35. M. Wormington, C. Panaccione, K. M. Matney, and D. K. Bowen, *Phil. Trans. R. Soc. Lond. A* **357**, 2827 (1999).
36. K. Adachi, H. Ogi, N. Takeuchi, N. Nakamura, H. Wantanabe, T. Ito, and Y. Ozaki, *J. Appl. Phys.* **124**, 085102 (2018).
37. J. F. Ziegler, J. P. Biersacke, and U. Littmark, The Stopping and Range of Ions in Solids vol 1 (Oxford, Pergamon), (1985).
38. J. Yu, Y. Wang, R. L. Moore, J.-Q. Lu, and R. J. Gutmann, *J. Electrochem. Soc.* **154**(1), H20 (2007).
39. Y. Minoura, T. Ohki, N. Okamoto, A. Yamada, K. Makiyama, J. Kotani, S. Ozaki, M. Sato, and N. Nakamura, *Jpn. J. Appl. Phys.* **59**, SGGD03 (2020).